Correlations to *Math Conne*
Student Edition and Standa

IMPACT Mathematics, Grade 4

The following chart shows how each activity correlates to the Macmillan/McGraw-Hill
Math Connects program and the NCTM Focal Points.

IMPACT Mathematics Activity *(Unit and Lesson)*	Math Connects Grade 4 *(Chapter and Lesson)*	NCTM Focal Points
A-1	4-2, 4-3, 4-5, 4-6, 6-1, 6-4, 6-6, 6-7, 6-8	G4-FP1
A-2	4-9	G4-FP1
A-3	4-1, 7-2	G4-FP1, G4-FP8C
A-4	8-1	G4-FP1, G4-FP8C
B-1	5-4	G4-FP4C
B-2	5-1, 5-2, 5-5	G4-FP4C
B-3	5-6, 5-8	G4-FP1, G4-FP4C
C-1	2-2	G4-FP8C
C-2	6-3, 7-2	G4-FP1, G4-FP8C
C-3	8-4	G4-FP1, G4-FP8C
D-1	13-1	G4-FP2, G4-FP8C
D-2	13-4	G4-FP2, G4-FP8C
D-3	13-5	G4-FP2, G4-FP8C
D-4	13-6	G4-FP2, G4-FP8C
E-1	14-2	G4-FP2, G4-FP8C
E-2	13-1, 13-7, 14-1, 14-7	G4-FP2, G4-FP8C
E-3	14-4	G4-FP2, G4-FP8C
E-4	14-2, 14-8	G4-FP2, G4-FP8C
F-1	Foundation for 11-6	G4-FP3, G4-FP5C
F-2	11-6	G4-FP3, G4-FP5C
F-3	Extension of 11-6	G4-FP3, G4-FP5C
G-1	Foundation for 12-10	G4-FP8C
G-2	Foundation for 12-10	G4-FP8C
G-3	12-10	G4-FP1, G4-FP8C
G-4	11-8	G4-FP1, G4-FP8C
H-1	11-1, 11-4	G4-FP8C
H-2	12-1, 12-2, 12-3	G4-FP8C
H-3	12-4, 12-6, 12-7	G4-FP8C
I-1	3-5	G4-FP7C
I-2	3-6	G4-FP7C
I-3	3-4	G4-FP7C
J-1	10-8	G4-FP5C
J-2	10-7	G4-FP5C
J-3	10-5	G4-FP5C

Correlations Chart

The following chart shows how each activity in *IMPACT Mathematics* correlates to the NCTM Focal Points and the Focal Points Connections.

NCTM Focal Points	Activity
Number and Operations and ***Algebra*** (G4-FP1) **Developing quick recall of multiplication facts and related division facts and fluency with whole number multiplication** Students use understandings of multiplication to develop quick recall of the basic multiplication facts and related division facts. They apply their understanding of models for multiplication (i.e., equal sized groups, arrays, area models, equal intervals on the number line), place value, and properties of operations (in particular, the distributive property) as they develop, discuss, and use efficient, accurate, and generalizable methods to multiply multidigit whole numbers. They select appropriate methods and apply them accurately to estimate products or calculate them mentally, depending on the context and numbers involved. They develop fluency with efficient procedures, including the standard algorithm, for multiplying whole numbers, understand why the procedures work (on the basis of place value and properties of operations), and use them to solve problems.	*A-1, A-2, A-3, A-4, B-3, C-2, C-3, G-3, G-4*
Number and Operations (G4-FP2) **Developing an understanding of decimals, including the connections between fractions and decimals** Students understand decimal notation as an extension of the base-ten system of writing whole numbers that is useful for representing more numbers, including numbers between 0 and 1, between 1 and 2, and so on. Students relate their understanding of fractions to reading and writing decimals that are greater than or less than 1, identifying equivalent decimals, comparing and ordering decimals, and estimating decimal or fractional amounts in problem solving. They connect equivalent fractions and decimals by comparing models to symbols and locating equivalent symbols on the number line.	*D-1, D-2, D-3, D-4, E-1, E-2, E-3, E-4*
Measurement (G4-FP3) **Developing an understanding of area and determining the areas of two-dimensional shapes** Students recognize area as an attribute of two-dimensional regions. They learn that they can quantify area by finding the total number of same-sized units of area that cover the shape without gaps or overlaps. They understand that a square that is 1 unit on a side is the standard unit for measuring area. They select appropriate units, strategies (e.g., decomposing shapes), and tools for solving problems that involve estimating or measuring area. Students connect area measure to the area model that they have used to represent multiplication, and they use this connection to justify the formula for the area of a rectangle.	*F-1, F-2, F-3*

Focal Points Connections	Activity
Algebra (G4-FP4C)	*B-1, B-2, B-3*
Geometry (G4-FP5C)	*F-1, F-2, F-3, J-1, J-2, J-3*
Data Analysis (G4-FP7C)	*I-1, I-2, I-3*
Number and Operations (G4-FP8C)	*A-3, A-4, C-1, C-2, C-3, D-1, D-2, D-3, D-4, E-1, E-2, E-3, E-4, G-1, G-2, G-3, G-4, H-1, H-2, H-3*

For a complete correlation to the NCTM Curriculum Focal Points, go to www.macmillanmh.com and select **Math**, then **Teacher View**. The complete Curriculum Focal Points may be viewed at www.nctm.org/focalpoints.

Contents in Brief

IMPACT Mathematics, Grade 4

Each unit includes Teacher Pages, Assessments, and Student Pages.

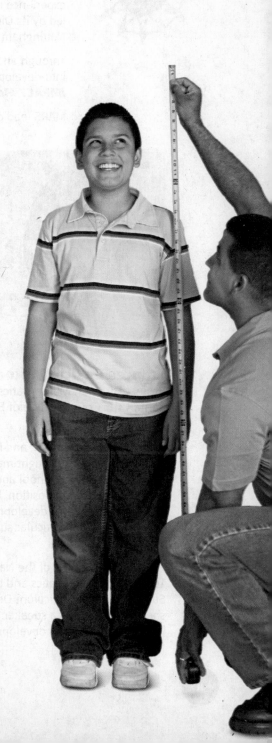

About the Authors

MARS
(Mathematics Assessment Resource Services)

MARS is a U.S.-based international team of people with diverse, research-based experience in mathematics education and its performance assessment. MARS is led by its Directorate: Sandra Wilcox (Michigan State U), Hugh Burkhardt (Shell Center, Nottingham U, UK), Alan Schoenfeld and Phil Daro (UC Berkeley).

Through an NSF grant, years of development, evaluation, and research have gone into developing the high-quality, performance-based assessments at the core of *IMPACT Mathematics*.

MARS lead designer for *IMPACT Mathematics* is **Rita Crust.**

Frances Basich Whitney
Project Director, Mathematics K–12
Santa Cruz County Office of Education
Santa Cruz, California

Frances received her B.A. and M.A. from Santa Clara University. She taught mathematics for 14 years at the high school and middle school levels. In her current position, Ms. Basich Whitney provides professional development primarily for K–8 teachers and curricular support to districts throughout California.

Frances is a member of the National Council of Teachers of Mathematics and the Association for Supervision and Curriculum Development, and she is very active as a speaker and workshop leader at professional development conferences.

Robyn Silbey
Mathematics Content Coach
Montgomery County Public Schools
Gaithersburg, Maryland

Robyn has been teaching in Montgomery County, Maryland, since 1974. She is currently working as a mathematics content coach. She has authored textbooks, software, supplemental materials, and magazine and journal articles on mathematics processes and topics from Kindergarten through Algebra I.

Robyn is a national consultant and presents workshops at national and international conferences. She serves in the Teaching Training Corps for the United States Department of Education and on the editorial panel of Teaching Children Mathematics, an NCTM periodical.

About the Consultants

Macmillan/McGraw-Hill wishes to thank the following professionals for their feedback. They were instrumental in providing valuable input toward the development of this program.

Jane D. Gawronski
Director of Assessment
and Outreach
San Diego State University
San Diego, California

Viken Hovsepian
Professor of Mathematics
Rio Hondo College
Whittier, California

About the Reviewers

Each of the educators reviewed five or more units of *IMPACT Mathematics*, giving feedback and suggestions for improving the effectiveness of the mathematics instruction.

Kathie Bossier
Director of Elementary and Middle
School Education
Community Unit School District 200
Wheaton, Illinois

Karen H. Dillon
Mathematics Coach
Erie 1 Boces
West Seneca, New York

LaVerne Dixon
Mathematics Coordinator
Riverview Gardens School District
St. Louis, Missouri

Ginna Gallivan
Mentor
South Buffalo Charter School
Buffalo, New York

Robert Jackson, Jr.
Mathematics Supervisor
St. Louis Public Schools
St. Louis, Missouri

Sarah J. Long
Assistant Superintendent,
Curriculum/Instruction
Poplar Bluff R-I
Poplar Bluff, Missouri

Karen Murray
Grade 5 Teacher
Lorraine Elementary PS #72
Buffalo, New York

Deborah Schluben
Mathematics Resource Specialist
Shawnee Mission School District
Shawnee Mission, Kansas

IMPACT Mathematics Overview

At the core of **IMPACT Mathematics** is investigative instruction aligned with performance-based assessment. Each unit of instruction begins with the assessment in mind.

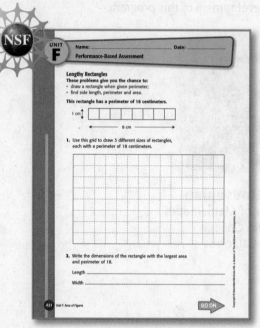

Grade 4 Teacher Guide, p. A21

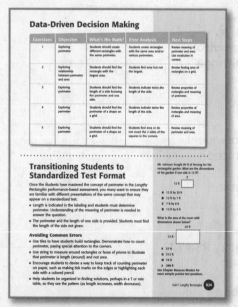

Grade 4 Teacher Guide, p. A24

MARS

MARS, the Mathematics Assessment Resource Service, is the author of the high-quality, field-tested performance assessments included in **IMPACT Mathematics**. This assessment drives the instruction for each unit. Each assessment gives students an opportunity to show what they *know, understand,* and *can do*.

With years of development and testing of these assessments, MARS is a leader in the field of performance-based assessment.

IMPACT Mathematics

IMPACT Mathematics was designed from the ground up to be used as a close companion to the K–5 *Macmillan/McGraw-Hill Mathematics* program. Some of the authors and consultants from Macmillan/McGraw-Hill's other math programs are also authors for **IMPACT Mathematics**.

Vertical Alignment

IMPACT Mathematics uses common vocabulary, planning features, technology, and manipulatives found in the K–5 *Macmillan/ McGraw-Hill Mathematics* program. Data-driven decision making is another link that vertically aligns the programs.

Units of **IMPACT Mathematics** consist of teacher pages, student pages, and assessments. Communication, investigation, and reflection are integral to each activity. The unit project and unit performance-based assessment give students an opportunity to show what they know, understand, and can do.

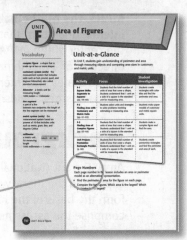

Grade 4 Teacher Guide, p. T57

① Teacher Pages

Hands-on investigations in which students use manipulatives and real objects to explore a new math concept

- Planning materials
- One investigation per activity, including guiding questions
- Differentiated instruction
- Project rubrics

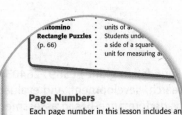

Page Numbers

Each page number in this lesson includes an model as an alternative representation.

- Find the perimeter or area for the figure o
- Compare the two figures. Which area is t perimeter is the largest?

② Student Pages

Real-world exercises, projects, and discussion to engage students in the classroom

- Blackline masters for easy duplication
- Real-world exercises
- Students explain, reason, and show work

Outside Your Cla

Where do you see perimeter and are around you?

- How much floor space do you need
- How much floor space do you need

Your after-school job is to sweep the are offered a choice on how to be r by the total number of square fee total number of square meters

hich payment method

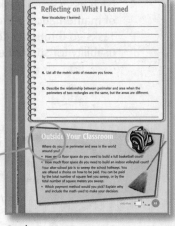

Grade 4   p. 65

③ Assessment Pages

Performance-based assessment per unit

- Student assessment
- Rubric for scoring
- Sample scored student papers
- Data-driven decision making for next steps

Error Analysis

	Error Analysis	
create ngles with rimeter.	Students create rectangles with the same area and/or various perimeters.	Re perime Use voc context.
should find the e with the area.	Students find area but not the largest.	Review find rectangles o
should find the a side knowing ter and one	Students indicate twice the length of the side.	Review prop rectangles a of perimet
find the e on	Students indicate twice the length of the side.	Revi re

Grade 4 Teacher Guide, p. A24

About MARS
(Mathematics Assessment Resource Service)

MARS, the Mathematics Assessment Resource Service, is a U.S.-based international team that created the performance-based assessments at the center of the *IMPACT Mathematics* program. MARS is under the direction of a Mathematics Board that includes teachers and recognized United States and international experts in the mathematics education and assessment fields.

Background

An NSF grant (National Science Foundation grant #ESI-9726403) has supported the many years of research, development, and evaluation that form the basis of the high-quality, performance-based assessments that comprise the assessment section of *IMPACT Mathematics.*

Development Process

Each assessment task is carefully constructed to assess the broad domain of mathematical performance that national and local standards specify. Tasks go through a development and review process to ensure validity and usability for student evaluation and continued improvement in instruction.

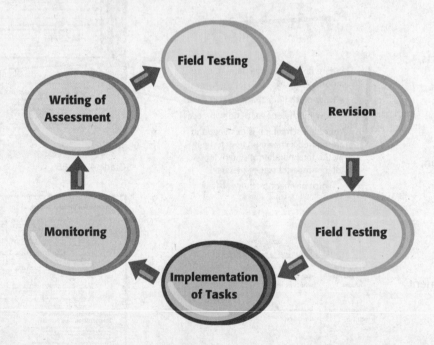

During the writing and revision process, the scoring rubric is refined and student work is collected. Rubrics, along with scored student work, accompany the MARS assessments, allowing teachers to evaluate student knowledge and progress and better inform instruction.

Evaluative Evidence

Over the years, MARS performance-based assessments have been used both throughout the United States and internationally. Evidence shows that the MARS assessments test a broader range of skills and knowledge than many state tests and are comparably challenging overall.

Figure 1. In one particular study, teachers used MARS assessments as part of a formative-assessment piece prior to taking the SAT-9 standardized test. The data show that students in classrooms receiving the MARS treatment outperformed control classrooms without MARS.

Source: Noyce Foundation Annual Report 2000

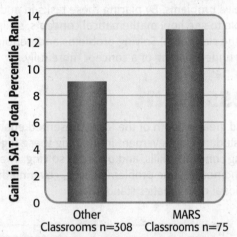

Figure 1
Average Gain in Math Percentile Rank Between 1999 SAT-9 and 2000 SAT-9

District Teachers' Involvement in MARS-based Professional Development

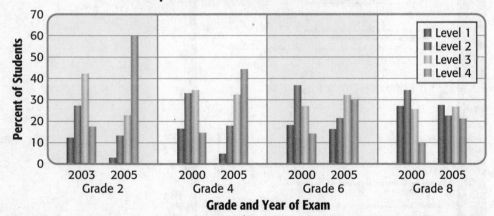

Figure 2
Student Achievement By Performance Levels on MARS Exam Comparison Between First Year and 2005

Figure 2. Over time, the evidence for MARS follows similar trends. The number of students performing at the highest levels (Level 4) of the MARS assessments climbs each year and at every grade level, while the number performing at the lower levels (Level 1) declines.

Source: Noyce Foundation Annual Report 2005

Performance-Based Assessment

At the center of each *IMPACT Mathematics* unit is a high-quality, research-based performance assessment. Using such an assessment helps determine student progress toward mastery of critical mathematical concepts.

What Is Performance-Based Assessment?

Performance assessments are an authentic form of assessment in which students are asked to perform tasks or solve problems. By placing these tasks in authentic (real-world) contexts, students are better able to see how mathematical concepts, skills, and problem solving abilities are useful outside of the classroom. Solving problems and performing tasks allows students to communicate their understanding of a concept more fully.

The Assessment

The broader range and greater depth of the tasks presented enables teachers to recognize, and thus encourage, students' achievement in meeting these higher standards for mathematical performance, including concepts, skills, and problem solving. The tasks demand substantial chains of reasoning and non-routine problem solving, covering the content and the process areas specified in national mathematics standards.

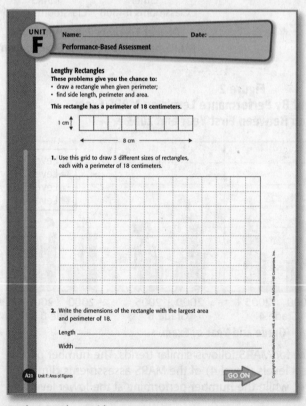

Grade 4 Teacher Guide, p. A21

Rubrics and Scoring

Each assessment is supported by a scoring rubric and actual graded student work. The scoring rubric lists point values to assign for alternative approaches and student responses. The sample student work shows how real student responses have been scored as a guide for teachers.

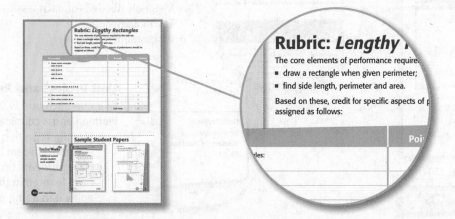

Data-Driven Decision Making and Standardized Tests

Following each assessment, the exercises are broken down by the core concepts being evaluated. Error analysis is provided to help teachers diagnose the misconception and prescribe an instructional path for individual students.

There may be times when a student performs very well on a performance-based assessment but has difficulty transferring this knowledge into the more traditional multiple-choice format of many standardized tests. *IMPACT Mathematics* provides teacher support for helping students make this transition and be successful in various testing situations.

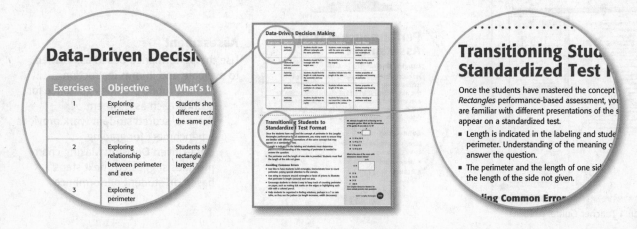

Teacher Pages Preview

The support for each unit includes a unit planner, differentiated instruction, assessment, and instructional pages.

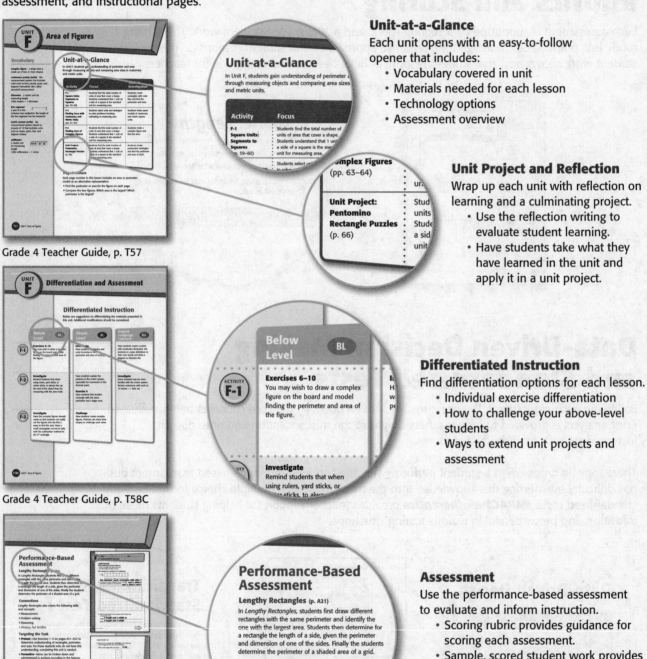

Grade 4 Teacher Guide, p. T57

Grade 4 Teacher Guide, p. T58C

Grade 4 Teacher Guide, p. T58D

Unit-at-a-Glance

Each unit opens with an easy-to-follow opener that includes:

- Vocabulary covered in unit
- Materials needed for each lesson
- Technology options
- Assessment overview

Unit Project and Reflection

Wrap up each unit with reflection on learning and a culminating project.

- Use the reflection writing to evaluate student learning.
- Have students take what they have learned in the unit and apply it in a unit project.

Differentiated Instruction

Find differentiation options for each lesson.

- Individual exercise differentiation
- How to challenge your above-level students
- Ways to extend unit projects and assessment

Assessment

Use the performance-based assessment to evaluate and inform instruction.

- Scoring rubric provides guidance for scoring each assessment.
- Sample, scored student work provides a benchmark for grading.
- Data-Driven Decision Making chart provides suggested "next steps" based on student performance.

Instructional Design

Each activity consists of instructional materials and student pages to allow students to investigate a mathematical concept, apply their knowledge through related exercises, and summarize their learning of the lesson in a reflection time.

① Investigate

Hands-on investigation in which students use manipulatives and real objects to explore a new math concept.

- Guiding Questions help teachers guide the class discussion to the desired learning outcomes.
- Connections and Extensions allow teachers to customize the instruction.
- Students develop tools they can use in future applications.

② Apply

After students explore mathematical concepts through hands-on investigations, they demonstrate understanding of each concept through writing and reasoning.

- Relevant, real-world examples and questions
- Opportunities to tie math learning to real-world connections
- Mini-projects to engage students in the learning process
- Many chances for students to write, show their work, and explain their reasoning

③ Reflect

Close each lesson with summarizing questions to help students draw conclusions and make connections.

- Higher-level questions help students see how the current lesson ties to prior knowledge and activities.
- Sample responses give teachers ideas of how students may reply.

④ Assess

Use the performance-based assessment to monitor student progress.

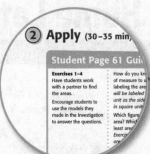

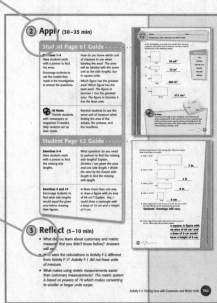

Grade 4 Teacher Guide, p. T61

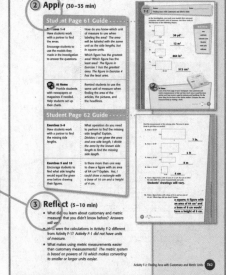

Grade 4 Teacher Guide, p. T62

Student Pages Preview

Each *IMPACT Mathematics* unit includes student materials to support the investigative instructional approach that begins in the teacher materials.

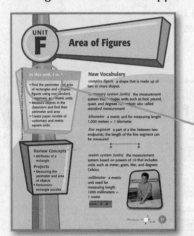

Grade 4   p. 57

Unit Opener

Each unit opens with an overview for students.

- Focus of math concepts
- New and review vocabulary
- Projects and games found in the unit

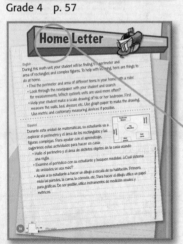

Grade 4   p. 58

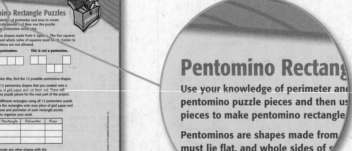

Home Letter

Learning opportunities outside the classroom are featured in the Home Letter.

- Overview of math being taught in each unit
- Ideas of how to engage students in learning at home
- Specific examples where math concepts can be found at home or in daily life

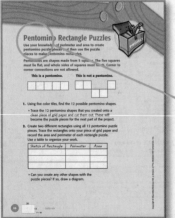

Grade 4   p. 66

Unit Project

The unit project integrates math from each unit and calls on prior knowledge for student completion.

- Requires students to organize ideas and put together a strategy for completing a project
- Requires multiple math concepts, skills, and mathematical processes
- Enriches understanding through writing and reflecting

Throughout each unit, students have an opportunity to solve exercises in a variety of contexts.

Hands-On Investigation

Each activity begins with a hands-on investigation to expose students to the math concept covered.

- Manipulatives, materials, and software engage students in lessons.
- Students construct knowledge through hands-on experiences and ongoing discussion among teacher and students.
- Sample student responses are provided for the Guiding Questions.

Real-World Feature

This feature highlights where students will see the math from each unit in the real world.

- Examples are given for math at home, at the playground, in science, at the grocery store, and more.
- Dialogue is encouraged between students and between student and family members at home.

Mini-Projects and Games

Multiple opportunities are given to engage students in discussions and communication.

- Short projects or investigations allow students to look at the world around them for math.
- Games and student interaction allow time for engaging math learning.

Reflection and Assessment

Each unit concludes with an opportunity for reflection and assessment.

- Reflection allows teachers to see how students have internalized the concepts.
- Performance-based assessments show what students can do.

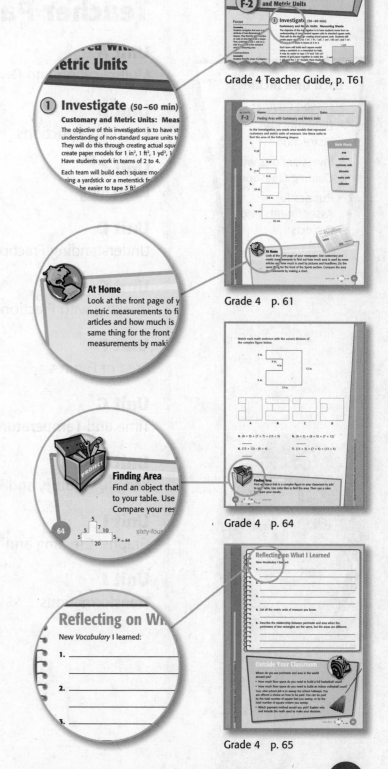

Grade 4 Teacher Guide, p. T61

Grade 4   p. 61

Grade 4   p. 64

Grade 4   p. 65

Table of Contents

Each Unit includes:
- Lesson Planner
- Differentiated Instruction
- Investigations with Guiding Questions
- Rubrics for Assessments and Projects

Teacher Pages

Assessment Pages

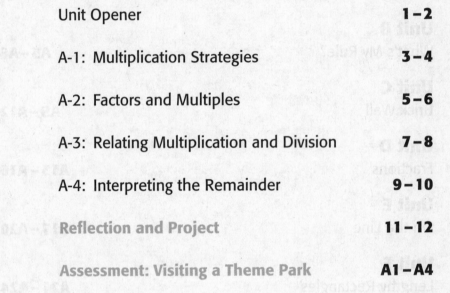

Student Pages

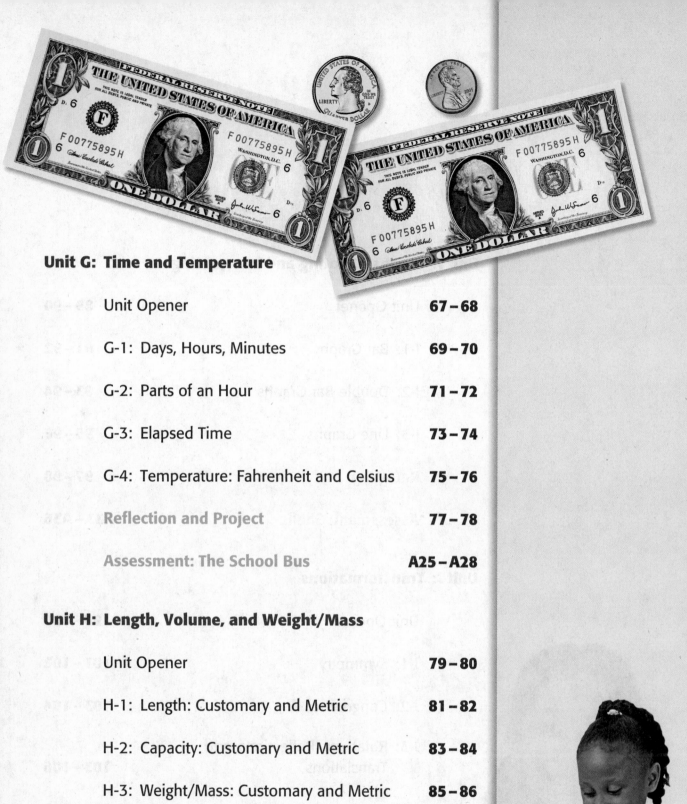

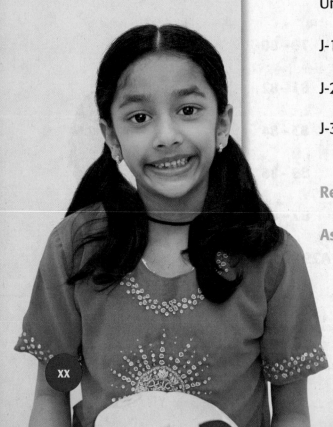

Program Resources

Blackline Masters

TeacherWorks™ _Plus_

Blackline masters on all **IMPACT Mathematics** student pages and assessment pages are available in the Teacher Guide and on the TeacherWorks™ Plus CD.

Manipulatives

included with *Macmillan/McGraw-Hill Mathematics* Program

Manipulative	Suggested Alternative
Student Clock	paper plate, brads
Demonstration Clock	paper plate, brads
Connecting Cubes	paper clips
Number Cubes	spinner, cards
Spinners	construction paper, paper clip, pencil
Two-Colored Counters	buttons, coins, beans
Pattern Blocks	construction paper
Geometric Solids/Models	cans, boxes, balls
Bucket Balance	ruler, paper cups, string
Base-Ten Blocks	grid paper
Money	real money, construction paper
Ruler	straightedge, book
Fraction Circles	construction paper
Fraction Models	
Geoboards	dot paper
Compass	paper clip
Protractor	
Plastic Cups	paper cups

Internet Resources

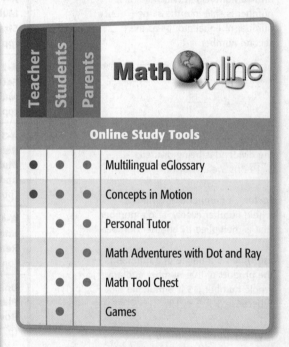

Math Online

Teacher	Students	Parents	Online Study Tools
●	●	●	Multilingual eGlossary
●	●	●	Concepts in Motion
	●	●	Personal Tutor
	●	●	Math Adventures with Dot and Ray
	●	●	Math Tool Chest
	●		Games

Multiplication and Division

Vocabulary

area the number of square units needed to cover the inside of a region or plane figure without any overlap

area = 6 square units

divide (division) an operation on two numbers in which the first number is split into the same number of equal groups as the second number

quotient ⟶ 6 R1 ⟵ remainder
divisor ⟶ 3)19 ⟵ dividend
$\underline{-18}$
1

divisor the number by which the dividend is being divided; 3)19 *3 is the divisor*

factor a number that divides a whole number evenly; also a number that is multiplied by another number

multiple a multiple of a number is the product of that number and any whole number; 15 is a multiple of 5 because $3 \times 5 = 15$

multiply (multiplication) an operation on two numbers to find their product; it can be thought of as repeated addition

product the answer to or result of a multiplication problem; it also refers to expressing a number as the product of its factors

Unit-at-a-Glance

In Unit A, students gain understanding of multiplication and division.

Activity	Focus	Student Investigation
A-1 Multiplication Strategies (pp. 3–4)	Students apply an understanding of models for multiplication, place value, and properties of multiplication.	Students use an area model and lattice multiplication.
A-2 Factors and Multiples (pp. 5–6)	Students practice and use quick recall of the basic multiplication facts and related division facts.	Students compare the relationships between factors and multiples.
A-3 Relating Multiplication and Division (pp. 7–8)	Students apply an understanding of models for multiplication, place value, and properties of multiplication.	Students use multiplication to check division.
A-4 Interpreting the Remainder (pp. 9–10)	Students select methods and apply them to estimate or to calculate products mentally.	Students decide how to interpret remainders.
Unit Project: Planning a Bowling Party (p. 12)	Students relate the concepts and skills they have learned to the real world.	Students use multiplication and division concepts to plan a party and design a budget.

Page Numbers

Each page number in this lesson includes dot cubes as an alternative representation.

Guiding Questions

- What division/multiplication sentence can you make using the number cubes as one of the factors?
- What are two multiples of the page number?

Unit Opener

Student Page 1 Guide · · · · · · · · ·

You can open the unit by having students read through the objectives they will accomplish during the unit. Have students restate objectives in their own words to ensure comprehension.

Scaffolding Questions

How are multiplication and repeated addition related? *Multiplication and repeated addition both combine equal groups.*

What math words do you know that relate to multiplication and division? *factor, product, quotient, dividend, divisor, remainder*

Vocabulary

The beginning of the unit is a great time to start a new wall chart.

Encourage students to write the definitions in their math journals. Writing their own definitions or creating drawings will help internalize the information.

WRITING IN MATH ▶ Remind students that the word *factor* has two meanings. A factor is a number that is multiplied by another number. It is also a number that divides a whole number evenly.

Student Page 2 Guide · · · · · · · · ·

Home Letter

Have students take the Home Letter home.

Look at the Projects and Discussions throughout the project to see if any additional opportunities are available for work at home.

ELL

Encourage students to visit the online eGlossary with parents to see vocabulary in 13 languages.

TeacherWorks *Plus*

See "Home E-mail" as an alternative for communication. From the Lesson Planner, select the e-mail document for this unit, double-click the file, and edit in the Worksheet Editor.

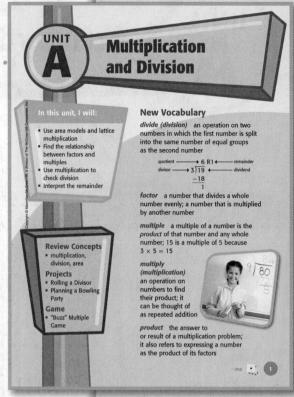

UNIT A

Multiplication and Division

In this unit, I will:
- Use area models and lattice multiplication
- Find the relationship between factors and multiples
- Use multiplication to check division
- Interpret the remainder

Review Concepts
- multiplication, division, area

Projects
- Rolling a Divisor
- Planning a Bowling Party

Game
- "Buzz" Multiple Game

New Vocabulary

divide (division) an operation on two numbers in which the first number is split into the same number of equal groups as the second number

$$\text{quotient} \longrightarrow 6 \text{ R1} \longleftarrow \text{remainder}$$
$$\text{divisor} \longrightarrow 3\overline{)19} \longleftarrow \text{dividend}$$
$$\underline{-18}$$
$$1$$

factor a number that divides a whole number evenly; a number that is multiplied by another number

multiple a multiple of a number is the *product* of that number and any whole number; 15 is a multiple of 5 because $3 \times 5 = 15$

multiply (multiplication) an operation on numbers to find their product; it can be thought of as repeated addition

product the answer to or result of a multiplication problem; it also refers to expressing a number as the product of its factors

one · · 1

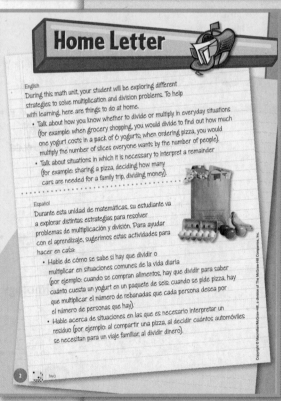

Home Letter

English

During this math unit, your student will be exploring different strategies to solve multiplication and division problems. To help with learning, here are things to do at home.
- Talk about how you know whether to divide or multiply in everyday situations (for example: when grocery shopping, you would divide to find out how much one yogurt costs in a pack of 6 yogurts; when ordering pizza, you would multiply the number of slices everyone wants by the number of people).
- Talk about situations in which it is necessary to interpret a remainder (for example: sharing a pizza, deciding how many cars are needed for a family trip, dividing money).

Español

Durante esta unidad de matemáticas, su estudiante va a explorar distintas estrategias para resolver problemas de multiplicación y división. Para ayudar con el aprendizaje, sugerimos estas actividades para hacer en casa.
- Hable de cómo se sabe si hay que dividir o multiplicar en situaciones comunes de la vida diaria (por ejemplo: cuando se compran alimentos, hay que dividir para saber cuánto cuesta un yogurt en un paquete de seis; cuando se pide pizza, hay que multiplicar el número de rebanadas que cada persona desea por el número de personas que hay).
- Hable acerca de situaciones en las que es necesario interpretar un residuo (por ejemplo: al compartir una pizza, al decidir cuántos automóviles se necesitan para un viaje familiar, al dividir dinero).

2 · · two

UNIT A

Activity Planner

KEY

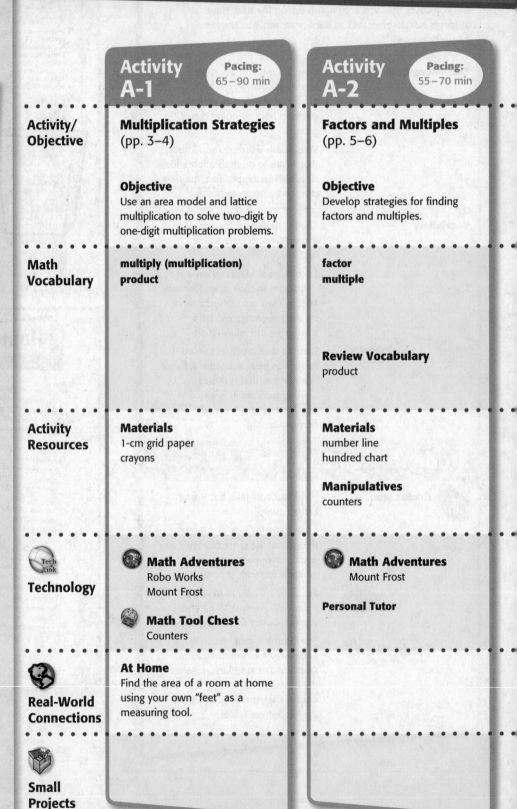

- Real-World Connections
- Projects
- Technology
- CD-ROM
- Math Tool Chest
- Math Adventures

	Activity A-1 Pacing: 65–90 min	**Activity A-2** Pacing: 55–70 min
Activity/ Objective	**Multiplication Strategies** (pp. 3–4) **Objective** Use an area model and lattice multiplication to solve two-digit by one-digit multiplication problems.	**Factors and Multiples** (pp. 5–6) **Objective** Develop strategies for finding factors and multiples.
Math Vocabulary	multiply (multiplication) product	factor multiple **Review Vocabulary** product
Activity Resources	**Materials** 1-cm grid paper crayons	**Materials** number line hundred chart **Manipulatives** counters
Technology	**Math Adventures** Robo Works Mount Frost **Math Tool Chest** Counters	**Math Adventures** Mount Frost **Personal Tutor**
Real-World Connections	**At Home** Find the area of a room at home using your own "feet" as a measuring tool.	
Small Projects		

Activity A-3	Pacing: 55–80 min	Activity A-4	Pacing: 55–80 min	Unit Project	Pacing: 30–40 min	
Relating Multiplication and Division (pp. 7–8) **Objective** Model and write corresponding multiplication and division equations.		**Interpreting the Remainder** (pp. 9–10) **Objective** Determine how to use a remainder.		**Planning a Bowling Party** (p. 12) **Objective** Use multiplication and division strategies to design a budget.		Activity/ Objective
dividend **divide (division)** **divisor** **quotient** **remainder** **Review Vocabulary** multiply (multiplication) product		**Review Vocabulary** dividend remainder quotient				Math Vocabulary
				Materials price list from local bowling alley		Activity Resources
Manipulatives base-ten blocks		**Manipulatives** base-ten blocks color tiles		**Manipulatives** play money		
Concepts in Motion		**Math Adventures** Number Voyage		**Math Tool Chest** Money		Technology
		At Home Write a story and corresponding division equation about interpreting a remainder.				Real-World Connections
Rolling a Divisor Roll number cubes and use counters to find factors.						Small Projects

Differentiated Instruction

Below are suggestions on differentiating the materials presented in this unit. Additional modifications should be considered.

	Below Level **BL**	Above Level **AL**	English Language Learners **ELL**
ACTIVITY A-1	When doing lattice multiplication, have students use a strip of paper to cover the squares and numbers that they do not need for each step.	Have students find the area of the classroom by measuring the length and width and then multiplying the dimensions using either an area model or lattice multiplication.	**Exercises 7–9** Help students focus on how many legs each animal has by looking at the pictures. Talk about the different characteristics of each animal.
ACTIVITY A-2	**Exercise 18** Before students begin their riddles, have them make a list of the factors and multiples of their number and which two numbers their number is between.	**Exercises 1–6** Have students use greater numbers that have more factors, such as 48 or 72.	
ACTIVITY A-3	**Exercises 10 and 11** Provide students with play money and coins to help them work out the problems.		Reinforce that the *divisor* is the number of groups you want to divide by, and the *dividend* is the total amount you want to divide.
ACTIVITY A-4	**Exercises 7–10** Have students work with a partner to answer the exercises.	**Exercises 7–9** Have students come up with their own stories that involve division and remainders and write 2 or 3 problems to go with them. Trade stories and problems with a partner and answer the questions.	Give examples of a remainder, such as the number of slices left after a pizza is divided by a certain number of people.

Performance-Based Assessment

Visiting a Theme Park (p. A2)

In *Visiting a Theme Park,* students first determine the number of cars needed with an explanation. Students then determine the number of packs of soda needed.

Connections

Visiting a Theme Park also covers the following skills and concepts:

- Number sense
- Multi-step problem solving
- Reasoning
- Interpreting remainders, division

Targeting the Task

- **Pretest** – Use exercises on page A2 to determine an understanding of division facts in a practical situation. For those students who do not have this understanding, completing this unit is needed.

- **Formative** – Items can be administered separately during the course of the lesson.

- **Summative** – Administer complete *Visiting a Theme Park* assessment.

Refer to "Data-Driven Decision Making" chart to determine student proficiency on concepts provided in "What's the Math?".

Differentiation

Similar problems can be developed to provide more experiences for students to deal with remainders in a meaningful way. For example: 55 fourth graders will visit the zoo. Each bus holds 30 students. How many buses will be needed? And once the 55 fourth graders are at the zoo, they will board mini-buses that hold 20 students each. How many mini-buses will they need to tour the zoo?

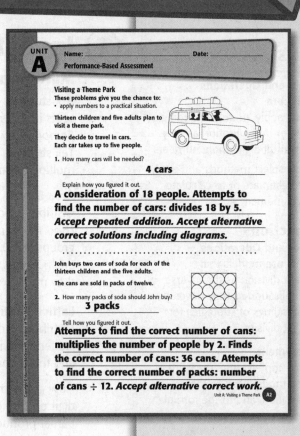

Multiplication Strategies

Focus

Number and Operations and Algebra

Students apply an understanding of models for multiplication as they multiply multidigit whole numbers.

Students select methods and apply them to estimate or to calculate products mentally.

Connections

Number and Operations

Students use models that represent division as the inverse of multiplication as they develop understandings of strategies for multidigit division.

Measurement

Students connect area measure to the area model used to represent multiplication, and to the formula for the area of a rectangle.

Vocabulary

multiply (multiplication)
product

Materials

1-cm grid paper
crayons

---

① Investigate (35–45 min)

Multiplication Strategies

Ask students what strategy they would use to find the total number of seats in a restaurant if there are 12 tables with 6 seats at each table. *Sample answers: using models, using a number line, drawing pictures* Tell students that they will be learning two new strategies for solving multiplication problems.

Area Model

Distribute 1-cm grid paper. Have students outline an array (6 × 12) to model the problem. Encourage students to color or shade groups of 10, count them, and then count the remaining ones. *6 tens and 12 ones; or 7 tens and 2 ones* Guide students to understand that they may use mental math to find the product.

Lattice Multiplication

Distribute 1-cm grid paper. Model a lattice grid for 12 x 6 and have students create their own. Write the first factor across the top of the grid and the second factor down the right side of the grid.

Now guide students through the multiplication process. Multiply each digit on the top of the grid by the digit on the right side of the grid. If the partial product is a two digit number, the tens go in the top part of the diagonal box. Once all digits have been multiplied, add the numbers in each diagonal row beginning in the lower right diagonal. Give students additional two-digit by one-digit problems to solve.

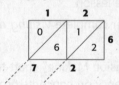

Guiding Questions

- For the lattice multiplication, you recorded partial products. Where do the tens go inside each diagonal box? Where do the ones go? *The tens go in the top part of the box, and the ones go in the bottom part of the box.*

- What do the numbers at the bottom of each diagonal column represent? *They represent the ones place and the tens place of the final product.*

- How are the two strategies similar? How are they different? *Sample answers: Both strategies help me visualize the multiplication. The area model uses mental math; the lattice method arranges the place values of the partial products as I multiply.*

② Apply (25–35 min)

Student Page 3 Guide · · · · ·

Exercises 1–4
Have students work with a partner. One partner can solve the problem using an area model while the other partner can use lattice multiplication.

How is the area model for Exercise 3 different from the other area models? *Sample answer: There are two groups of 10 ones. The other area models only have one group of 10 ones.*

Student Page 4 Guide · · · · ·

Exercises 5–8
Encourage students to draw pictures to help them visualize the problems.

What are some other ways you could find the total number of shoes for each problem? *Sample answers: draw a picture; act it out, use a number line, make an array; skip count*

Exercise 9
Guide students to count the number of people in the classroom and then set up their multiplication strategies. Allow time to share strategies.

By what number did you multiply the number of people in the classroom to find the total number of shoes? Explain. *2; each person has 2 feet, so they will each wear 2 shoes*

 At Home
Demonstrate how to measure "feet" by touching the heel of one foot to the toe of your other foot so that all students measure a room in their homes using the same strategy.

How could two students measure the same room and get different answers? *Sample answer: They are not using a standard unit of measure.*

③ Reflect (5–10 min)

- Name the four multiplication strategies you know. *multiplication algorithm, making an array, area models, lattice multiplication*

- How are the new strategies similar to strategies you already know? How are they different? *Sample answer: Lattice is similar to the multiplication algorithm, but it arranges the numbers so that place value and regrouping are easier to see. The area model is similar to making an array, but it uses grids instead of models or drawings.*

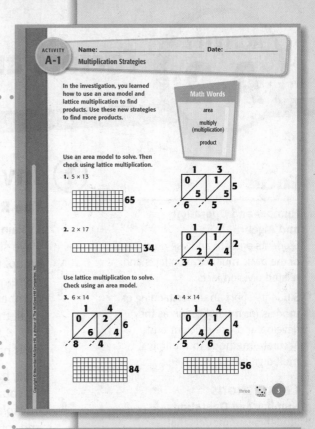

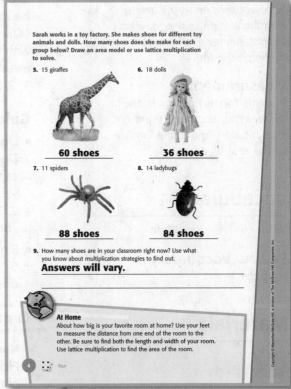

Factors and Multiples

Focus

Number and Operations and Algebra

Students practice and use quick recall of the basic multiplication facts and related division facts.

Students apply an understanding of models for multiplication as they develop and use efficient and accurate methods to multiply multidigit whole numbers.

Connections

Number and Operations

Students use models that represent division as the inverse of multiplication as they develop understandings of strategies for multidigit division.

Measurement

Students connect area measure to the area model used to represent multiplication, and to the formula for the area of a rectangle.

Vocabulary

factor   multiple

Review Vocabulary
product

Materials

counters   number line
hundred chart

---

① Investigate (30–35 min)

The Relationship Between Factors and Multiples

Explain that a *factor* is a number that divides another number evenly. Have students work in small groups and distribute 12 counters to each group. Challenge them to create a rectangular array with even rows and no remaining counters, beginning with 1 and moving through the numbers to 12. Ask students to share their responses. Create a class list of all the factors of 12 on the board. Make sure students understand that 5, 7, 8, and 9 are not factors of 12 because they cannot make equal rows of counters.

Next, have each group of students make groups of 2 with their 12 counters. Guide the students to see that 2, 4, 6, 8, 10, and 12 are *multiples* of 2. Help students see the relationship between factors and multiples: *12 is a multiple of 2, and 2 is a factor of 12.* Repeat, having students make groups of 3, 4, 5, and 6 with their 12 counters. Make sure students understand that if they cannot make even groups with the counters, then 12 is *not* a multiple of that number. After the investigation, students should find that 12 is a multiple of the numbers 1, 2, 3, 4, and 6.

Guiding Questions

- Does a number have a limited number of whole number factors? Does a number have a set number of multiples? Give examples to explain your answer. *A number has a set number of factors, but not a set number of multiples. Sample explanation: The factors of 12 are 1, 2, 3, 4, 6, and 12. The multiples of 2 are 2, 4, 6, 8, 10, 12, and so on. The multiples of a number are unlimited.*

- Since 3 and 5 have a product of 15, what do you know about 3 and 5? *I know that 3 and 5 are factors of 15, and 15 is a multiple of 3 and of 5.*

Connections and Extensions

Number and Operations: Buzz Game
Pick a number. Tell the students that you are looking for the multiples of that number. Start at 1 and go around the room counting numbers. When you get to a multiple of the chosen number, the player must say "buzz." If the player says the multiple instead of the word "buzz," the player is out. For example, if you were finding the multiples of 3, the game would go: "1, 2, buzz, 4, 5, buzz, etc." Challenge students by using greater numbers.

② Apply (20–25 min)

Student Page 5 Guide ·····

Exercises 1–6 Encourage students to use counters or grid paper to find the factors of each number.	Why did some numbers have more factors than others? *Sample answers: Some numbers have "twin" factors, such as 4 × 4 = 16. They may have fewer factors than another number; some numbers can be divided evenly in only 2 ways, others in 3 or more ways.*
Exercises 7 and 8	What did you find to be similar about the multiples of each factor? *They all had the original number as a multiple.*

Student Page 6 Guide ·····

Exercises 9–17 Provide students with counters, number lines, or hundred charts to help them solve the riddles.	What was your strategy for solving the riddles? *Sample answer: I used a number line so I could identify all of the possible numbers. Then I found the multiples or factors for the number provided.* For Exercises 15–17, both factors and multiples are included as clues. Are they both necessary to solve the riddles? Explain. *Yes. Sample explanation: For Exercise 16, the numbers 12, 15, and 18 work for the first three clues, but only 15 works for all four clues.*
Exercise 18 Give students possible numbers to use, such as 10, 12, or 16. Allow students time to share their riddles with a partner or in small groups.	What process did you use when you wrote your riddles? *Sample answer: I picked my number, found its factors and multiples, and then wrote clues that would help someone choose my number.*

③ Reflect (5–10 min)

- How are factors and multiples related? *If Number A is a factor of Number B, then Number B is a multiple of Number A.*

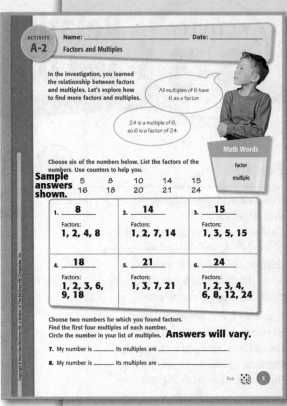

ACTIVITY A-3

Relating Multiplication and Division

Focus

Number and Operations and Algebra

Students apply an understanding of models for multiplication as they develop and use efficient and accurate methods to multiply multidigit whole numbers.

Students solve problems by developing skill with efficient procedures, understanding why the procedures work, and using the procedures in real problems.

Connections

Number and Operations

Students use models that represent division as the inverse of multiplication as they develop understandings of strategies for multidigit division.

Vocabulary

dividend   quotient
divide (division)   remainder
divisor

Review Vocabulary
multiply (multiplication)
product

Materials

base-ten blocks

① Investigate (20–30 min)

Finding the Regrouping Step in Division; Using Multiplication to Check Division

Ask students what they know about multiplication and division. Encourage students to use words such as *product, quotient,* and *remainder* as they share their ideas. Record students' responses on the board. Is there a regrouping step in multiplication? *Yes.* How about in addition and subtraction? *Yes.* Today, we will discover whether or not there is a regrouping step in division. We will also see how to use multiplication to check the answer to a division problem.

Arrange students into pairs and distribute a collection of tens and ones blocks to each pair. Write this problem on the board or overhead: "There are 75 fourth graders at Rosemont School. They are divided into 3 different classes. How many students are in each class?" Discuss with students how they might model the problem. Guide students to suggest that they divide 75 by 3. Remind students to think about the regrouping step as they complete their models. When students have completed their models, have volunteers write the division algorithm for each step of the division on the board. Next, have students check their work by multiplying their answer by 3. $25 \times 3 = 75$

Guiding Questions

- What did you do to model and solve the problem? *We modeled a group of 7 tens and 5 ones and divided the blocks into 3 equal groups.*

- Was there a regrouping step? If so, where was it? *Yes; we regrouped 1 ten for 10 ones after we distributed 2 tens to each of the three groups.*

- How did you use multiplication to check your answer? *We multiplied 3 by 25. We knew our answer was correct because the product matched the dividend.*

- What would happen if there were 76 fourth graders in the school? How would that change your answer? *There would be 25 students in two of the classes and 26 students in the third class.*

- How would you check a division problem that has a remainder? *Sample answer: I would add the remainder in after multiplying.*

Connections and Extensions

- **Algebra**
  Write and solve 6 problems similar to the ones shown in Exercises 1 through 6. Use a divisor of 3. What pattern do you see in the remainders? Repeat for a divisor of 4. What pattern do you see in the remainders? Can you write a rule to show what you have discovered?

② Apply (30–40 min)

Student Page 7 Guide · · · · ·

Exercises 1–6 Have students work with a partner. Focus students' attention on the patterns between the exercises.	What patterns do you see in the exercises? *The divisor is the same for all of the problems; the dividend increases by 1 each time; there is a remainder of 1 for every other quotient.* Can the remainder be 2? Explain. *No. The divisor is 2. If there are 2 remaining, they can be divided evenly into 1 more group.*
Exercise 7 Make sure students see the patterns in Exercises 1 through 6 before assigning Exercise 7.	If you are dividing a number by 2, how can you tell if the quotient will have a remainder? *The even numbers will have no remainder; the odd numbers will have a remainder of 1.*
Rolling a Divisor Engage students in a discussion about the results of their projects. Encourage them to notice patterns.	*Sample patterns: 20 divides evenly by 1, 2, 4, and 5; the remainder is the same when dividing by 3 and by 6 because the division equations are related.*

Student Page 8 Guide · · · · ·

Exercises 8 and 9 Tell students that their pictures should show the multiplication and division equations.	How are the division and multiplication equations alike for both exercises? *They have the same numbers.*
Exercises 10 and 11 Ask students to justify their responses.	How did you know whether to multiply or divide? *Exercise 10 is about sharing, so I divided. Exercise 11 is about money earned each hour, so I multiplied.*

③ Reflect (5–10 min)

- How are division and multiplication related? *Sample answers: They are inverse operations; multiplication checks division.*

- Is there a regrouping step in division? If so, when does it happen? *The regrouping step is when the next place value is being divided. The remaining values of the greater place value are regrouped and added to the lesser place value to be divided again.*

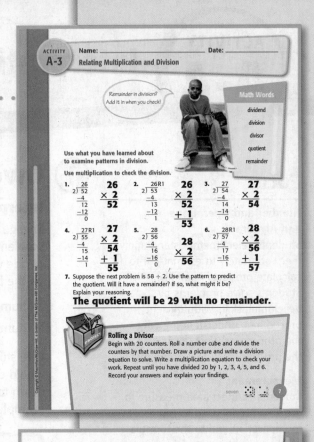

Activity A-3: Relating Multiplication and Division **T8**

Interpreting the Remainder

Focus

Number and Operations and Algebra

Students select methods and apply them accurately to estimate or to calculate products mentally. Students solve problems by developing skills with efficient procedures, understanding why the procedures work, and using the procedures in real problems.

Measurement

Students connect area measure to the area model used to represent multiplication and to the formula for the area of a rectangle.

Connections

Number and Operations

Students develop strategies for multidigit division by using models that represent division as the inverse of multiplication.

Review Vocabulary
dividend
quotient
remainder

Materials

base-ten blocks
color tiles

① Investigate (25–35 min)

Interpreting the Remainder

Engage students in a discussion about the remainder in a division problem. Tell students that for some problems, they will need to decide what to do with the remainder. Write the following options on the board:

Thumbs up: add 1 to the quotient

Thumbs down: drop the remainder

Give students the following situations. Have them decide what they would do with the remainders. Ask students to hold their thumbs up or down to show how they would interpret each remainder. Discuss each example as a class.

Magazines cost $3 each. How many magazines can Ray buy with $10? *Drop the remainder; thumbs down.*	A tennis ball can holds 3 tennis balls. How many cans are needed to store 10 tennis balls? *Add 1 to the quotient; thumbs up.*

Guiding Questions

- How are the remainders the same? How are they different? *The remainders are the same numbers, but how they are interpreted within the context of the problem is different.*

- Why is the remainder dropped in the problem about the magazines? *The remainder of 1 means that there is only $1 left, which is not enough to buy another magazine.*

- Why is 1 added to the quotient in the problem about the tennis balls? *Another can is needed to store the tenth tennis ball.*

- Would you ever have a situation where you would subtract 1 from the quotient to interpret the remainder? Explain. *No; the quotient shows equal groups, and the remainder is the number left over. The remainder would not be taken away from the number of equal groups.*

Connections and Extensions

- **Measurement**
  You have 36 color tiles. What is the largest rectangle you can make with a side length of 8 color tiles? Explain your reasoning. *An 8 by 4 rectangle with 32 tiles would be the largest. The 4 remaining tiles cannot be used to make another complete row of 8 tiles. For an 8 by 5 rectangle, you would need 40 tiles, which is more than you have.*

② Apply (25–35 min)

Student Page 9 Guide • • • • •

Exercises 1–6
Give students base-ten blocks to model each problem.

For which problems did you drop the remainder? Explain. *2, 3, and 4. Sample answer: Each situation called for equal groups of complete units. There could not be a group of partial units, so I dropped the remainder.*

 At Home

Have students share their stories with the class.

Which division equation did you write to represent the situation?

How did your family deal with the remainder?

Student Page 10 Guide • • • • •

Exercises 7–9
Encourage students to use base-ten blocks or draw a picture to model each problem.

Guide students to observe that all of the problems require two or more steps to solve.

What do you need to do before dividing? *Add the numbers of family members together.*

How did you solve Exercise 8? *Sample answer: I added 9 + 8, then multiplied by 2, then divided by 8. I added 1 to the quotient because they would need to buy another pack of water to have enough for everyone.*

Exercise 10
Have students work with a partner or in small groups. Then discuss students' responses as a class.

How are your stories for A and B alike? How are they different? *The division problem and solution are the same; the situation was different.*

③ Reflect (5–10 min)

- How can you tell when you need to drop the remainder? *I have to drop the remainder when I need a full unit, such as an amount of money to buy something.*

- How can you tell when you need to add 1 to the quotient? *I have to add 1 to the quotient when a partial unit cannot be used, such as another car to fit the remaining people.*

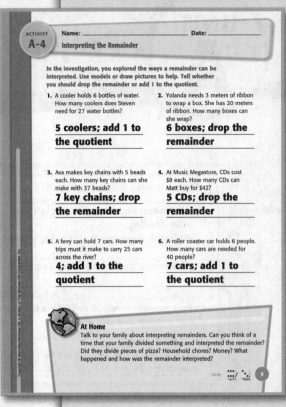

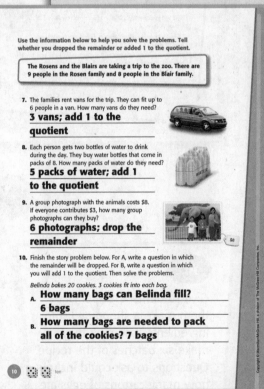

UNIT A

Projects and Discussion

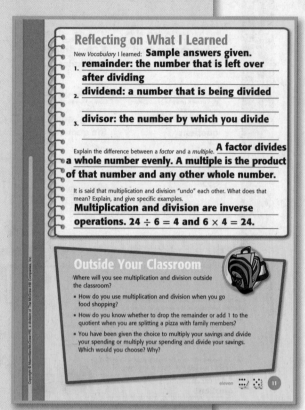

Reflecting on What I Learned

New *Vocabulary* I learned: **Sample answers given.**

1. **remainder: the number that is left over after dividing**

2. **dividend: a number that is being divided**

3. **divisor: the number by which you divide**

Explain the difference between a *factor* and a *multiple*. **A factor divides a whole number evenly. A multiple is the product of that number and any other whole number.**

It is said that multiplication and division "undo" each other. What does that mean? Explain, and give specific examples. **Multiplication and division are inverse operations. 24 ÷ 6 = 4 and 6 × 4 = 24.**

Outside Your Classroom

Where will you see multiplication and division outside the classroom?

- How do you use multiplication and division when you go food shopping?
- How do you know whether to drop the remainder or add 1 to the quotient when you are splitting a pizza with family members?
- You have been given the choice to multiply your savings and divide your spending or multiply your spending and divide your savings. Which would you choose? Why?

eleven · 11

 ## Vocabulary and Essential Learnings

Vocabulary

- Have students discuss in small groups the vocabulary terms and the definitions that they learned or reviewed in this unit.
- Generate a master list of terms on the board or have students create a Foldable®.
- Have students record three terms of their choice, along with a brief definition or picture for each one.

Essential Learnings

Arrange students in pairs. Have partners review the activities on pages 3 through 10 and discuss what they learned.

Allow time for students to share their essential learnings in small groups or as a class.

 ## Outside Your Classroom

You may wish to arrange students into four groups. Then have groups share their responses with the class. Allow time for classmates to extend or enrich the groups' responses.

Possible student responses:

- *Sample answers: comparing unit prices when different-sized packaging is available; buying a specified number of servings for everyone in the family; dividing the contents of a bottle or package by the number of people in a family*
- *Sample answers: drop the remainder and give the leftover pieces to parents or other adults; add 1 to the quotient so that everyone can have another piece of pizza*
- *Sample answer: I want my savings multiplied so I have more money and my spending divided so I spend less. The opposite is also acceptable with correct reasoning.*

 AL

Give students a recipe. Have them make a shopping list for ingredients assuming they make six batches of the recipe. Questions to ask could include how many cartons of eggs are needed.

Planning a Bowling Party

Materials

price list from local bowling alley or the prices listed on student page 12
play money

Pacing: 30–40 min

Introducing the Project

Guide students to review the concepts taught in the unit. You may wish to have students skim the pages in the unit to refresh their memories.

Ask students to think about other times that they have planned an activity such as going to the movies or going to the mall. Tell students they will be planning a day with two friends at the bowling alley.

Completing the Project

Discuss what the term *budget* means and how it applies to their projects. Have students read the questions in Step 1 and think about how their lists might look. Students may wish to compare their ideas with a partner or in small groups. Tell students to consider using their discussions to guide the creation of their lists. Then have students complete Steps 2 and 3 independently.

The table shown in Step 2 is an example only.

Extending the Project

Distribute play money (bills) and have students pay a "cashier" for their purchases. Have students divide the remaining money equally among the 3 friends.

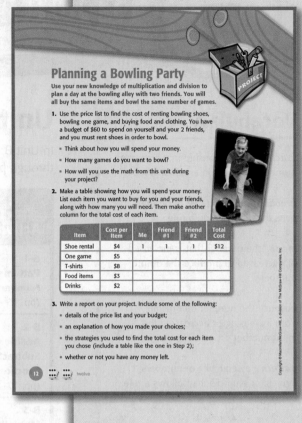

Planning a Bowling Party

Use your new knowledge of multiplication and division to plan a day at the bowling alley with two friends. You will all buy the same items and bowl the same number of games.

1. Use the price list to find the cost of renting bowling shoes, bowling one game, and buying food and clothing. You have a budget of $60 to spend on yourself and your 2 friends, and you must rent shoes in order to bowl.
   - Think about how you will spend your money.
   - How many games do you want to bowl?
   - How will you use the math from this unit during your project?

2. Make a table showing how you will spend your money. List each item you want to buy for you and your friends, along with how many you will need. Then make another column for the total cost of each item.

Item	Cost per Item	Me	Friend #1	Friend #2	Total Cost
Shoe rental	$4	1	1	1	$12
One game	$5				
T-shirts	$8				
Food items	$3				
Drinks	$2				

3. Write a report on your project. Include some of the following:
   - details of the price list and your budget;
   - an explanation of how you made your choices;
   - the strategies you used to find the total cost for each item you chose (include a table like the one in Step 2);
   - whether or not you have any money left.

12 twelve

Suggested Scoring Rubric

4	The student completes the project with accuracy and creativity. The student's report accurately and completely describes the project and is written in clear, concise language including appropriate math terminology and shows the strategies used to solve.
3	The student completes the project. The student's report has some inaccuracies and uses very little math terminology. The strategies used to solve are not clear.
2	The student does not complete all components of the project. The student's report is inaccurate, incomplete, and contains incorrect or no math terminology. No work was included to show the strategies used to solve.
1	The student's project is either incomplete or inaccurate. The student's report is inaccurate, incomplete, and contains incorrect math terminology.

UNIT B

Exploring Functions

Vocabulary

function a relationship in which one number depends on another number

function table a table of ordered pairs that is based on a rule

input the number that is increased or decreased to produce the output number

output the number that results from increasing or decreasing the input number

pattern a sequence of numbers, figures, or symbols that follows a rule or design

2, 4, 6, 8, 10

Unit-at-a-Glance

In Unit B, students gain understanding of number relationships through patterns and functions.

Activity	Focus	Student Investigation
B-1 Patterns in Numbers (pp. 15–16)	Students identify, describe, and extend numeric patterns.	Students use different manipulatives to create growing and repeating patterns.
B-2 Addition and Subtraction Functions (pp. 17–18)	Students identify, describe, and extend numeric patterns. They develop an understanding of how to describe a sequence of numbers or objects using a rule.	Students create a garden design using a function rule.
B-3 Multiplication and Division Functions (pp. 19–20)	Students identify, describe, and extend numeric patterns. They develop an understanding of how to describe a sequence of numbers or objects using a rule.	Students find a relationship between a map scale and real distances and create a function rule.
Unit Project: Create a Function Machine Game (p. 22)	Students relate the concepts and skills they have learned to the real world.	Students apply what they have learned about patterns and functions to create a game using a function machine.

Page Numbers

Each page number is accompanied by a function equation in which ▲ equals the input and the output (□) equals the page number.

Guiding Questions

- What is the input?
- What is another pair of numbers that would work for this equation? Create a function table.
- Write or tell a story problem that fits the equation.

Unit Opener

You can open the unit by having students read through the objectives they will accomplish during the unit. Have students restate objectives in their own words to ensure comprehension.

Scaffolding Questions

What is an example of a skip counting pattern? How are the numbers related? *5, 10, 15, 20, 25, 30; Each number is 5 more than the number before it.*

How do you solve these problems?

$3 + 6 = 13 - \underline{4}$

$24 \div \underline{3} = 4 \times 2$

Vocabulary

WRITING IN MATH

The beginning of the unit is a great time to start a new wall chart.

Encourage students to write the definitions in their math journals. Writing their own definitions or creating drawings will help internalize the information.

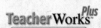
Home Letter

Have students take the Home Letter home.

Look at the Projects and Discussions throughout the unit to see if any additional opportunities are available for work at home.

ELL

Encourage students to visit the online eGlossary with parents to see vocabulary in 13 languages.

TeacherWorks *Plus*

See "Home E-mail" as an alternative for communication. From the Lesson Planner, select the e-mail document for this unit, double-click the file, and edit in the Worksheet Editor.

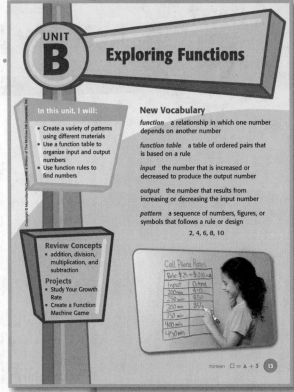

UNIT B Exploring Functions

In this unit, I will:
- Create a variety of patterns using different materials
- Use a function table to organize input and output numbers
- Use function rules to find numbers

Review Concepts
- addition, division, multiplication, and subtraction

Projects
- Study Your Growth Rate
- Create a Function Machine Game

New Vocabulary

function a relationship in which one number depends on another number

function table a table of ordered pairs that is based on a rule

input the number that is increased or decreased to produce the output number

output the number that results from increasing or decreasing the input number

pattern a sequence of numbers, figures, or symbols that follows a rule or design

2, 4, 6, 8, 10

thirteen □ = ▲ + 3   13

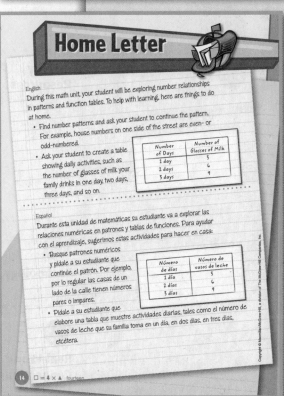

Home Letter

English

During this math unit, your student will be exploring number relationships in patterns and function tables. To help with learning, here are things to do at home.

- Find number patterns and ask your student to continue the pattern. For example, house numbers on one side of the street are even- or odd-numbered.
- Ask your student to create a table showing daily activities, such as the number of glasses of milk your family drinks in one day, two days, three days, and so on.

Number of Days	Number of Glasses of Milk
1 day	3
2 days	6
3 days	9

Español

Durante esta unidad de matemáticas su estudiante va a explorar las relaciones numéricas en patrones y tablas de funciones. Para ayudar con el aprendizaje, sugerimos estas actividades para hacer en casa:

- Busque patrones numéricos y pídale a su estudiante que continúe el patrón. Por ejemplo, por lo regular las casas de un lado de la calle tienen números pares o impares.
- Pídale a su estudiante que elabore una tabla que muestre actividades diarias, tales como el número de vasos de leche que su familia toma en un día, en dos días, en tres días, etcétera.

Número de días	Número de vasos de leche
1 día	3
2 días	6
3 días	9

14 □ = 4 × ▲   fourteen

UNIT B

Activity Planner

KEY

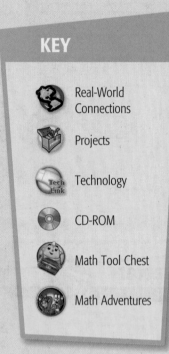

- Real-World Connections
- Projects
- Technology
- CD-ROM
- Math Tool Chest
- Math Adventures

	Activity B-1 Pacing: 60–75 min	**Activity B-2** Pacing: 70–85 min
Activity/ Objective	**Patterns in Numbers** (pp. 15–16) **Objective** Describe, extend, and apply number patterns to solve problems.	**Addition and Subtraction Functions** (pp. 17–18) **Objective** Use function rules with addition and subtraction.
Math Vocabulary	function table pattern	function output input **Review Vocabulary** function table pattern
Activity Resources	**Manipulatives** clocks connecting cubes counters coins pattern blocks	**Materials** yardsticks or measuring tape **Manipulatives** counters
Technology	**Math Tool Chest** Counters Pattern Blocks	**Math Adventures** Mount Frost Robo Works
Real-World Connections	**At Home** Make function tables about number relationships at home.	
Small Projects		**Growth Rate** Measure your height and use a function table to determine how tall you might be after a specific number of years.

Activity B-3	Pacing: 75–90 min	Unit Project	Pacing: 45 min	

Activity B-3
Multiplication and Division Functions
(pp. 19–20)

Objective
Use function rules with multiplication and division.

Unit Project
Create a Function Machine Game
(p. 22)

Objective
Create a game using a function machine.

Activity/ Objective

Review Vocabulary
function
function table
input
output

Math Vocabulary

Materials
yardsticks or measuring tape
teacher-made maps of the
   classroom

Manipulatives
rulers

Materials
boxes	scissors
glue sticks	string or yarn
index cards	tape
markers	chart paper

Manipulatives
number cubes
spinners

Activity Resources

Math Adventures
Robo Works

Personal Tutor

Technology

In Science
Create a function table representing the amount of garbage you produce each day, each month, and each year.

Real-World Connections

Small Projects

Differentiation and Assessment

Differentiated Instruction

Below are suggestions on differentiating the materials presented in this unit. Additional modifications should be considered.

Below Level (BL) | Above Level (AL) | English Language Learners (ELL)

ACTIVITY B-1

Below Level

Exercise 3
Have students write "+ 6" on the line between each column to help them calculate the number of hours.
Students can add a *process* column to function tables so they can *see* the rule.

Above Level

Exercises 3 and 4
Have students expand the range of days and predict the number of hours for 10 days and 20 days (or about one month). Then encourage them to check their predictions by calculating the exact number of hours. Students can add a *process* column to function tables so they can *see* the rule.

English Language Learners

Exercises 3 and 4
Talk about the different meanings of the word *table*. A table can be a piece of furniture, and it can also be a way to organize information with rows and columns. Students can add a *process* column to function tables so they can *see* the rule.

ACTIVITY B-2

Below Level

Exercises 4–6
Have students write the function rule between the two columns of each function table and refer to the rule when solving the problems.

Above Level

Exercise 5
Have students create a new problem with their time zone as the input numbers and a different time zone as the output numbers. Provide students with a time zone chart if needed.

English Language Learners

Have students add the words *input* and *output* to a word bank. Have them circle the smaller words *in* and *out* within each word to help remind them that the input number goes *in* the equation and the output number comes *out*.

ACTIVITY B-3

Below Level

Exercises 6–8
Have students write the function rule between the two columns of each function table. Also, encourage students to look for patterns in the tables to check their answers.

Above Level

Exercises 6–8
Have students revise one of the function tables using a different function rule. Ask them to switch their problem with a partner to solve.

English Language Learners

In Science
Have students add the words *landfill, garbage,* and *trash* to a word bank and explain the meanings of the terms. Discuss other words that might be new, such as *recycle* and *reuse*.

Performance-Based Assessment

What's My Rule? (p. A5)

In *What's My Rule?*, students first complete a table according to a rule they figure out. Students then must write their own rule and complete a table with their rule.

Connections

What's My Rule? also covers the following skills and concepts:

- Pattern recognition
- Multiplication
- Division
- Reasoning

Targeting the Task

- **Pretest** – Use Exercises 1–4 in the *What's My Rule?* assessment to determine students' understanding of relationships between two sets of numbers. For those students who do not have this understanding, completing this unit is needed.
- **Formative** – *What's My Rule?* can be broken down and administered in sections according to the lessons.
- **Summative** – Administer the complete *What's My Rule?* performance-based assessment.

Differentiation

Students can be given input/output tables to familiarize them with finding the rule. Tables such as the following may be used.

Rule:	
Input	**Output**
2	16
3	24
4	?
5	?
6	48

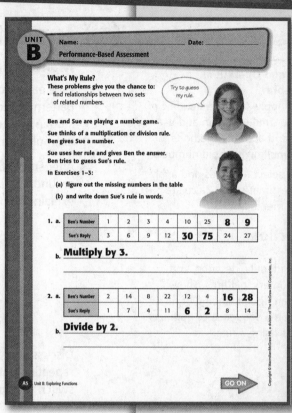

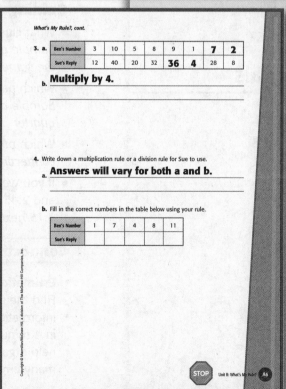

Patterns in Numbers

Focus

Number and Operations and Algebra

Students apply an understanding of models for multiplication and use efficient and accurate methods to multiply multidigit whole numbers.

Students select methods and apply them to estimate or to calculate products mentally.

Connections

Algebra

Students identify, describe, and extend numeric patterns. They develop an understanding of how to describe a sequence of numbers or objects using a rule.

Vocabulary

function table

pattern

Materials

clocks
counters
pattern blocks
connecting cubes
coins

① Investigate (30–35 min)

Making Repeating Patterns and Growing Patterns

Give each small group of students a different set of manipulatives—pattern blocks, counters, connecting cubes, coins, and clocks. Tell students to use their materials to make a pattern. Provide several examples on the board.

After students have finished making their patterns, invite them to walk around and look at other groups' patterns. Ask them to identify and explain the pattern unit represented by each display.

Discuss students' observations of the patterns. Review examples of repeating patterns and growing patterns. If time allows, have groups switch manipulatives and make a new pattern.

Guiding Questions

- What clues did you use to find the pattern in each group's display? *Sample answer: I looked from left to right and tried to find what was the same and what was different each time.*

- Which patterns displayed are repeating patterns? *Answers will vary. Sample answer: coin pattern: dime, dime, quarter, dime, dime, quarter*

- Which patterns displayed are growing patterns? *Sample answer: the connecting cubes: 3 rows of 2; 4 rows of 3; 5 rows of 4*

- If you were to continue a clock pattern that showed 1:15, 1:45, 2:15, and 2:45, what time would you show next? Explain. *I would show 3:15 next; the time increases by $\frac{1}{2}$ hour each time.*

Connections and Extensions

Estimation Skills

Find the number of times you can jump rope in 2 minutes. Use this information to estimate about how many times you can jump rope in 4 minutes, 6 minutes, 8 minutes, and 10 minutes. Make a table to help organize your data. Using this information, can you estimate how many times you can jump rope in 60 minutes?

② Apply (25–30 min)

Student Page 15 Guide ·····

Exercises 1 and 2
Have students describe the relationship of the number of days to the number of hours.

What pattern do you see? *Sample answer: The number of hours increases by 6 each day. If you multiply 6 times the number of days, the product is the number of hours.*

Exercises 3 and 4
Have students share how they completed the function table.

How does the function table help you organize the pattern? *Sample answer: It puts the number of days and the number of hours in order. I can read the pattern by reading across or up and down.*

At Home
Have students discuss other number relationships they could use to create a function table.

Student Page 16 Guide ·····

Exercises 5–8
Have students discuss results in small groups and then as a class.

In Exercises 7 and 8, how did you find the pattern for the ticket numbers? *Sample answer: I compared the numbers. There was a difference of 105 between each number.*

Exercises 9 and 10
Review how to set up a function table with students.

In Exercise 9, how did you know what numbers to put on the boxes? *Sample answer: I made a function table. I started with 25 cartons for Box 1 and then added 25 for each box. So, Boxes 1 through 4 were 25, 50, 75, and 100.*

③ Reflect (5–10 min)

- How does a function table help us to identify number patterns? *Sample answer: It helps us to compare number relationships by organizing the information in rows and columns.*

- When might you use a function table to help you solve a problem? *Sample answer: to find out how many CDs I can buy for $5, $10, or $15*

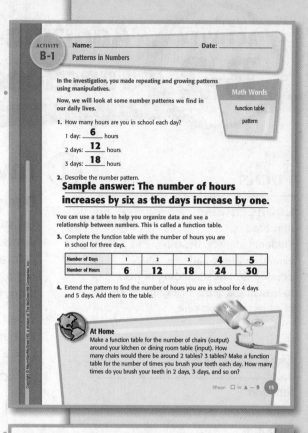

Addition and Subtraction Functions

Focus

Connections

Algebra
Students identify, describe, and extend numeric patterns. They develop an understanding of how to describe a sequence of numbers or objects using a rule.

Vocabulary

function

input

output

Review Vocabulary
function table
pattern

Materials

yardstick or measuring tape
counters

① Investigate (40–45 min)

Designing a Garden: Using Function Rules

Tell students this story: Sylvia is planning a design for her tulip garden. She wants each row to have space for two more tulip plants than the row before it. Have students draw a plan for her garden showing the number of tulip bulbs planted in each row. Students may use counters to help them figure out the placement of the bulbs before drawing their designs.

When students are finished with their designs, discuss the function rule that applies to each design. Draw a function table to illustrate the rule. $\square = \blacktriangle + 2$

Sylvia's Garden Design

Rule: $\square = \blacktriangle + 2$	
Input (▲): number of bulbs in row	Output (□): number of bulbs in next row
1	3
3	5
5	7
7	9
9	11

Guiding Questions

- How did you create the design for your tulip garden? How many tulip bulbs are in the first row? What shape is your garden? *Sample answer: I started the first row with one tulip bulb. Then I started making rows that were a little longer on each side and added two more bulbs in each row. My garden is in the shape of a triangle.*

- Look at the number of bulbs in each row. Is there a pattern? *Sample answer: Yes; the bulbs increase by 2 as the rows increase by 1.*

- Can you write number sentences that compare two rows at a time, moving from the first row to the last row? *Sample answer: 1 + 2 = 3; 3 + 2 = 5, etc.*

- Using the rule, how many tulips would be in row 15? *29 tulips*

Connections and Extensions

Graphing

Show students a bar graph displaying fundraiser pizza sales for four students. If each person sold 15 more pizzas, how many pizzas would each student sell? Use a function table to show the changes. Then, create a new graph to represent the new sales numbers.

School Fundraiser Pizza Sales

② Apply (25–30 min)

Student Page 17 Guide · · · · ·

Exercises 1–3
Have students share responses in small groups. Talk about the relationship between the input number, the output number, and the function rule.

If you know the output number and the rule, can you find the input number? If so, give an example. *Sample answer: Yes; if I know that the output number is 18 and the rule is □ = ▲ + 3, then the input number is 18 − 3, or 15.*

Growth Rate
Remind students that at some point, growth rates slow down and then stop.

Encourage students to round their heights to the nearest inch.

Student Page 18 Guide · · · · ·

Exercises 4–6
Have students discuss results in small groups and then as a class. Connect the rule to the input and output numbers in the function table.

In Exercise 4, what rule did you use to find the output numbers? *□ = ▲ + 12*

In Exercise 6, what rule did you use? *□ = ▲ − 15*

How could you find out how many books were left at the library after the donation? *I could add all the output numbers together.*

Exercises 7 and 8
Have students share their function tables with a partner.

How did you know how big to make your table? *When the output was 18, I could answer the question, so the table was big enough.*

③ Reflect (5–10 min)

- What is the relationship between the input and output numbers and the addition or subtraction function rule? *Sample answer: The function rule tells what to do to the input number to get the output number.*

- When might you use addition and subtraction function rules and function tables to help you solve a problem? *Sample answer: I might use them when I need to add or subtract the same number from different amounts, such as taking away three sheets of paper from each stack or adding two chairs to each table.*

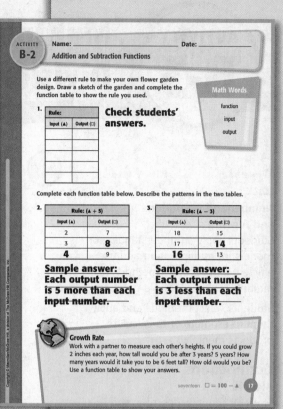

ACTIVITY B-2
Name: _____ Date: _____
Addition and Subtraction Functions

Use a different rule to make your own flower garden design. Draw a sketch of the garden and complete the function table to show the rule you used.

Math Words
function
input
output

1.
Rule:	
Input (▲)	Output (□)

Check students' answers.

Complete each function table below. Describe the patterns in the two tables.

2.
Rule: (▲ + 5)	
Input (▲)	Output (□)
2	7
3	**8**
4	9

3.
Rule: (▲ − 3)	
Input (▲)	Output (□)
18	15
17	**14**
16	13

Sample answer: Each output number is 5 more than each input number.

Sample answer: Each output number is 3 less than each input number.

Growth Rate
Work with a partner to measure each other's heights. If you could grow 2 inches each year, how tall would you be after 3 years? 5 years? How many years would it take you to be 6 feet tall? How old would you be? Use a function table to show your answers.

seventeen □ = 100 − ▲   **17**

You can use function tables to solve problems. Complete each function table. Use an equation to define the function rule.

4. Each row in an auditorium has 12 more seats than its row number. In which row can a group of 16 people sit together?
   row 4
   Function rule: □ = ▲ + 12

Input (▲) Row Number	Output (□) Number of Seats
1	13
2	**14**
3	**15**
4	**16**

5. The time in California is 3 hours earlier than the time in New York. What time is it in California when it is 2:00 in New York?
   11:00
   Function rule: □ = ▲ − 3

Input (▲) New York Time	Output (□) California Time
12:00	9:00
2:00	**11:00**
4:00	1:00
6:00	**3:00**

6. In the library, 15 books from each shelf were donated to charity. How many books were left on a shelf that started with 35 books?
   20 books
   Function rule: □ = ▲ − 15

Input (▲) Number of Books per shelf Before Donation	Output (□) Number of Books per shelf After Donation
65	50
55	**40**
45	**30**
35	**20**

Use a function table to solve the problem.

7. Juanita has a brother who is 3 years older than she is. Juanita is 10 years old. Make a function table to show their ages. How old will Juanita be when her brother is 18?
   15

   Check students' function tables.

8. What function rule did you use for Exercise 7?
   □ = ▲ + 3 or brother = Juanita + 3

18 2 × ▲ = □ eighteen

ACTIVITY B-3
Multiplication and Division Functions

Focus

Number and Operations and Algebra

Students apply an understanding of models for multiplication and use efficient and accurate methods to multiply multidigit whole numbers.

Students select methods and apply them to estimate or to calculate products mentally.

Connections

Algebra

Students identify, describe, and extend numeric patterns. They develop an understanding of how to describe a sequence of numbers or objects using a rule.

Review Vocabulary

function
function table
input
output

Materials

yardsticks or measuring tape
teacher-made maps of the
   classroom
rulers

① Investigate (40–45 min)

Map Scales: Comparing Measurements

Give each small group of students measuring tools and a simple map of the classroom showing its perimeter and a few landmarks, such as the board and the teacher's desk. Have students find the scale of the map by comparing the length and width of the room to the length and width on the classroom map (for example: 1 inch = 4 feet). Have students label the scale on the map. Ask them to also label each side of the room on the map with the length and width in both inches and feet. Discuss the relationship of the map scale to the room.

Guiding Questions

- How did you find the scale of your map? *Sample answer: First we measured the side lengths of the room on the map in inches. Next, we measured the length and width of the classroom in feet. Then we made a function table to compare the lengths, starting with the greatest length and working backward.*

- How can you use the function table to find the number of feet equal to 7 inches, 6 inches, 5 inches, 4 inches, and so on? *Sample answer: The number of inches is in the input column and the number of feet is in the output column.*

- What rule can your write for the function table? *Answers will vary. Sample answer: The number of feet is equal to the number of inches times four:* $\square = \blacktriangle \times 4$.

Connections and Extensions

Algebra
Have students find function rules involving two operations and extend the function tables. Remind students of the order of operations.

Input(▲)	Output(□)
5	11
6	13
7	15
8	17

$\square = 2\blacktriangle + 1$

Input(▲)	Output(□)
48	10
40	8
36	7
28	5

$\square = \blacktriangle \div 4 - 2$

Input(▲)	Output(□)
7	30
8	35
2	5
4	15

$\square = 5\blacktriangle - 5$

Measurement
Have students make a table showing the relationship of the number of inches to feet, or feet to yards. Then have them write the function rule that relates the two units of measurement. This activity can also be done with weight and capacity, in both customary and metric units.

② Apply (30–35 min)

Student Page 19 Guide

Exercises 1–5
Have students share their strategies for finding the function rules and their completed function tables with a partner.

Have students compare their story problems.

How can you tell if your function rule should involve multiplication, division, addition, or subtraction? *Sample answer: I can compare the input and output numbers. When the output numbers are less than the input numbers, the function rule might involve subtraction or division. When the output numbers are greater than the input numbers, the function rule might involve addition or multiplication.*

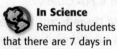 **In Science**
Remind students that there are 7 days in 1 week and 365 days in 1 year.

Encourage students to think about the effects of garbage produced each day. Talk about ways they can reduce trash by reusing and recycling.

Student Page 20 Guide

Exercises 6–8
Encourage students to explain the function rules in their own words and note patterns in their tables.

In Exercise 8, what patterns do you see in your function table? *As the number of apartment units increases by ten, the number of floors increases by five. Five is half of ten, so it fits the rule.*

Exercises 9 and 10
Have students discuss results with a partner and then with the class.

In Exercise 10, how did you find the sale price for the baseball caps? *Sample answer: I divided the normal price of the baseball caps by 4; $16 ÷ 4 = $4.*

③ Reflect (5–10 min)

- How could you find the value for □ given the rule □ = ▲ ÷ 7, when ▲ is 63? *I would substitute 63 for ▲; 63 ÷ 7 = 9. So, □ = 9.*

- When might you use a function table for the rule □ = 4 × ▲? *Sample answers: when you are trying to find the number of wheels given a number of cars; when you are trying to find the number of chair legs given a number of chairs*

ACTIVITY **B-3** Name: _____ Date: _____
Multiplication and Division Functions

In the investigation, you wrote a function rule that used multiplication. Let's explore more multiplication and division function rules. Complete the table. Write the rule.

1.

Input (▲)	Output (□)
2	8
3	12
4	16
5	**20**

□ = ▲ × 4

2.

Input (▲)	Output (□)
100	10
90	9
80	8
70	**7**

□ = ▲ ÷ 10

3.

Input (▲)	Output (□)
48	6
40	5
32	**4**
24	3

□ = ▲ ÷ 8

4.

Input (▲)	Output (□)
1	3
3	9
6	18
9	27

□ = ▲ × 3

5. Write a story problem that uses the function rule in Exercise 4.
Sample answer: For every aluminum can that Sam recycles, he gets paid 3 cents.

 In Science
The average person throws away about 5 pounds of garbage each day. Many times, garbage is collected and taken to a landfill. Create a function table that shows how much garbage a person throws away in 1 week, 1 month, and 1 year. What could you do to reduce the amount of trash you throw away each day?

nineteen □ = ▲ − 10 **19**

Complete each function table. Use the table to solve the problem. Then write the function rule.

6. You need 3 cups of flour for one batch of muffins. How many cups of flour do you need for 4 batches?
12 cups
Function rule: □ = ▲ × 3

Input (▲) Batches	Output (□) Cups
1	3
2	**6**
3	**9**
4	**12**
5	**15**

7. You earn $15 every 3 hours you work. You want to make enough money to buy a $45 video game. How many hours do you need to work to buy the video game?
9 hours
Function rule: □ = ▲ × 5

Input (▲) Hours	Output (□) Dollars
3	$15
6	**$30**
9	**$45**

8. Each apartment building on your block has half as many floors as the number of apartment units. How many floors are there in a building with 20 apartment units? 30 apartment units? 40 apartment units?
10 floors, 15 floors, and 20 floors
Function rule: □ = ▲ ÷ 2

Input (▲) Apartment Units	Output (□) Floors
20	**10**
30	**15**
40	**20**

Use the sign to complete the problems.

9. The local clothing store is having a clearance sale. You can find the sale prices on the sign. What function rule describes the price relationships?
□ = ▲ ÷ 4

10. Baseball caps are also on sale. They normally cost $16. What is the sale price for baseball caps?
$4

Clearance Sale

	Original	Sale Price
Sweaters	$48	$12
Pants	$44	$11
Shirts	$40	$10
Shoes	$36	$9
Baseball caps	$16	**$4**

20 □ = 5 × ▲ twenty

Vocabulary and Essential Learnings

Vocabulary

- Have students discuss in small groups the vocabulary terms and the definitions that they learned or reviewed in this unit.

- Generate a master list of terms on the board or have students create a Foldable®.

- Have students record three terms of their choice, along with a brief definition or picture for each one.

Essential Learnings

Arrange students in pairs. Have partners review the activities on pages 15 through 20 and discuss what they learned.

Allow time for students to share their essential learnings in small groups or as a class.

Outside Your Classroom

Possible student responses:

- Do you have enough time to listen to 5, 10, 15, or 20 songs? *I have enough time to listen to 5 (15 minutes), 10 (30 minutes), and 15 (45 minutes) songs, but not enough time to listen to 20 (60 minutes) songs.*

- How many points did each team score at the end of 5 rounds? *Team A scored 22 points, and Team B scored 20 points at the end of 5 rounds.*

- How many cans do you need to buy to get 10 free cans? *I need to buy 30 cans to get 10 free cans.*

Reflecting on What I Learned

New *Vocabulary* I learned: **Sample answers given.**

1. **function: a relationship in which one number depends on another number**
2. **input: the number that is increased or decreased to produce the output number**
3. **pattern : a sequence of numbers, figures, or symbols that follows a rule or design**

What did you learn about function tables and function rules?
I can make a function table to organize my input and output numbers. A function rule tells me how an input number and output number are related.

List one relationship between input and output numbers and the function rule you learned.
When you follow the function rule, you add, subtract, multiply, or divide the input number to find the output number.

Outside Your Classroom

Where will you use functions outside the classroom?

- You have 50 minutes before dinner. The length of a song is about 3 minutes. Do you have enough time to listen to 5, 10, 15, or 20 songs?

- In the first round of the game, Team A scored 6 points and Team B scored 4 points. After the first round, both teams scored 4 points each round. How many points did each team score at the end of 5 rounds?

- For every 6 cans of soup you buy, you get 2 free cans. How many cans do you need to buy to get 10 free cans of soup?

twenty-one □ = 7 × ▲   **21**

AL

Your cell phone plan has a setup fee of $25.00. It includes 100 free minutes and charges $0.10 for each additional minute. What would your monthly bill be if you used 250 minutes?

Extension: Have students compare this plan with one in which the setup fee is $50.00 with unlimited free minutes.

Create a Function Machine Game

Materials

boxes   scissors
glue sticks   string or yarn
index cards   tape
markers   chart paper
number cubes
spinners

Pacing: 45 min

Introducing the Project

Before students begin working on the project, have them name number games they have played. Invite students to describe what makes a good game to play. Write these characteristics on chart paper and post for students to refer to during the project.

Completing the Project

Have students read the questions in Step 1 and respond to them in small groups. Tell students to use their responses to guide them in the creation of their Function Machine Game. Ask them to think about what a function machine does and how they can design it so it is easy to use. Then, have students complete Steps 2 and 3 independently.

Extending the Project

Ask students to evaluate their games and revise them if needed. Perhaps change the rule from addition or subtraction to multiplication or division.

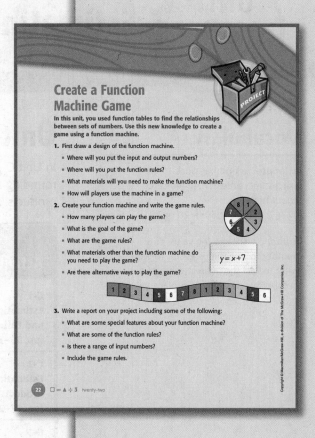

Create a Function Machine Game

In this unit, you used function tables to find the relationships between sets of numbers. Use this new knowledge to create a game using a function machine.

1. First draw a design of the function machine.
   - Where will you put the input and output numbers?
   - Where will you put the function rules?
   - What materials will you need to make the function machine?
   - How will players use the machine in a game?

2. Create your function machine and write the game rules.
   - How many players can play the game?
   - What is the goal of the game?
   - What are the game rules?
   - What materials other than the function machine do you need to play the game?
   - Are there alternative ways to play the game?

   $y = x + 7$

3. Write a report on your project including some of the following:
   - What are some special features about your function machine?
   - What are some of the function rules?
   - Is there a range of input numbers?
   - Include the game rules.

22   □ = ▲ ÷ 3   twenty-two

Suggested Scoring Rubric

4	The student completes the project with accuracy and creativity. The student's report accurately and completely describes the project and is written in clear, concise language including appropriate math terminology.
3	The student completes the project. The student's report has some inaccuracies and uses very little math terminology.
2	The student does not complete all the components of the project. The student's report has some inaccuracies and uses very little math terminology.
1	The student's project is either incomplete or inaccurate. The student's report is inaccurate, incomplete and contains incorrect or no math terminology.

UNIT C — Estimating

Vocabulary

estimate a number close to an exact value; an estimate indicates *about* how much
47 + 22 is about 50 + 20 or 70

round to change the value of a number to one that is easier to work with; to find the nearest value of a number based on a given place value

Unit-at-a-Glance

In Unit C, students gain understanding of estimation through rounding and finding compatible numbers for sums, differences, products, and quotients.

Activity	Focus	Student Investigation
C-1 Estimating Sums and Differences (pp. 25–26)	Students determine the relative sizes of amounts (or distances) using estimation.	Students estimate the number of beans in a jar.
C-2 Estimating Products (pp. 27–28)	Students select the methods and apply them to estimate or calculate products mentally.	Students estimate the area of classroom objects using grid paper.
C-3 Estimating Quotients (pp. 29–30)	Students select the methods and apply them to estimate or calculate products mentally.	Students estimate the number of miles traveled each hour between two cities.
Unit Project: Planning a Vacation (p. 32)	Students relate the concepts and skills they have learned to the real world.	Students use concepts of estimation to plan a vacation and write a travel diary.

Page Numbers

Each page number in this lesson includes base-ten blocks as a representation.

Guiding Questions

- How many one blocks (unit blocks) do you need to make a 10 rod?
- How many rods and blocks would you have if you added the two pages together?
- Round the page number to the nearest tens place.

Unit Opener

Student Page 23 Guide · · · · · · · ·

You can open the unit by having students read through the objectives they will accomplish during the unit. Have students restate objectives in their own words to ensure comprehension.

Scaffolding Questions	Can you round 245 to the greatest place value? *200*
	Write the fact family for 3, 6, and 18. *3 × 6 = 18; 6 × 3 = 18; 18 ÷ 3 = 6; 18 ÷ 6 = 3*
Vocabulary	The beginning of the unit is a great time to start a new wall chart.
WRITING IN MATH ▶	Encourage students to write the definitions in their math journals. Writing their own definitions or creating drawings will help internalize the information.
	Students may have trouble with *overestimating* and *underestimating*. Remind students that although an estimate will usually be higher or lower than the actual answer, an overestimate is when the estimate is much higher than the actual answer, whereas an underestimate is when the estimate is much lower than the actual answer.

Student Page 24 Guide · · · · · · · ·

Home Letter	Have students take the Home Letter home.
	Look at the Projects and Discussions throughout the unit to see if any additional opportunities are available for work at home.
ELL	Encourage students to visit the online eGlossary with parents to see vocabulary in 13 languages.
TeacherWorks *Plus*	See "Home E-mail" as an alternative for communication. From the Lesson Planner, select the e-mail document for this unit, double-click the file, and edit in the Worksheet Editor.

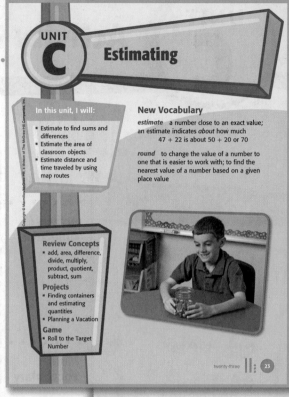

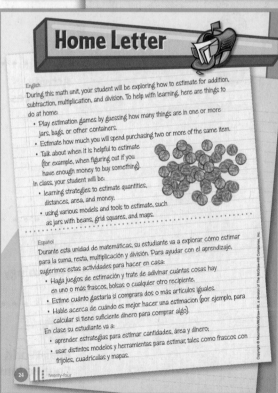

UNIT C
Activity Planner

KEY

🌐 Real-World Connections

📦 Projects

💻 Technology

💿 CD-ROM

🎮 Math Tool Chest

🎭 Math Adventures

	Activity C-1 Pacing: 55–75 min	**Activity C-2** Pacing: 60–80 min
Activity/ Objective	**Estimating Sums and Differences** (pp. 25–26) **Objective** Use estimation strategies to estimate sums and differences.	**Estimating Products** (pp. 27–28) **Objective** Use estimation strategies to estimate products.
Math Vocabulary	**estimate** **round (rounding)** **Review Vocabulary** difference sum	**Review Vocabulary** area multiply estimate product
Activity Resources	**Materials** different sizes of jars with caps beans **Manipulatives** number cubes	**Materials** one-inch grid paper book covers (of various sizes) 11" x 17" paper
Technology	**Personal Tutor**	🌐 **Math Adventures** Robo Works
Real-World Connections		**In Science** Find out about how much garbage your family throws away in one day, one week, one month, and one year.
Small Projects	**Container Estimates** Estimate the number of items in different containers and sort the containers based on those estimates.	

Activity C-3 — Pacing: 55–75 min	**Unit Project** — Pacing: 40 min	

Activity C-3
Pacing: 55–75 min

Unit Project
Pacing: 40 min

Estimating Quotients
(pp. 29–30)

Planning a Vacation
(p. 32)

Activity/
Objective

Objective
Use estimation strategies
to estimate quotients.

Objective
Use concepts taught in the unit
to plan a vacation and write a
travel diary.

Math
Vocabulary

Review Vocabulary
divide
quotient

Activity
Resources

Materials
travel books and brochures
restaurant menus
United States maps
Internet

Math Adventures
Robo Works
Personal Tutor

Math Tool Chest
Money
Tables

Technology

Real-World
Connections

Small
Projects

Differentiated Instruction

Below are suggestions on differentiating the materials presented in this unit. Additional modifications should be considered.

Below Level **BL**	Above Level **AL**	English Language Learners **ELL**
ACTIVITY C-1 **Exercises 7–13** Have students work with an above-level peer to complete these exercises.		Provide students with an example of an *overestimate* and an *underestimate*. For example, a good estimate of 229 + 306 would be 500. An *overestimate* could be 600 and an *underestimate* could be 400.
ACTIVITY C-2 **Exercise 4** Guide students to first determine how many tiles the rug is covering, and then add this amount to their estimate of the number of tiles showing.	**Measurement Connection** Have pairs of students sketch a room floor and give the estimated area and one side length. Have students trade drawings and solve for the missing length.	Review with students that *area* is the number of square units needed to cover the inside of an object. Review how to find area by multiplying length times width.
ACTIVITY C-3 **Exercise 8** Have students work with a partner to complete this exercise.	**Measurement Connection** Have students calculate how long it would take the cheetah to travel other distances, such as from their house to a vacation spot.	

Performance-Based Assessment

Brick Wall (p. A10)

In *Brick Wall,* students first make an estimate and then explain how they determined that estimate.

Connections

Brick Wall also covers the following skills and concepts:

- Problem solving
- Reasoning
- Computation
- Estimation

Targeting the Task

- **Pretest** – *Brick Wall* is one item with a required explanation and can be given to determine students' understanding of estimation and strategies for estimation. For students who do not have this understanding, completing this unit is needed.

- **Formative** – Provide students with opportunities to estimate e.g., number of books in the school library, total number of tables in all the rooms in the school, etc.

- **Summative** – Administer *Brick Wall* completely.

Differentiation

Students need a context for estimation. Why wouldn't they want an exact answer? Provide several types of estimation experiences for students.

- Measurement: For example, students take some one-inch squares around the room and estimate how many inches something is, or measure their heights and estimate the height of the door.

- Computational: Bring in receipts or store flyers from the grocery store and have students estimate how much they can buy or how much they should budget.

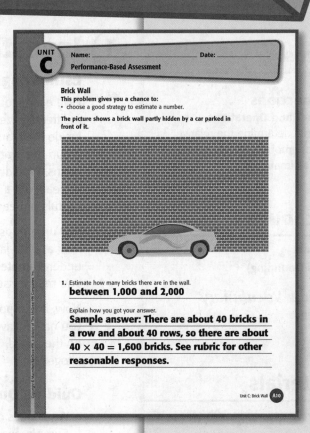

UNIT C

Name: _____ Date: _____

Performance-Based Assessment

Brick Wall
This problem gives you a chance to:
- choose a good strategy to estimate a number.

The picture shows a brick wall partly hidden by a car parked in front of it.

1. Estimate how many bricks there are in the wall.
   between 1,000 and 2,000

   Explain how you got your answer.
   Sample answer: There are about 40 bricks in a row and about 40 rows, so there are about 40 × 40 = 1,600 bricks. See rubric for other reasonable responses.

Unit C: Brick Wall **A10**

Estimating Sums and Differences

Focus

Connections
Number and Operations
Students determine the relative sizes of amounts (or distances) using estimation.

Vocabulary

estimate
round (rounding)

Review Vocabulary
difference
sum

Materials

different sizes of jars with caps
beans
number cubes

① Investigate (20–25 min)

Estimating

Give each group of students a jar filled with beans. Each jar should be a different size. Have each group estimate about how many beans are inside their jar. Have one person write the estimate on paper. After each group has written their estimate, ask them to take out one capful of beans. Would you like to change your estimate? If so, write it down. Repeat with a second capful of beans. Then have students pour the two capfuls of beans back into the jar.

Pair up groups and have them compare their estimates. Have them look at both jars of beans to compare. Did you overestimate? Did you underestimate? What is the difference between your two estimates? You may revise your estimate for the last time.

Now, if you pour your beans together, about how many beans would you have? Have students add their estimates together and write them on the board. Then, as a class, estimate how many beans you have altogether.

Guiding Questions

- What clues did you use to estimate the number of beans in your jar? *Sample answers: We counted the number of beans in the jar that we could see. We compared the leftover space after we took away the capfuls of beans to the space filled with the beans.*

- What are some things that helped you decide to change your estimate? Did you overestimate or underestimate? *Answers will vary.*

- When might you estimate to find the sum or difference of two quantities? *Sample answers: when I want to know about how many pages I have left to read in a book; when I want to know about how much money I need to buy something at the store*

Connections and Extensions

Estimation
Play *Roll to the Target Number.* Choose a target number, such as 5,000, or 9,000. In pairs, have one student roll three number cubes, one at a time, to create a number (5, 6, and 2 is 562). He or she rounds the number and then has his or her partner record the rounded number on a piece of paper. The first student continues rolling the number cubes, rounding, and estimating the sum until he or she gets close to the target number. Then the other partner rolls, rounds, and adds. The partner who is closer to the target number wins. An alternative method is to subtract from the target number until the estimate is close to zero.

Student Page 25 Guide ·····

Exercises 1–3 Have students compare responses with a partner and then review as a class.	What did you do to find the estimate for Jar B? *I compared the space filled with marbles in Jar A to the space filled with marbles in Jar B.*
Exercises 4–6 Have students share with a partner how they estimated the total number of balls in the boxes.	How did you solve Exercise 6? *It looked like the space left over at the top of Box B was the same as the space filled with balls in Box A, so I added 300 to 600 to get 900.*

Student Page 26 Guide ·····

Exercises 7–10 Have students share how they rounded the numbers. Encourage volunteers to share what they did by writing it on the board.	How did you estimate the total cost for Exercise 10? *I rounded $16 to $20 and I rounded $22 to $20 and added them together to get $40.*
Exercises 11–13 Encourage students to talk about how they used estimation to solve the exercises.	How did you solve Exercise 12? *I tried various combinations.* Discuss the different combinations as a class.
Container Estimates Put containers in the center of the classroom and invite other students to estimate and compare them.	Set out bins or bags labeled with target numbers, such as 50, 100, 500, or 1,000. Students place two or more containers inside the box or bag that when added together would come close to that sum.

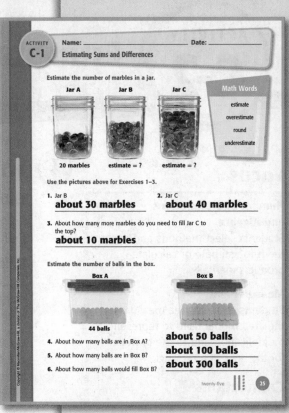

ACTIVITY C-1

Name: _____ Date: _____

Estimating Sums and Differences

Estimate the number of marbles in a jar.

Jar A   Jar B   Jar C

Math Words
estimate
overestimate
round
underestimate

20 marbles   estimate = ?   estimate = ?

Use the pictures above for Exercises 1–3.

1. Jar B **about 30 marbles**
2. Jar C **about 40 marbles**
3. About how many more marbles do you need to fill Jar C to the top? **about 10 marbles**

Estimate the number of balls in the box.

Box A   Box B

44 balls

4. About how many balls are in Box A? **about 50 balls**
5. About how many balls are in Box B? **about 100 balls**
6. About how many balls would fill Box B? **about 300 balls**

twenty-five **25**

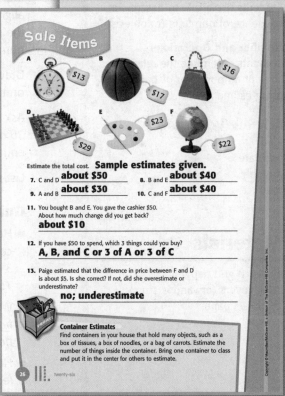

Sale Items

A $13   B $17   C $16

D $29   E $23   F $22

Estimate the total cost. **Sample estimates given.**

7. C and D **about $50**
8. B and E **about $40**
9. A and B **about $30**
10. C and F **about $40**

11. You bought B and E. You gave the cashier $50. About how much change did you get back? **about $10**

12. If you have $50 to spend, which 3 things could you buy? **A, B, and C or 3 of A or 3 of C**

13. Paige estimated that the difference in price between F and D is about $5. Is she correct? If not, did she overestimate or underestimate? **no; underestimate**

Container Estimates
Find containers in your house that hold many objects, such as a box of tissues, a box of noodles, or a bag of carrots. Estimate the number of things inside the container. Bring one container to class and put it in the center for others to estimate.

26 twenty-six

③ Reflect (5–10 min)

- What are some strategies that you can use to estimate sums and differences? *Round each number to the greatest place value, then add or subtract.*

- Why is it important to know how to estimate sums and differences? *Sometimes you don't need to know the exact number, so it saves time if you can estimate how many or how much.*

Estimating Products

Focus

Number and Operations and Algebra
Students select methods and apply them to estimate or calculate products mentally.

Measurement
Students connect area measure to the area model used to represent multiplication and to the formula for the area of a rectangle.

Connections

Algebra
Students use a rule to describe a sequence of numbers (or objects).

Number and Operations
Students determine the relative sizes of amounts (or distances) using estimation.

Review Vocabulary
area
estimate
multiply
product

Materials

one-inch grid paper
book covers (of various sizes)
11" x 17" paper

① Investigate (25–30 min)

Estimating Area

Sometimes when multiplying, it is easier to estimate the product than to find an exact answer.

Distribute a sheet of grid paper to each student. Estimate how many grid squares will cover their math books. Invite students to share how they estimated. When finished, have students find the exact area and record their findings.

Have students work in pairs to estimate the area of various things around the classroom, such as book covers, table tops, bulletin boards, etc. Ask them to record each object, its estimate, and its area in grid squares. When finished, have students share and discuss their findings. Encourage them to share their calculation strategies when the grid squares did not align edge-to-edge with the object. Students may say they estimated the number of grid squares to one more or one fewer than the actual number of squares.

Draw a simple diagram with measurements on the board to represent a kitchen floor.

Ask students how to round the dimensions. *20 and 30* Using mental math, 2 times 3 equals 6, so 20 times 30 equals 600.

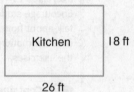

List some number pairs on the board for students to estimate.

Guiding Questions

- How did you find the number of grid squares that covered the index card? *Answers will vary; I put 5 grid squares along the length and 3 grid squares along the width. Then I multiplied the 5 and 3 and got 15 grid squares.*

- When might it be helpful to estimate products? *Sample answers: figuring out about how many treats you should bring for the class, how many people can sit in the lunch room*

- How would you estimate 473 × 5? *I would round 473 to 500 and leave 5 the same; 500 times 5 equals 2,500.*

Connections and Extensions · · · · · · · · · · · · · ·

Measurement
Give students an estimated area of a room floor, such as 800 square feet. Have them draw possible dimensions for the room and label the sides in feet.

Student Page 27 Guide · · · · ·

Exercise 1 Have students explain how they estimated the area of the 11" × 17" paper.	How did you estimate to find the area of the paper? *I rounded 17 to 20 and 11 to 10; 20 × 10 = 200. The area is about 200 grid squares.*
Exercises 2 and 3 Have students explain how they rounded the factors before multiplying.	What numbers did you use to estimate the area? *Exercise 2, round 37 to 40; Exercise 3, round 23 to 20 and 46 to 50*
Exercise 4 Have students work with a partner. Have each pair share with the class how they solved the problem.	How did you solve this problem? Is there another way? Which way is quicker? *Answers will vary.*

Student Page 28 Guide · · · · ·

Exercise 7 Invite students to have a partner solve their estimation problem.	What container did you use and how many items were inside of it? *Answers will vary.*
Exercises 8 and 9 Invite students to share their estimation strategies with the class.	In Exercise 8, is there a quick way to estimate the cost of 11 bicycles? *Yes, I rounded it to 10 × 200. Then I multiplied 2 × 1 and added 3 zeros.*
In Science Have students first determine how many people are in their family.	Talk about the number of days in a month and year. Encourage students to make a table to display their findings.

③ **Reflect** (5–10 min)

- What are some strategies you use to estimate when multiplying? *Round numbers to their greatest place value and then multiply.*
- If you estimate these problems, how are they the same and how are they different: 560 × 7 and 580 × 7? *Both 560 and 580 round to 600. So, both estimates would be 600 × 7 = 4,200; the actual products will differ.*

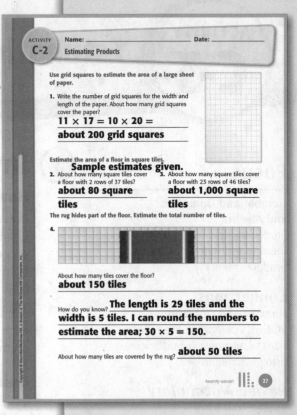

ACTIVITY C-2

Name: _____ Date: _____

Estimating Products

Use grid squares to estimate the area of a large sheet of paper.

1. Write the number of grid squares for the width and length of the paper. About how many grid squares cover the paper?

11 × 17 = 10 × 20 =

about 200 grid squares

Estimate the area of a floor in square tiles.
Sample estimates given.

2. About how many square tiles cover a floor with 2 rows of 37 tiles? **about 80 square tiles**

3. About how many square tiles cover a floor with 23 rows of 46 tiles? **about 1,000 square tiles**

The rug hides part of the floor. Estimate the total number of tiles.

4.

About how many tiles cover the floor? **about 150 tiles**

How do you know? **The length is 29 tiles and the width is 5 tiles. I can round the numbers to estimate the area; 30 × 5 = 150.**

About how many tiles are covered by the rug? **about 50 tiles**

twenty-seven 27

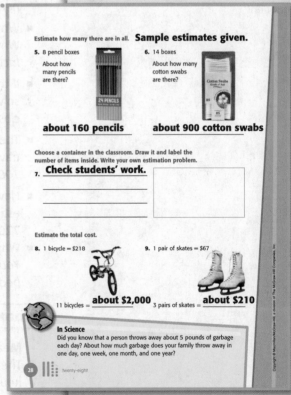

Estimate how many there are in all. **Sample estimates given.**

5. 8 pencil boxes
About how many pencils are there?

about 160 pencils

6. 14 boxes
About how many cotton swabs are there?

about 900 cotton swabs

Choose a container in the classroom. Draw it and label the number of items inside. Write your own estimation problem.

7. **Check students' work.**

Estimate the total cost.

8. 1 bicycle = $218

11 bicycles = **about $2,000**

9. 1 pair of skates = $67

3 pairs of skates = **about $210**

In Science
Did you know that a person throws away about 5 pounds of garbage each day? About how much garbage does your family throw away in one day, one week, one month, and one year?

28 *twenty-eight*

ACTIVITY C-3

Estimating Quotients

Focus

Number and Operations and Algebra
Students select methods and apply them to estimate or calculate products mentally.

Connections

Number and Operations
Students determine the relative sizes of amounts (or distances) using estimation.

Review Vocabulary
divide
quotient

① Investigate (20–25 min)

How Far Each Day?

Draw a simple map on the board. Label two cities, Philadelphia and Charleston, and draw a route from one city to the other. Label the route 453 miles. Tell students the following story. The Alvarez family traveled from Philadelphia, Pennsylvania to Charleston, South Carolina to visit relatives. They drove 453 miles in 9 hours.

Ask students to estimate about how many miles they traveled each hour. Invite students to share their estimates and write them on the board.

Guiding Questions

- To solve this problem, do you need an exact answer? *No, you only need an estimate.*

- Which multiplication fact helped you solve this division problem? Why was it helpful? *9 × 5 = 45; I can quickly divide using this basic fact, 45 ÷ 9 = 5 and 450 ÷ 9 = 50.*

- If the Alvarez family traveled 463 miles in 9 hours, how would you solve the problem? *9 × 5 = 45, and 9 × 6 = 54; 9 × 5 = 45 is the closest. So, my estimate is the same, about 50 miles each hour.*

- There are 96 crackers to share on this trip. If there are 4 people traveling, about how many crackers does each person get? *100 ÷ 4 or about 25 each*

- Have students identify which multiplication facts would help them estimate the quotients for the following: 320 ÷ 8; 4,800 ÷ 6; 720 ÷ 8; and 6,500 ÷ 8. *4 × 8; 8 × 6; 9 × 8; 8 × 8*

- Why do you think multiplication facts help you solve division problems? *You use the same three numbers when you multiply and divide because division "undoes" multiplication.*

Connections and Extensions

Measurement
The cheetah is the fastest land mammal. It can run up to 65 miles per hour. The squirrel is much slower. It can only run up to 12 miles per hour. Compare the estimated length of time it will take a cheetah and a squirrel to run from Indianapolis, Indiana to Bismarck, North Dakota. See the table on Student Page 30 for mileage. *cheetah: about 30 hours; squirrel: about 200 hours*

The average person walks 3 miles per hour. At this rate about how long would it take you to walk from Indianapolis, Indiana to Bismarck, North Dakota? *about 600 hours*

T29 Unit C: Estimating

② Apply (30–40 min)

Student Page 29 Guide · · · · ·

Exercise 1 Have students examine the multiplication fact used to solve the problem.	What do you notice about 9 times 3, 9 times 30, and 9 times 300? Do you see a pattern? *The product is 27 with 0, 1, or 2 zeros after it.*
Exercises 2 and 3 Have students share with a partner and then the class how they solved the problems.	For Exercise 3, why didn't you use $9 \times 4 = 36$ to help you divide? *The problem does not have 9 or 4 as the number in common with 36, it has the number 6.*

Student Page 30 Guide · · · · ·

Exercises 4–7 Students may have difficulty deciding which digits in the dividend they should divide by first.	Underline the first two digits in each number. Then ask yourself "What multiplication fact has this number as a product?"
Exercise 8 Help students set up the problem by guiding them to divide the number of miles Rosa traveled each day by 4.	Ask students to review their answer from Exercise 5 to help them set up this problem.
Exercises 9 and 10 These exercises have divisors that do not divide equally into the dividends. Share and discuss how to solve these types of problems.	In Exercise 9, how did you find the estimate when 5 does not divide equally into 16? $5 \times 3 = 15$, $5 \times 2 = 10$, and $5 \times 4 = 20$. 15 is closest to 16, so it is the best estimate; $150 \div 5 = 30$.

③ Reflect (5–10 min)

- What are some strategies that you can use to estimate a quotient? *Look at the numbers in the problem and think of a multiplication fact that has those numbers. Divide to estimate the quotient. Add zeros if needed.*

- When might you estimate to find the quotient? *Sample answers: approximate cost of one item given the total cost of 4 items; sharing a box of cookies*

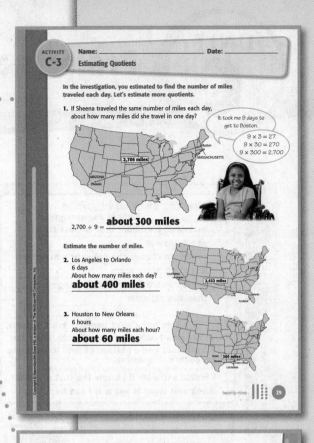

ACTIVITY C-3 Name: _____ Date: _____
Estimating Quotients

In the investigation, you estimated to find the number of miles traveled each day. Let's estimate more quotients.

1. If Sheena traveled the same number of miles each day, about how many miles did she travel in one day?

It took me 9 days to get to Boston.
$9 \times 3 = 27$
$9 \times 30 = 270$
$9 \times 300 = 2,700$

2,706 miles

$2,700 \div 9 =$ **about 300 miles**

Estimate the number of miles.

2. Los Angeles to Orlando
6 days
About how many miles each day?
about 400 miles

2,432 miles

3. Houston to New Orleans
6 hours
About how many miles each hour?
about 60 miles

360 miles

twenty-nine **29**

	Nashville, TN	Kansas City, MO	Bismarck, ND	Reno, NV
Indianapolis, IN	287 miles	485 miles	1,852 miles	2,073 miles

Use the table to estimate.
Each traveler's route starts in Indianapolis.

4. If Jake traveled 7 hours to Nashville, about how many miles did he travel each hour?
about 40 miles each hour

5. Rosa traveled 9 days to Bismarck. About how many miles did she travel each day?
about 200 miles each day

6. Liz traveled 400 miles each day. About how many days did it take her to get to Reno?
about 5 days

7. Sammy traveled about 60 miles each hour. About how long did it take him to get to Kansas City?
about 8 hours

8. If Rosa traveled 4 hours each day, who traveled more miles each hour, Rosa or Jake? Explain why. **Rosa traveled more miles each hour. She traveled 200 miles each day for 4 hours; $200 \div 4 = 50$. 50 miles each hour is $>$ 40 miles each hour.**

Estimate.

9. On her vacation, Rosa spent $161 for 5 meals. About how much did she spend for each meal?
about $30

10. Sammy spent about $57 for 8 meals. About how much did he spend for each meal?
about $7

30 ||| thirty

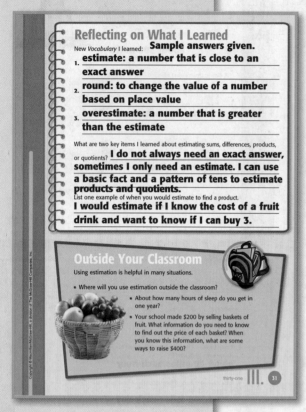

Reflecting on What I Learned

New *Vocabulary* I learned: **Sample answers given.**

1. **estimate: a number that is close to an exact answer**

2. **round: to change the value of a number based on place value**

3. **overestimate: a number that is greater than the estimate**

What are two key items I learned about estimating sums, differences, products, or quotients? **I do not always need an exact answer, sometimes I only need an estimate. I can use a basic fact and a pattern of tens to estimate products and quotients.**

List one example of when you would estimate to find a product. **I would estimate if I know the cost of a fruit drink and want to know if I can buy 3.**

Outside Your Classroom

Using estimation is helpful in many situations.

- Where will you use estimation outside the classroom?
  - About how many hours of sleep do you get in one year?
  - Your school made $200 by selling baskets of fruit. What information do you need to know to find out the price of each basket? When you know this information, what are some ways to raise $400?

thirty-one 31

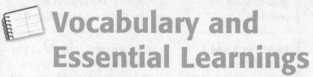

Vocabulary and Essential Learnings

Vocabulary

- Have students discuss in small groups the vocabulary terms and the definitions that they learned or reviewed in this unit.

- Generate a master list of terms on the board or have students create a Foldable®.

- Have students record three terms of their choice, along with a brief definition or picture for each one.

Essential Learnings

Arrange students in pairs. Have partners review the activities on pages 25 through 30 and discuss what they learned.

Allow time for students to share their essential learnings in small groups or as a class.

Outside Your Classroom

You may wish to arrange students into groups. Allow time for classmates to extend or enrich the groups' responses.

Possible student responses:

- Where will you see estimation?
  Sample answers: when I am shopping and need to figure out if I have enough money to buy several things that are the same price; when I need to know about how many things are packed in a box

- About how many hours of sleep do you get in one year?
  I sleep about 10 hours every night and there are 365 days in a year; so, I sleep about 3,500 hours every year.

- Criteria for fruit basket sale:
  I will need to know about how many baskets were sold. For $400, I could double the price or sell twice as many baskets.

AL

What information would you need to know to figure out how many people a box of cereal will feed?

How many ounces of cereal? What is the amount of one serving?

Planning a Vacation

Materials

travel books and brochures
restaurant menus
United States maps
Internet

Pacing:
40 min

Introducing the Project

Guide students to review the concepts taught in the unit.

Have students explore travel books and maps. Talk about what things are important to plan before going on a trip. Have students share a vacation experience. Provide experiences where they are asked to find a hotel or an attraction and its cost. Then have them round the price to the nearest dollar, ten dollars, or hundred dollars to make it easier for their estimation calculations. Explain what things could be included in their travel diary.

Completing the Project

Keep travel materials, menus, and maps available for the students. Have students read the questions in Step 1 and respond to them in small groups. Throughout the project, assist them in finding information they need to make their vacation plans.

Extending the Project

Have students compare travel options: train, air, bus. Would they be more or less expensive? Have students plan how much money they would need to save per week if their vacation is 6 months away.

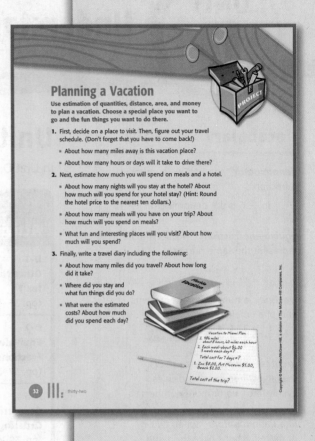

Planning a Vacation

Use estimation of quantities, distance, area, and money to plan a vacation. Choose a special place you want to go and the fun things you want to do there.

1. First, decide on a place to visit. Then, figure out your travel schedule. (Don't forget that you have to come back!)
   - About how many miles away is this vacation place?
   - About how many hours or days will it take to drive there?

2. Next, estimate how much you will spend on meals and a hotel.
   - About how many nights will you stay at the hotel? About how much will you spend for your hotel stay? (Hint: Round the hotel price to the nearest ten dollars.)
   - About how many meals will you have on your trip? About how much will you spend on meals?
   - What fun and interesting places will you visit? About how much will you spend?

3. Finally, write a travel diary including the following:
   - About how many miles did you travel? About how long did it take?
   - Where did you stay and what fun things did you do?
   - What were the estimated costs? About how much did you spend each day?

Suggested Scoring Rubric

4	The student completes the project with accuracy and creativity. The student's travel diary describes the vacation and includes accurate estimates.
3	The student completes the project. The student's travel diary describes the vacation, but some of the estimations are incorrect (no more than half).
2	The student does not complete all components of the project and more than half of the estimates are incorrect.
1	The student's project is either incomplete or inaccurate. The student's travel diary is inaccurate, incomplete, and contains incorrect estimates.

Understanding Fractions

Vocabulary

denominator   the bottom number in a fraction

In $\frac{5}{6}$, 6 is the denominator.

equivalent fractions   fractions that represent the same number

$$\frac{3}{4} = \frac{6}{8}$$

fraction   a number that represents part of a whole or part of a set

$\frac{1}{2}, \frac{1}{3}, \frac{1}{4}, \frac{3}{4}$ ← numerators
← denominators

greatest common factor (GCF) the largest number that divides evenly into two or more numbers

like denominators   when two or more fractions have the same denominator, they have like denominators.

In $\frac{1}{4}$ and $\frac{3}{4}$, 4 is the like denominator.

numerator   the number above the bar in a fraction; the part of the fraction that tells how many of the equal parts are being used

simplest form   a fraction in which the numerator and the denominator have no common factor greater than 1

Unit-at-a-Glance

In Unit D, students gain an understanding of fractions.

Activity	Focus	Student Investigation
D-1 Other Names for 1 (pp. 35–36)	Students develop an understanding of equivalent fractions by comparing models to symbols.	Students cut paper to find fractions equal to one.
D-2 Equivalent Fractions (pp. 37–38)	Students develop an understanding of equivalent fractions by comparing models to symbols.	Students make models that represent equivalent fractions.
D-3 Comparing and Ordering Fractions (pp. 39–40)	Students develop an understanding of equivalent fractions by comparing models to symbols and locating them on a number line.	Students use fraction tiles and a number line to compare and order fractions.
D-4 Adding and Subtracting Fractions with Like Denominators (pp. 41–42)	Students apply their understanding of fractions to reading, writing, and estimating fractions in problem solving.	Students use fraction tiles and other models to add and subtract fractions with like denominators.
Unit Project: Representing Survey Data (p. 44)	Students relate the concepts and skills they have learned to the real world.	Students conduct a survey and use fraction concepts to record the data.

Page Numbers

Each page number in this lesson includes a fraction which equals the page number.

Guiding Questions

- Explain how to reduce the fraction to its simplest form. In simplest form, the fraction will be the page number.
- Write the page-number fractions for this unit in order on a number line.
- Have students draw models or use manipulatives to represent the fraction.

Unit Opener

Student Page 33 Guide

You can open the unit by having students read through the objectives they will accomplish during the unit. Have students restate objectives in their own words to ensure comprehension.

Scaffolding Questions	What do you already know about fractions? *Answers will vary.*
	How are fractions related to whole numbers? *Fractions represent a part of a whole.*
Vocabulary **WRITING IN MATH**	The beginning of the unit is a great time to start a new wall chart.
	Encourage students to write the definitions in their math journals. Writing their own definitions or creating drawings will help internalize the information.
	Remind students that the word *factor* has two meanings. A factor is a number that is multiplied by another number. It is also a number that divides a whole number evenly.

Student Page 34 Guide

Home Letter

Have students take the Home Letter home.

Look at the Projects and Discussions throughout the unit to see if any additional opportunities are available for work at home.

ELL

Encourage students to visit the online eGlossary with parents to see vocabulary in 13 languages.

TeacherWorks *Plus*

See "Home E-mail" as an alternative for communication. From the Lesson Planner, select the e-mail document for this unit, double-click the file, and edit in the Worksheet Editor.

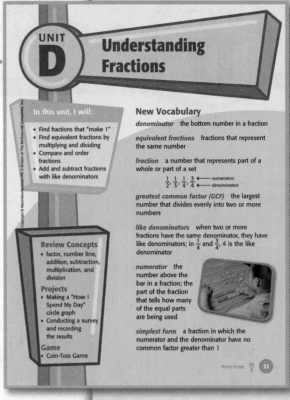

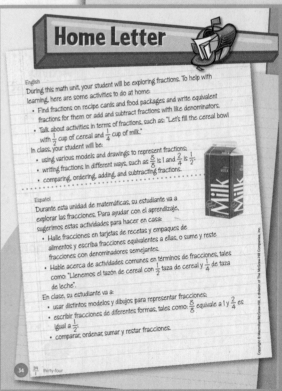

UNIT D

Activity Planner

KEY

- Real-World Connections
- Projects
- Technology
- CD-ROM
- Math Tool Chest
- Math Adventures

	Activity D-1 — Pacing: 55–70 min	Activity D-2 — Pacing: 65–80 min
Activity/ Objective	**Other Names for 1** (pp. 35–36)	**Equivalent Fractions** (pp. 37–38)
	Objective Find fractions equivalent to one.	**Objective** Identify equivalent fractions using multiplication and division.
Math Vocabulary	denominator fraction numerator	equivalent fractions **Review Vocabulary** denominator numerator
Activity Resources	**Materials** 8.5" × 11" construction paper scissors markers **Manipulatives** rulers	**Materials** fraction kit (from Activity D-1) index cards **Manipulatives** counters
Technology	**Math Tool Chest** Fractions **Math Adventures** Blipp's Satellite Service **Personal Tutor**	**Math Adventures** Blipp's Satellite Service **Games** Fair and Square
Real-World Connections		**At Home** Find a recipe. Use equivalent fractions to list the ingredients.
Small Projects		

Activity D-3	Pacing: 55–70 min	Activity D-4	Pacing: 55–70 min	Unit Project	Pacing: 45 min	
Comparing and Ordering Fractions (pp. 39–40) **Objective** Compare and order fractions.		**Adding and Subtracting Fractions with Like Denominators** (pp. 41–42) **Objective** Add and subtract fractions with like denominators.		**Representing Survey Data** (p. 44) **Objective** Conduct a survey and use fractions to represent the data.		Activity/ Objective
		greatest common factor (GCF) like denominators simplest form				Math Vocabulary
Review Vocabulary number line		**Review Vocabulary** equivalent fractions factor				
		Materials index cards with recipes fruit—apples, bananas, pineapple, oranges		**Materials** examples of categorical surveys examples of circle graphs chart paper		Activity Resources
Manipulatives fraction tiles rulers number cubes		**Manipulatives** fraction tiles analog clock				
Math Tool Chest Fractions Number line **Math Adventures** Mount Frost		**Math Tool Chest** Fractions **Math Adventures** Blipp's Satellite Service		**Math Tool Chest** Circle Graphs **Personal Tutor**		Technology
At Home Play Coin-Toss game.						Real-World Connections
		Make a Circle Graph Write fractions for time spent on daily activities. Make a circle graph to represent the data.				Small Projects

Unit D: Activity Planner   **T34B**

Differentiated Instruction

Below are suggestions on differentiating the materials presented in this unit. Additional modifications should be considered.

Below Level **BL**	Above Level **AL**	English Language Learners **ELL**
ACTIVITY D-1 Allow students to use fraction tiles or fraction circles as they complete the exercises.	**Exercises 9–18** For fractions greater than one, challenge students to write a mixed number.	
ACTIVITY D-2 **Exercises 4–11** Have students work with a partner to find equivalent fractions.		Link *equivalent* to the word *equal*. Show items that are equal in size or amount such as two cups filled with the same amount of water.
ACTIVITY D-3 Have students use fraction circles to help them see that the greater the number of pieces (denominator), the smaller each piece. This will help them to compare fractions with the same numerator but different denominators.	Have students play a game using a spinner or number cube. Have them record each outcome in a tally table and then write the outcomes as fractions. Students can compare and order the results.	Link the terms *least* and *greatest* to smallest and biggest. Line up fraction tiles to represent the fractions and help illustrate the order from least to greatest or smallest to biggest.
ACTIVITY D-4 Have students use fraction tiles to add and subtract and then find the simplest form. Explain that the simplest form uses the fewest number of tiles. **Make a Circle Graph** Students may find it easier to first divide the circle into 24 equal parts and then shade.	**Exercise 10** Have students look at the statements in Exercise 10. Challenge them to write another equation for each statement.	**Exercise 10** Check students' understanding of the terms *sum* and *difference*. Clarify by writing addition and subtraction sentences, circling and labeling the answers as *sum* or *difference*.

Performance-Based Assessment

Fractions (p. A14)

In *Fractions,* students first explore fractions less than 1 and then find a fraction less than $\frac{1}{2}$ and then a fraction between $\frac{1}{2}$ and 1.

Connections

The *Fractions* assessment also covers the following skills and concepts:

- Estimation
- Comparing fractions
- Fraction equivalence
- Problem solving

Targeting the Task

- **Pretest** – Use Exercises 1–3 to determine students' understanding of fractions less than 1. For those students who do not have this understanding, completing this unit is needed.

- **Formative** – Use the exercise individually to assess students during the course of the unit.

- **Summative** – Administer the complete *Fractions* assessment.

Differentiation

Teachers can scaffold this lesson for struggling students by controlling the numbers in the numerator and denominator. For example, when asking students to create two fractions equal to $\frac{1}{2}$, write in the denominators. Choose numbers that students have fraction pieces for so they can build the fractions.

Students who have a fairly good grasp of fraction quantities could practice checking their work by drawing a picture instead of using concrete materials.

Students should be encouraged to look for patterns in the fractions such as "if the number in the denominator is twice the numerator, the fraction is exactly $\frac{1}{2}$."

Finally, students who are doing well can be challenged by comparing more than two fractions.

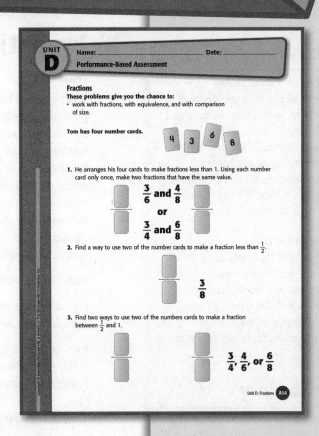

Other Names for 1

Focus

Number and Operations

Students apply their understanding of fractions to reading, writing, and estimating decimals or fractions in problem solving. They develop an understanding of equivalent fractions and decimals by comparing models to symbols and locating them on a number line.

Connections

Number and Operations

Students' work with models of fractions and multiplication and division facts develops an understanding of equivalent fractions and simplifying fractions.

Vocabulary

denominator

fraction

numerator

Materials

8.5" × 11" construction paper
scissors
markers
rulers

① Investigate (30–35 min)

Making 1

Ask students how a fraction is related to a whole. *A fraction names a part of a whole.* Have students explore naming a whole using fractions by folding and cutting paper into equal-sized pieces and making a fraction kit. Divide students into small groups. Provide each group with six sheets of construction paper. Have students begin by labeling one sheet as one whole. Fold and cut another sheet in half. Guide students to label each part as a fraction of the whole. Talk about the relationship between the denominator and the number of equal parts in the whole. Students should repeat the folding and cutting to model thirds, fourths, sixths, and eighths.

Write this equation on the board: $\frac{1}{2} + \frac{1}{2} = \frac{2}{2} = 1$

Discuss other ways to make one whole.

Sample answers: $\frac{1}{3} + \frac{1}{3} + \frac{1}{3} = \frac{3}{3} = 1$

Explain that a fraction can be thought of as a division problem. Therefore, if the numerator and denominator are the same, the quotient will be 1. Note: Students will use their fraction kits in Activity D-2 also.

Guiding Questions

- How do you know what fraction to use to label each part of the whole? *Sample answer: The numerator is 1 because it is one part of the whole, and the denominator is the total number of parts I cut the whole into.*

- What do you notice about the denominator and the number of fraction parts that name one whole? *Sample answer: The denominator is equal to the number of fraction parts that equal one whole.*

- What if I used a larger sheet of paper and folded it and cut it into halves. Would my $\frac{1}{2}$ piece and your $\frac{1}{2}$ piece equal 1? Why or why not? *No; Sample explanation: You cannot mix the fraction parts from different-sized wholes to make 1. The fraction pieces are different sizes.*

- Does $\frac{24}{24}$ equal one whole? Why or why not? What operation can you use to check your answer? *Yes. Sample explanation: numerator and denominator are the same; division, 24 ÷ 24 = 1*

Connections and Extensions

Measurement

Measure a partner's arm length in inches. Between which two inch marks does your partner's arm measure? Is your partner's arm closer to one inch than the other? Write your partner's arm length in inches and in a fraction of an inch.

Student Page 35 Guide · · · · ·

Exercise 1
Have students compare responses with a partner and then as a class.

What does the denominator in a fraction tell us? What does the numerator tell us? *The denominator tells us the total number of equal parts that make one whole. The numerator tells us how many equal parts there are.*

Exercises 2–5
In Exercises 2 and 3, encourage students to note that the fraction parts are not the same size.

Have students tell a partner how they know if the parts do or do not make a whole.

Why can you make one whole using the shaded parts in Exercise 4 but not in Exercises 2 and 3? *In Exercise 4, the fractional parts are the same size. In Exercises 2 and 3, the fractional parts are different sizes.*

If you put the shaded parts together in Exercise 2, does it show less than or more than one whole? *more than one whole*

Student Page 36 Guide · · · · ·

Exercises 6–9
Have students share what strategies they used to divide each figure into equal parts.

How did you know how to divide each whole into equal parts? Explain. *The denominator tells me how many equal parts there are. If the denominator is 10, I draw 10 equal parts.*

Exercises 10–20
Encourage students to focus on comparing the numerator and the denominator to see if a fraction is less than, equal to, or greater than 1.

How can you check to see if a fraction is equal to 1? *If the denominator and numerator are the same (except zero), the fraction equals 1.*

How do you know that a fraction is greater than 1? *numerator is greater than the denominator*

③ **Reflect** (5–10 min)

- What are some fractions that name one whole? *Sample answers:* $\frac{5}{5}, \frac{7}{7}, \frac{25}{25}$
- What is the same about all fractions equal to 1? *The numerator and denominator are the same.*
- What does the denominator in a fraction tell us? *the number of equal parts the whole is divided into*

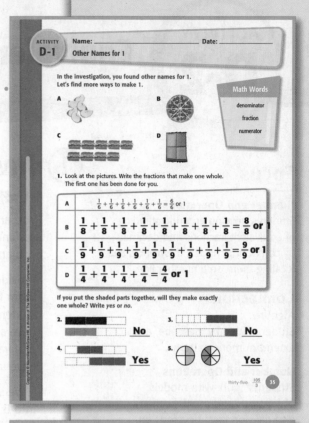

ACTIVITY D-1
Other Names for 1
Name: _____ Date: _____

Math Words
denominator
fraction
numerator

In the investigation, you found other names for 1. Let's find more ways to make 1.

A   B

C   D

1. Look at the pictures. Write the fractions that make one whole. The first one has been done for you.

A	$\frac{1}{6}+\frac{1}{6}+\frac{1}{6}+\frac{1}{6}+\frac{1}{6}+\frac{1}{6}=\frac{6}{6}$ or 1
B	$\frac{1}{8}+\frac{1}{8}+\frac{1}{8}+\frac{1}{8}+\frac{1}{8}+\frac{1}{8}+\frac{1}{8}+\frac{1}{8}=\frac{8}{8}$ or 1
C	$\frac{1}{9}+\frac{1}{9}+\frac{1}{9}+\frac{1}{9}+\frac{1}{9}+\frac{1}{9}+\frac{1}{9}+\frac{1}{9}+\frac{1}{9}=\frac{9}{9}$ or 1
D	$\frac{1}{4}+\frac{1}{4}+\frac{1}{4}+\frac{1}{4}=\frac{4}{4}$ or 1

If you put the shaded parts together, will they make exactly one whole? Write *yes* or *no*.

2. **No**   3. **No**
4. **Yes**   5. **Yes**

thirty-five $\frac{105}{3}$ 35

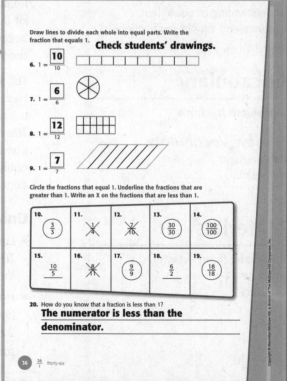

Draw lines to divide each whole into equal parts. Write the fraction that equals 1. **Check students' drawings.**

6. $1 = \frac{10}{10}$
7. $1 = \frac{6}{6}$
8. $1 = \frac{12}{12}$
9. $1 = \frac{7}{7}$

Circle the fractions that equal 1. Underline the fractions that are greater than 1. Write an X on the fractions that are less than 1.

10.	11.	12.	13.	14.
$\frac{3}{3}$	$\frac{1}{4}$	$\frac{10}{7}$	$\frac{30}{30}$	$\frac{100}{100}$
15.	16.	17.	18.	19.
$\frac{10}{5}$	$\frac{8}{3}$	$\frac{9}{9}$	$\frac{6}{2}$	$\frac{18}{18}$

20. How do you know that a fraction is less than 1?
The numerator is less than the denominator.

36 $\frac{36}{1}$ thirty-six

Equivalent Fractions

Focus

Number and Operations
Students develop an understanding of equivalent fractions and decimals by comparing models to symbols and locating them on a number line.

Connections

Algebra
Students identify, describe, and extend numeric patterns.

Number and Operations
Students' work with models of fractions and multiplication and division facts develops an understanding of equivalent fractions and simplifying fractions.

Vocabulary

equivalent fractions

Review Vocabulary
denominator
numerator

Materials

fraction kit (from Activity D-1)
index cards
counters

① Investigate (35–40 min)

Finding Equivalent Fractions

You are having some guests to your home for a party. You bake a rectangular cake. If three guests come, how would you cut the cake so you and each guest get an equal part? *Cut the cake into 4 equal pieces.*

Provide each student with a sheet of paper to represent the cake. Have them fold the paper to show cutting the cake into equal pieces. Remind students that there is more than one way to divide paper equally. Then have students shade one part. Talk about one piece of the cake in terms of a fraction of the whole, or $\frac{1}{4}$. Write the fraction on the board. Then have students locate the $\frac{1}{4}$ piece in their fraction kit (from Activity D-1).

Have students fold the sheet of paper again to show cutting the cake into 8 equal pieces. Guide them to see that two $\frac{1}{8}$ pieces equals $\frac{1}{4}$. Reaffirm this by having students place two $\frac{1}{8}$ pieces from their fraction kit over the $\frac{1}{4}$ piece. Explain that $\frac{1}{4}$ and $\frac{2}{8}$ are equivalent fractions because they name the same part of the whole. Give students time to use their fraction kits to explore equivalent fractions.

Tell students that multiplication can be used to find equivalent fractions. Have students look at the sets of equivalent fractions and think about the relationship between the numerators and denominators in each set. *The numerator and denominator are multiplied by the same non-zero number.* Have students use multiplication to find other fractions equivalent to $\frac{1}{4}$. Be sure students multiply the numerator and denominator by the same number.

Guiding Questions

- Look at the set of equivalent fractions for $\frac{1}{2}$. What pattern do you see? *The numerator and denominator both increase by a factor of 2 and the denominator is always 2 times the numerator.*

- How can you use multiplication to find a fraction equivalent to $\frac{1}{2}$ that has a denominator of 10? *Sample answer: I know that to get from 2 to 10, I need to multiply by 5. So I multiply the numerator by the same factor; 1 × 5 = 5. The equivalent fraction is $\frac{5}{10}$.*

Connections and Extensions

Matching Fractions
Using index cards, have students make a set of 30 fraction cards containing 15 pairs of equivalent fractions. Shuffle the cards and place them facedown in equal rows on a desk. Players take turns turning over two cards. If the fractions on the cards are equivalent, the player keeps the pair and takes another turn. The player with the most equivalent pairs wins.

② Apply (25–30 min)

Student Page 37 Guide · · · · · ·

Exercise 1 Have students compare responses with a partner and then as a class.	Compare the drawings. How do they relate to equivalent fractions? *Both drawings show the same amount.* When can you use division to find equivalent fractions? *When the numerator and denominator have a common factor.*
Exercises 2 and 3 Have students share their answers with a partner and then with the class.	How did you know if the two fractions were equivalent? *Sample answer: I multiplied or divided the numerator and denominator of the first fraction by the same number to get the second fraction.*

Student Page 38 Guide · · · · ·

Exercises 4–11 Make a list of the different answers for Exercises 8–11 and discuss the number of possible answers.	For Exercise 9, could you divide to find an equivalent fraction? Why or why not? *No; 2 and 5 do not have a factor in common.*
Exercises 12–15 Encourage students to share how they used each pattern to find the missing fractions.	For which exercises did you divide to find the missing fraction? For which did you multiply? *I divided for Exercises 13 and 14; I multiplied for Exercise 12.*
At Home Have students find a recipe that includes fractions and write equivalent fractions for them.	Have students share their recipes and ask other students to try to determine the original fractions.

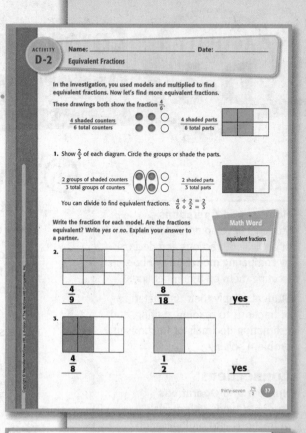

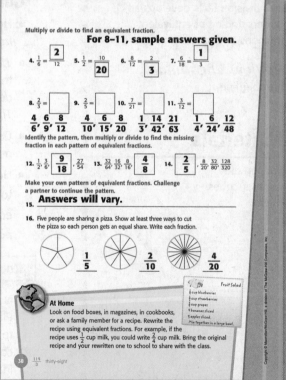

③ Reflect (5–10 min)

- What does it mean when we say two fractions are equivalent? *The fractions name the same part of a whole.*

- How do you use multiplication and division to find equivalent fractions? *Multiply or divide the numerator and denominator by the same non-zero number.*

Comparing and Ordering Fractions

Focus

Number and Operations

Students develop an understanding of equivalent fractions and decimals by comparing models to symbols and locating them on a number line.

Students apply their understanding of fractions to reading, writing, and estimating decimals or fractions in problem solving.

Connections

Number and Operations

Students' work with models of fractions and multiplication and division facts develops an understanding of equivalent fractions and simplifying fractions.

Review Vocabulary
number line

Materials

fraction tiles
number cubes
rulers

① Investigate (20–25 min)

First, Next, and Last

How can you decide which is greater, $\frac{3}{8}$ of a mile or $\frac{7}{8}$ of a mile?

Provide students with fraction tiles. Have them use the tiles to model each fraction and decide which is greater. $\frac{7}{8}$ Have students use the fraction tiles to explore the relationship between other fractions, such as $\frac{3}{4}$ and $\frac{2}{3}$.

Give students the following scenario: Nathan ran $\frac{3}{8}$ of a mile, Zoe ran $\frac{7}{8}$ of a mile, Simon ran $\frac{3}{4}$ of a mile, and Pedro ran $\frac{2}{3}$ of a mile. Who ran the farthest distance? Who ran the shortest distance? Put the runners in order from the farthest distance to the shortest distance they ran. *Zoe, Simon, Pedro, Nathan*

Guiding Questions

- How do you use fraction tiles to compare fractions? *Model each fraction using the tiles; the longer fraction model is the greater fraction.*

- What do you notice about the denominators of $\frac{3}{8}$ and $\frac{7}{8}$? How does this help you compare the fractions? *They are the same; when the denominators are the same, I only have to compare the numerators. The greater the numerator, the greater the fraction.*

- Can you compare $\frac{2}{3}$ and $\frac{3}{4}$ by comparing the numerators? Why or why not? *Sample answer: No; the denominators are different.*

- How can you use what you know about equivalent fractions to compare $\frac{3}{4}$ and $\frac{7}{8}$? *Sample answer: I can change $\frac{3}{4}$ to an equivalent fraction with a denominator of 8; $\frac{3}{4} = \frac{6}{8}$. Both fractions now have the same denominator so I can compare the numerators.*

Connections and Extensions

Number and Operations: Rolling Fractions Game
Players take turns rolling two number cubes, using the numbers rolled to make a fraction and recording the fraction on paper. Players then compare fractions. The player with the lesser fraction earns one point. Play continues for five rounds.

Measurement
Select at least five items that are shorter than 1 foot for students to measure. Have students measure the items to the nearest inch and record the measurement as a fraction of a foot. Remind students that there are 12 inches in 1 foot. Students can then write the measurements in order from least to greatest.

② Apply (30–35 min)

Student Page 39 Guide . . . . .

Exercises 1–3
Have students compare responses with a partner and then with the class. Discuss the different methods students can use to solve the problems.

Which is greater, $\frac{1}{10}$ of a mile or $\frac{1}{5}$ of a mile? How do you know? *$\frac{1}{5}$ of a mile; Tenths are smaller than fifths.*

Exercise 4
Have students share their story problems with a partner to solve.

What strategy did you use to solve your partner's story problem? *Answers may vary.*

Student Page 40 Guide . . . . .

Exercises 5–15
Encourage students to use the different strategies they have learned in the unit to solve these problems.

How did you compare the fractions in Exercise 5? *Sample answer: I compared the numerators because the denominators are the same; $5 > 2$, so $\frac{5}{6} > \frac{2}{6}$.*

Exercises 16–18
Ask students to share their methods with the class.

What method did you use to put the fractions in order? *Answers will vary.*

 At Home
Have students bring their coin-toss lists to school and record their results on a number line from 0 to 1.

Talk about ways to compare the numbers while you do this. Talk about each fraction's relationship to 0, $\frac{1}{2}$, and 1. Then, make a line plot to display the data.

③ Reflect (5–10 min)

- How does knowing equivalent fractions help you compare fractions? *I can change the fractions I am comparing to equivalent fractions so that they will have the same denominator. Then I can compare the numerators.*

- When might you need to compare and order fractions? Give an example. *Sample answers: dividing pizza, figuring out distances, deciding if one measurement is longer or shorter than another measurement*

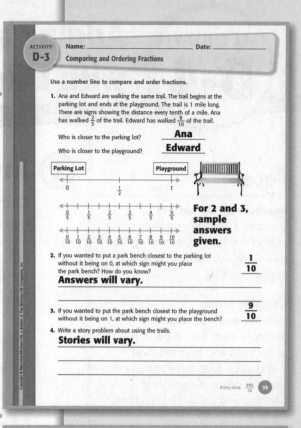

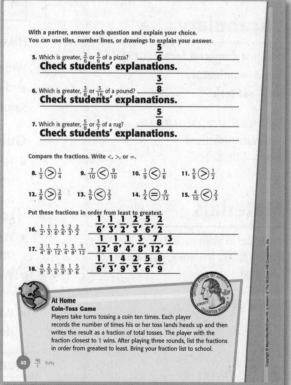

Adding and Subtracting Fractions with Like Denominators

Focus

Number and Operations

Students apply their understanding of fractions to reading, writing, and estimating decimals or fractions in problem solving.

Connections

Number and Operations

Students' work with models of fractions and multiplication and division facts develops an understanding of equivalent fractions and simplifying fractions.

Vocabulary

greatest common factor (GCF)
like denominators
simplest form

Review Vocabulary
equivalent fractions
factor

Materials

index cards with recipes
fruit—apples, bananas, pineapple, oranges
fraction tiles
analog clock

---

① Investigate (20–25 min)

Combining Recipes

Distribute recipe cards and fraction tiles to each pair of students. You may also wish to bring in the fruit and model the fractions using the fruit. Have students determine the total amount of each item they need to make both recipes. Use fraction tiles or other models as needed.

Fruit Salad	**Fruit Smoothie**
$\frac{1}{2}$ apple, chopped	$\frac{1}{2}$ apple
$\frac{1}{6}$ banana	$\frac{2}{6}$ banana
$\frac{3}{8}$ pineapple, diced	$\frac{2}{8}$ pineapple, diced
$\frac{3}{4}$ orange, sliced	$\frac{1}{4}$ orange, sliced

Have students share their totals and explain their answers.

Write the equation for each item on the board. For example: $\frac{1}{2} + \frac{1}{2} = \frac{2}{2}$ and $\frac{1}{6} + \frac{2}{6} = \frac{3}{6}$. Guide students to see that the denominator stays the same and the numerators are added together.

Guiding Questions

- How can you use fraction tiles to find out how much of each ingredient you need? Did anyone use other models or drawings? *Sample answer: Model each fraction with the fraction tiles and then combine the fraction tiles to find the total.*

- Were you able to add any of the fractions in your head? *Sample answer: Yes, two halves equal one whole.*

- Were any of the sums greater than 1? Explain. *No; the sums all had numerators that were equal to or less than the denominators.*

- What happens to the denominator when adding fractions with like denominators? *The denominator stays the same.*

Connections and Extensions

Measurement
Have students examine an analog clock and think of minutes as fractions of an hour. For example, 15 minutes is $\frac{15}{60}$ or $\frac{1}{4}$ of an hour. Have students design a schedule for a class that lasts one hour. Have them write lengths of activities in both minutes and in fractions of an hour. Encourage students to use addition to check that their fractions total 1 hour.

② Apply (30–35 min)

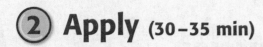

Student Page 41 Guide · · · · ·

Exercises 1–5
Have students share how they found each difference with the class.

How did addition of like fractions help you with subtraction of fractions? *Sample answer: When we add or subtract like fractions, we keep the denominators the same.*

Exercises 6–8
Have students discuss how to find common factors. Guide students through the first example, and show them how to divide by the greatest common factor to find simplest form.

What is the greatest common factor for the fraction $\frac{6}{18}$? What is the fraction in simplest form? *6 is the greatest common factor; $\frac{1}{3}$*

Student Page 42 Guide · · · · ·

Exercises 9 and 10
Have students discuss results in small groups and then as a class.

What strategy did you use to solve the problems? Did you use a different model than others in your group? *Answers will vary.*

Making a Circle Graph
How I Spend My Day

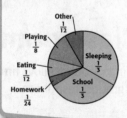

Remind students that each hour is $\frac{1}{24}$ of a day. Have them make a list of activities they do in a day and about how many hours they spend on each. Encourage students to write each fraction in simplest form. Guide them to make a circle graph of their data.

③ Reflect (5–10 min)

- When do you think you might add and subtract fractions in everyday life? *Sample answers: when measuring lengths and widths of things that have fractions of inches; when baking and needing to know how much of each ingredient to use*

- How do you know when a fraction is in simplest form? *It is in simplest form when the only common factor of the numerator and denominator is 1.*

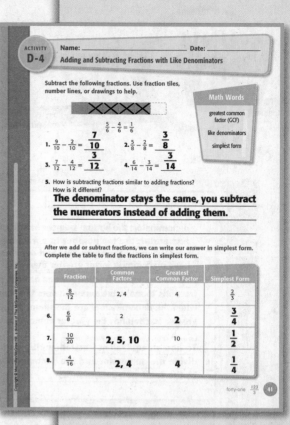

ACTIVITY D-4
Name: _____ Date: _____
Adding and Subtracting Fractions with Like Denominators

Subtract the following fractions. Use fraction tiles, number lines, or drawings to help.

Math Words
greatest common factor (GCF)
like denominators
simplest form

$\frac{5}{6} - \frac{4}{6} = \frac{1}{6}$

1. $\frac{9}{10} - \frac{2}{10} = \frac{7}{10}$
2. $\frac{5}{8} - \frac{2}{8} = \frac{3}{8}$
3. $\frac{7}{12} - \frac{4}{12} = \frac{3}{12}$
4. $\frac{6}{14} - \frac{3}{14} = \frac{3}{14}$

5. How is subtracting fractions similar to adding fractions? How is it different?
The denominator stays the same, you subtract the numerators instead of adding them.

After we add or subtract fractions, we can write our answer in simplest form. Complete the table to find the fractions in simplest form.

Fraction	Common Factors	Greatest Common Factor	Simplest Form
$\frac{8}{12}$	2, 4	4	$\frac{2}{3}$
6. $\frac{6}{8}$	2	2	$\frac{3}{4}$
7. $\frac{10}{20}$	2, 5, 10	10	$\frac{1}{2}$
8. $\frac{4}{16}$	2, 4	4	$\frac{1}{4}$

forty-one $\frac{123}{3}$ 41

Check students' work.

9. Add or subtract the fractions. Draw a number line or use fraction tiles to show your work. Write your answer in simplest form.

a. $\frac{9}{12} - \frac{6}{12} = \frac{1}{4}$

b. $\frac{1}{4} + \frac{2}{4} = \frac{3}{4}$

c. $\frac{1}{8} + \frac{2}{8} = \frac{3}{8}$

d. $\frac{7}{10} - \frac{1}{10} = \frac{3}{5}$

e. $\frac{5}{9} + \frac{2}{9} = \frac{7}{9}$

10. Match each sum or difference above to a statement. Write the letter of the equation in the correct box.

a sum between $\frac{1}{2}$ and 1 **b and e**	a sum between zero and $\frac{1}{2}$ **c**
a difference between $\frac{1}{2}$ and 1 **d**	a difference between zero and $\frac{1}{2}$ **a**

Make a Circle Graph
Make a list of the activities you do in a day. Include the amount of time you spend doing each activity. Write the time as a fraction of a day. Then, make a circle graph to show your data. (HINT: There are 24 hours in 1 day, and the sum of the fractions must equal 1.)

How I Spend My Day

42 $\frac{84}{2}$ forty-two

Activity D-4: Adding and Subtracting Fractions with Like Denominators **T42**

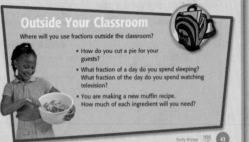

Reflecting on What I Learned

New *Vocabulary* I learned:

1. denominator: the bottom number in a fraction
2. numerator: the top number in a fraction
3. simplest form: the numerator and denominator have no common factor greater than 1

How do you compare two fractions that have different denominators?

Find an equivalent fraction for one or both of the fractions to make the denominators the same; when the denominators are the same, the greater fraction has the greater numerator.

List one thing you learned about equivalent fractions.

To find an equivalent fraction, multiply or divide the numerator and the denominator by the same non-zero number.

Outside Your Classroom

Where will you use fractions outside the classroom?

- How do you cut a pie for your guests?
- What fraction of a day do you spend sleeping? What fraction of the day do you spend watching television?
- You are making a new muffin recipe. How much of each ingredient will you need?

forty-three $\frac{430}{10}$ 43

Vocabulary and Essential Learnings

Vocabulary

- Have students discuss in small groups the vocabulary terms and the definitions that they learned or reviewed in this unit.
- Generate a master list of terms on the board, or have students create a Foldable®.
- Have students record three terms of their choice along with a brief definition or picture for each one.

Essential Learnings

Arrange students in pairs. Have partners review the activities on pages 35 through 42 and discuss what they learned.

Allow time for students to share their essential learnings in small groups or as a class.

Outside Your Classroom

You may wish to arrange students into groups. Allow time for classmates to extend or enrich the groups' responses.

Possible student responses:

- How do you cut a pie for your guests? *When I am cutting pie or other foods for guests, I will need to know the amount of pie and the number of pieces to cut to determine the size of each piece.*
- What fraction of a day do you spend sleeping? What fraction of the day do you spend watching television? *I know that there are 24 hours in one day. The hours I sleep and the hours I watch television are each parts of the 24 hours, so 24 will be my denominator. The number of hours I spend on each activity will be the numerators.*
- You are baking a muffin recipe. How much of each ingredient will you need? *I need to know how many muffins I want to bake and what the measurements are for each ingredient.*

AL

Present these statements to students and have them determine how much of each pie was eaten.

- There is $\frac{1}{3}$ of a chocolate pie left. $\frac{2}{3}$ *was eaten.*
- There are slices equal to $\frac{1}{8}$ and $\frac{3}{8}$ of cherry pie left. $\frac{4}{8}$ or $\frac{1}{2}$ *was eaten.*

Representing Survey Data

Materials

examples of categorical surveys
examples of circle graphs
chart paper

Pacing:
45 min

Introducing the Project

Show students examples of categorical surveys in which participants responded to a question by choosing one option. Then, with the students, brainstorm ideas for their own survey topics and/or questions. List these ideas on chart paper.

Completing the Project

Keep the list of survey topics and examples posted while students work on the project. Set up a survey table in the front of the room and have each student come to the front and ask students their survey question. Then complete Steps 2 and 3 independently. Remind students that to find the fractions, they will count the total number of votes and the number of votes for each choice.

Help students draw their circle graphs. Draw the greatest fraction first. Is it more than $\frac{1}{2}$ or less than $\frac{1}{2}$ of the votes? Students may find it helpful to divide their circles into parts and then shade.

Extending the Project

Encourage students to write questions about their data. The questions can have to do with comparing and ordering fractions, adding and subtracting fractions, or reading the data. Have students trade questions with a partner from a different group and solve.

Representing Survey Data

Use your new knowledge about fractions to represent survey data in a circle graph.

1. First, plan and conduct a survey.
   - Choose a survey question that has at least three answer choices to ask 10 people. For example, "What is your favorite sport?" or "What is your favorite color?"
   - Record the results in a tally chart.
   - Turn the results into fractions: $\frac{\text{number of votes for choice}}{\text{total number of survey votes}}$
2. Next, make a circle graph to represent the data from your survey.
   - Draw a circle. Draw the sections of your graph for each choice.
   - Label each choice and its fraction part. Make sure fractions are in simplest form.
3. Finally, write a report explaining your survey and results.
   - Include the tally chart and the circle graph in your report. Explain the results. (Sample graphs shown.)
   - Which choice received the most votes? Which received the fewest? What fraction is each?
   - Which two choices added together received more than $\frac{1}{2}$ of the votes? Which choices received about $\frac{1}{3}$ of the votes?

What is your favorite sport?	
Baseball	卌 I
Basketball	I
Soccer	卌 IIII
Tennis	IIII

Favorite Sports

44 $\frac{68}{2}$ forty-four

Copyright © Macmillan/McGraw-Hill, a division of The McGraw-Hill Companies, Inc.

Suggested Scoring Rubric

4	The student completes the project with accuracy and creativity. The student's report accurately and completely describes the project and is written in clear, concise language including appropriate math terminology.
3	The student completes the project. The student's report has some inaccuracies and uses very little math terminology.
2	The student does not complete all components of the project. The student's report is inaccurate, incomplete, and contains incorrect or no math terminology.
1	The student's project is either incomplete or inaccurate. The student's report is inaccurate, incomplete, and contains incorrect math terminology.

UNIT E

Working with Fractions and Decimals

Vocabulary

decimal a number that uses place value, numbers, and a decimal point to show part of a whole

decimal equivalents decimals that represent the same number

0.9 and 0.90

decimal point a period separating the ones and the tenths in a decimal number

0.8 or $3.77

hundredth a place-value position; one of the one hundred equal parts

In the number 0.05, 5 is in the hundredths place.

mixed number a number that has a whole number part and a fraction part

$6\frac{3}{4}$

tenth a place-value position; one of ten equal parts, or $\frac{1}{10}$

In the number 0.25, 2 is in the tenths place.

Unit-at-a-Glance

In Unit E, students gain understanding of decimals.

Activity	Focus	Student Investigation
E-1 What Is a Decimal? (pp. 47–48)	Students relate decimals to the base-ten number system, identifying a decimal as one way to name parts of one.	Students use coins and grid paper to model decimals and explore the relationship between ones, tenths, and hundredths.
E-2 Renaming Fractions and Decimals (pp. 49–50)	Students relate decimals to fractions and use them to find the same part of one.	Students explore various models and describe each model using fractions and decimals.
E-3 Ordering Fractions and Decimals on a Number Line (pp. 51–52)	Students use a number line to compare and order decimals and fractions from 0 through 1.	Students compare and order decimals and fractions on a number line.
E-4 Decimals, Fractions, and Mixed Numbers (pp. 53–54)	Students expand an understanding of decimals and fractions to include mixed numbers and decimal equivalents.	Students compare and order data represented as mixed numbers and decimals.
Unit Project: Spending $100 (p. 56)	Students relate the concepts and skills they have learned to the real world.	Students use knowledge of decimal representation of money and parts of 1 to create a spending plan and to graph the expense categories.

Page Numbers

Each page number is represented as a point on a number line.

Guiding Questions

- Fill in the missing numbers on the number line. Count by 1s, 5s, 10s, etc.
- If each page number were divided by 100, what would the decimal look like?

Unit Opener

Student Page 45 Guide

You can open the unit by having students read through the objectives they will accomplish during the unit. Have students restate objectives in their own words to ensure comprehension.

Scaffolding Questions

How are decimals similar to whole numbers and how are they different? *Decimals and whole numbers both use place value to describe an amount; decimals name parts of a whole, such as tenths or hundredths.*

How are decimals similar to fractions and how are they different? *Fractions and decimals both name parts of 1; decimals are written with a decimal point and fractions are written with a fraction bar, with a numerator over a denominator.*

Vocabulary

WRITING IN MATH ▶

The beginning of the unit is a great time to start a new wall chart.

Encourage students to write the definitions in their math journals. Writing their own definitions or creating drawings will help internalize the information.

Remind students that fractions name parts of a whole and that equivalent fractions can be found by multiplying or dividing the numerator and denominator by the same number.

Student Page 46 Guide

Home Letter

Have students take the Home Letter home.

Look at the Projects and Discussions throughout the unit to see if any additional opportunities are available for work at home.

ELL

Encourage students to visit the online eGlossary with parents to see vocabulary in 13 languages.

TeacherWorks *Plus*

See "Home E-mail" as an alternative for communication. From the Lesson Planner, select the e-mail document for this unit, double-click the file, and edit in the Worksheet Editor.

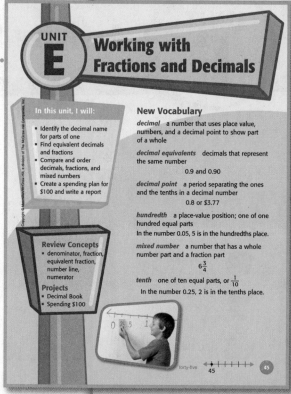

UNIT E — Working with Fractions and Decimals

In this unit, I will:
- Identify the decimal name for parts of one
- Find equivalent decimals and fractions
- Compare and order decimals, fractions, and mixed numbers
- Create a spending plan for $100 and write a report

Review Concepts
- denominator, fraction, equivalent fraction, number line, numerator

Projects
- Decimal Book
- Spending $100

New Vocabulary

decimal a number that uses place value, numbers, and a decimal point to show part of a whole

decimal equivalents decimals that represent the same number

0.9 and 0.90

decimal point a period separating the ones and the tenths in a decimal number

0.8 or $3.77

hundredth a place-value position; one of one hundred equal parts

In the number 0.05, 5 is in the hundredths place.

mixed number a number that has a whole number part and a fraction part

$6\frac{3}{4}$

tenth one of ten equal parts, or $\frac{1}{10}$

In the number 0.25, 2 is in the tenths place.

forty-five **45**

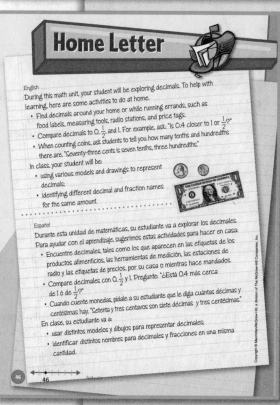

Home Letter

English

During this math unit, your student will be exploring decimals. To help with learning, here are some activities to do at home.
- Find decimals around your home or while running errands, such as food labels, measuring tools, radio stations, and price tags.
- Compare decimals to 0, $\frac{1}{2}$, and 1. For example, ask: "Is 0.4 closer to 1 or $\frac{1}{2}$?"
- When counting coins, ask students to tell you how many tenths and hundredths there are. "Seventy-three cents is seven tenths, three hundredths."

In class, your student will be:
- using various models and drawings to represent decimals;
- identifying different decimal and fraction names for the same amount.

Español

Durante esta unidad de matemáticas, su estudiante va a explorar los decimales. Para ayudar con el aprendizaje, sugerimos estas actividades para hacer en casa:
- Encuentre decimales, tales como los que aparecen en las etiquetas de los productos alimenticios, las herramientas de medición, las estaciones de radio y las etiquetas de precios, por su casa o mientras hace mandados.
- Compare decimales con 0, $\frac{1}{2}$ y 1. Pregunte: "¿Está 0.4 más cerca de 1 o de $\frac{1}{2}$?"
- Cuando cuente monedas, pídale a su estudiante que le diga cuántas décimas y centésimas hay. "Setenta y tres centavos son siete décimas y tres centésimas."

En clase, su estudiante va a:
- usar distintos modelos y dibujos para representar decimales;
- identificar distintos nombres para decimales y fracciones en una misma cantidad.

46 forty-six

UNIT E

Activity Planner

KEY

 Real-World Connections

 Projects

 Technology

 CD-ROM

 Math Tool Chest

Math Adventures

	Activity E-1 Pacing: 50–65 min	**Activity E-2** Pacing: 65–80 min
Activity/ Objective	**What Is a Decimal?** (pp. 47–48) **Objective** Model decimals and name parts of a whole using decimals.	**Renaming Fractions and Decimals** (pp. 49–50) **Objective** Identify decimals and fractions that name the same part.
Math Vocabulary	decimal tenth decimal equivalents decimal point hundredth **Review Vocabulary** fraction	**Review Vocabulary** decimal equivalents denominator equivalent fractions numerator
Activity Resources	**Materials** 10 × 10 grid paper meterstick newspapers magazines **Manipulatives** coins (pennies, dimes)	**Materials** grid paper meterstick paper plate index cards **Manipulatives** coins (pennies, dimes) connecting cubes counters
Technology	**Math Adventures** Mount Frost Blipp's Satellite Service	**Math Adventures** Blipp's Satellite Service **Personal Tutor**
Real-World Connections		
Small Projects	**Decimal Book** Create a Decimal Book from decimals found in newspapers or magazines.	

Activity E-3	Pacing: 55–70 min	Activity E-4	Pacing: 55–75 min	Unit Project	Pacing: 45 min	
Ordering Fractions and Decimals on a Number Line (pp. 51–52)		**Decimals, Fractions, and Mixed Numbers** (pp. 53–54)		**Spending $100** (p. 56)		**Activity/ Objective**
Objective Compare and order decimals and fractions using a number line.		**Objective** Compare and order decimals, fractions, and mixed numbers.		**Objective** Create a spending plan using decimals and fractions to represent money amounts.		
		mixed number				**Math Vocabulary**
Review Vocabulary number line						
Materials index cards markers tape		**Materials** paper		**Materials** catalogs ads in newspapers samples of circle graphs and bar graphs		**Activity Resources**
		Manipulatives play money ($1 bills, dimes, pennies)				
🏅 **Math Adventures** Mount Frost		🛠 **Math Tool Chest** Money **Personal Tutor**		🛠 **Math Tool Chest** Graphs		🖥 **Technology**
		In Science Explore density. Compare densities of substances to the density of water.				🌎 **Real-World Connections**
Decimal Book Have students utilize their Decimal Books to compare and order more decimals.						📦 **Small Projects**

UNIT E

Differentiation and Assessment

Differentiated Instruction

Below are suggestions on differentiating the materials presented in this unit. Additional modifications should be considered.

Below Level **BL**	Above Level **AL**	English Language Learners **ELL**
ACTIVITY E-1 **Exercises 1–6** Allow students to use base-ten blocks and place-value charts to model and read decimals.	**Decimal Book** Have students begin to explore decimals with place value to thousandths.	Help students with the terms *tenths* and *hundredths*. The "th" sound may be difficult for them to pronounce. Have students explain the difference between *tens* and *tenths* and *hundreds* and *hundredths*.
ACTIVITY E-2 Encourage students to use fraction tiles, grid paper, or diagrams to help them write fractions as decimals and vice versa.	**Investigate** Have students explore using division to change fractions to decimals. Provide them with a calculator to help them divide the numerator by the denominator.	Explain that *equivalent* means *equal to* or *the same as.* Have students draw pictures to demonstrate understanding. Include comparison words such as *longer, shorter, greater,* and *less.*
ACTIVITY E-3 **Exercises 1–6** Provide additional benchmarks/ tick marks on the number lines to help students locate both the fractions and the decimals. 0.10 0.20 0.1 0.2 $\frac{1}{10}$ $\frac{1}{5}$ ⟷	**Exercises 7–11** Have students write their own story problem using decimals, fractions, and a number line, then share it with a partner to solve.	Talk about words that signify comparing and ordering, such as *least, greatest, fewest,* and *most.* Have students locate these and other words in the exercises and be sure they understand what is being asked.
ACTIVITY E-4 Have students use a place-value chart to help them compare and order decimal numbers. Remind them to align the decimal points.	**Exercises 10–12** Have students write new grocery-store problems using fractions, decimals, and mixed numbers. Have them share with a partner to solve.	**Exercises 10–12** Have students look at the word problems and discuss any words that they find confusing. Provide visuals to help them understand the information given and what they are asked to find.

Performance-Based Assessment

On The Line (p. A18)

In *On the Line,* students first place fractions and decimal numbers on a number line and then explain their meanings.

Connections

On the Line also covers the following skills and concepts:

- Comparing and ordering fractions and decimals
- Problem solving
- Reasoning
- Communication

Targeting the Task

- **Pretest**–Use Exercises 1 and 2 to determine students' understanding of the meanings and relationships of fractions and decimals.
- **Formative**–The exercises can be administered individually during the course of the related unit.
- **Summative**–Administer the complete *On The Line* assessment.

Differentiation

Students struggling with ordering decimals and fractions need more practice with the benchmarks. An easy way to use benchmarks is by folding paper strips. Fold a strip into fourths and have students number the benchmark fractions $0, \frac{1}{4}, \frac{1}{2}, \frac{3}{4}, 1$. Work with real or play money to break $1 into the same benchmarks, and have students label the decimal equivalents under the fraction.

Move the lesson forward by having students fold a strip into eighths, but continue to skip count by fourths in order to get benchmarks $1\frac{1}{4}, 1\frac{1}{2}, 1\frac{3}{4}$.

After the benchmarks are labeled, give students an extra fraction and an extra decimal to put on the line. Increase the complexity of the lesson by choosing decimals and fractions that are close to each other such as $\frac{2}{3}$ and $\frac{3}{5}$.

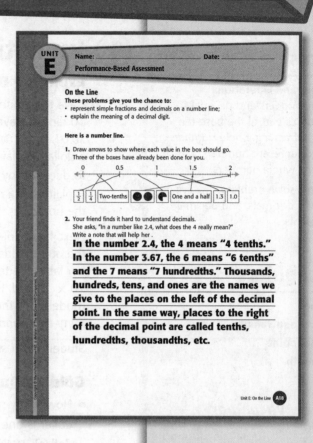

ACTIVITY E-1

What Is a Decimal?

Focus

Number and Operations

Students understand decimal notation as part of the base-ten system of writing whole numbers used to represent numbers between whole numbers.

Students solve problems involving fractions, decimals, and decimal equivalents.

Vocabulary

decimal
decimal equivalents
decimal point
hundredth
tenth

Review Vocabulary
fraction

Materials

10 × 10 grid paper
meterstick
newspapers
magazines
coins (100 pennies, 10 dimes)

① Investigate (20–25 min)

Exploring Decimals

Have the students work in pairs. Provide each pair with 100 pennies and 10 dimes. Have students write the value of a penny and a dime. *1¢ or $0.01, and 10¢ or $0.10* Guide them to think about pennies as parts of a dollar. Explain that a penny is one-hundredth of a dollar. Link fractions to decimals by writing $\frac{1}{100} = 0.01$ on the board. Repeat using dimes. Explain that a dime is one-tenth of a dollar and write $\frac{1}{10} = 0.1$ on the board.

Next, have one student in the pair model 3 dimes and 2 pennies. Have the other student record the value as a decimal. *$0.32* Then have him or her label the tenths and the hundredths places. Provide students with a 10 × 10 grid. Have them shade in squares to represent the decimal modeled by the coins. Discuss how to read the decimal number 0.32. *thirty-two hundredths*

Students can switch roles and repeat, using a different decimal number.

Guiding Questions

- How many pennies equal one dollar? *100* What fraction of a dollar is one penny? $\frac{1}{100}$ How many dimes equal one dollar? *10* What fraction of a dollar is one dime? $\frac{1}{10}$

- What is the relationship between tenths and hundredths? *10 hundredths equal 1 tenth.*

- How are decimals similar to fractions? *They both name part of a whole.*

- When you write a decimal number, you use a decimal point. Why is the decimal point necessary? *The decimal point separates the whole from the parts.*

- How did you know how many squares to shade on the grid? *Sample answer: Each square represents $\frac{1}{100}$. So, I shaded 10 squares for each dime and 1 square for each penny.*

Connections and Extensions •••••••••••

Measurement
Link decimal numbers to the metric system. Show students a meterstick and discuss how the meter is divided into centimeters. Each centimeter is $\frac{1}{100}$ of a meter. Have students measure objects in centimeters and record the measurement as a decimal part of a meter.

Student Page 47 Guide ·····

Exercises 1–6
Discuss the relationship between the part of the grid that is shaded and the decimal. Go over how to write decimals in both standard and word form.

Is there another way to write your answer for Exercise 4? *Yes; I can write the shaded part as 0.50 or 0.5.*

Discuss how both are acceptable answers.

Student Page 48 Guide ·····

Exercises 7 and 8
Discuss the relationship between tenths and hundredths.

Have students write the equivalent fraction for each decimal to reinforce that the decimals are equivalent.
$$\frac{4}{10} = \frac{40}{100}, \frac{9}{10} = \frac{90}{100}$$

Exercises 9–13
Review place value with the class. Students may use the charts on page 47 to help them with the exercises. Have students share their answers with the class.

How do the words *tenths* and *hundredths* help you to know how many places the decimal number will have? *Tenths will have one place to the right of the decimal point; hundredths will have two places.*

Exercises 14 and 15
Have students share their answers with the class. Encourage students to use grid paper or models to support their answers.

For Exercise 15, students may use a drawing to compare 0.58 and $\frac{1}{2}$ or they could use equivalent fractions. Discuss the different methods as a class.

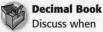 **Decimal Book**
Discuss when decimals are used, such as in measurements, batting averages, and track-and-field times.

Have students find decimal numbers in newspapers, magazines, or on the Internet. Invite them to draw a model of the decimal on one page and then write the decimal number in word form on the opposite page.

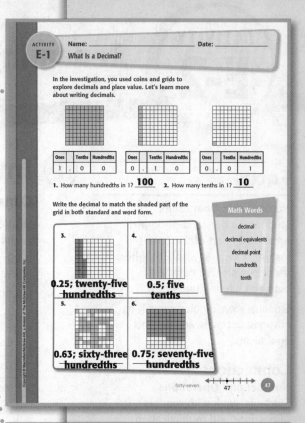

ACTIVITY E-1
Name: _____ Date: _____
What Is a Decimal?

In the investigation, you used coins and grids to explore decimals and place value. Let's learn more about writing decimals.

Ones	Tenths	Hundredths
1	0	0

Ones	Tenths	Hundredths
0	1	0

Ones	Tenths	Hundredths
0	0	1

1. How many hundredths in 1? **100**   2. How many tenths in 1? **10**

Write the decimal to match the shaded part of the grid in both standard and word form.

Math Words
decimal
decimal equivalents
decimal point
hundredth
tenth

3. **0.25; twenty-five hundredths**
4. **0.5; five tenths**
5. **0.63; sixty-three hundredths**
6. **0.75; seventy-five hundredths**

forty-seven   47   47

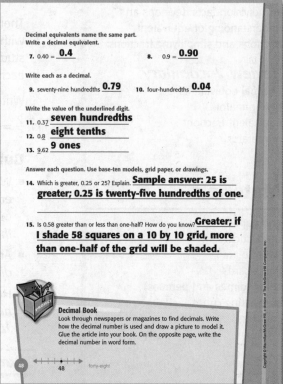

Decimal equivalents name the same part. Write a decimal equivalent.
7. 0.40 = **0.4**   8. 0.9 = **0.90**

Write each as a decimal.
9. seventy-nine hundredths **0.79**   10. four-hundredths **0.04**

Write the value of the underlined digit.
11. 0.3_7_ **seven hundredths**
12. 0._8_ **eight tenths**
13. _9_.62 **9 ones**

Answer each question. Use base-ten models, grid paper, or drawings.
14. Which is greater, 0.25 or 25? Explain. **Sample answer: 25 is greater; 0.25 is twenty-five hundredths of one.**

15. Is 0.58 greater than or less than one-half? How do you know? **Greater; if I shade 58 squares on a 10 by 10 grid, more than one-half of the grid will be shaded.**

Decimal Book
Look through newspapers or magazines to find decimals. Write how the decimal number is used and draw a picture to model it. Glue the article into your book. On the opposite page, write the decimal number in word form.

48   48   forty-eight

③ **Reflect** (5–10 min)

- How does the decimal point help you understand the decimal number? *Sample answer: The decimal point separates the whole from the parts.*

- When might you use decimals numbers? *Sample answers: prices, distances, measurements*

Renaming Fractions and Decimals

Focus

Number and Operations

Students understand decimal notation as part of the base-ten system of writing whole numbers used to represent numbers between whole numbers.

Students solve problems involving fractions, decimals, and decimal equivalents.

Connections

Number and Operations

Students' work with models of fractions and multiplication and division facts develops an understanding of equivalent fractions and simplifying fractions.

Review Vocabulary

decimal equivalents
denominator
equivalent fractions
numerator

Materials

grid paper
meterstick
paper plate
index cards
coins (dimes and pennies)
connecting cubes
counters

① Investigate (30–35 min)

Connecting Decimals to Fractions

Display the following: 8 dimes; 2 pennies; 10 connecting cubes, 6 red and 4 orange; a meterstick with an arrow pointing to 65 centimeters; a 10 × 10 grid with 20 squares shaded. Have students work with a partner. Instruct them to look at each display and describe it using fractions and decimals. Have them record their work in a table.

Item	Fraction	Decimal
Coins	$\frac{82}{100}$ of a dollar	$0.82
Connecting cubes	$\frac{6}{10}$ are red	0.6 are red
Meterstick	$\frac{65}{100}$ of a meter	0.65 of a meter
Grid	$\frac{20}{100}$ is shaded	0.20 is shaded

Then display the following: a paper plate divided into 5 equal sections with 2 parts shaded; a group of 8 counters, 4 red and 4 yellow. Have students use what they know about equivalent fractions to describe each as a decimal. Have them record their work in their tables.

Write the fractions and their decimal equivalents on the board.

$$\frac{2}{5} = \frac{2 \times 2}{5 \times 2} = \frac{4}{10} = 0.4 \qquad \frac{4}{8} = \frac{1}{2} = \frac{5}{10} = 0.5$$

Guiding Questions

- What patterns do you notice between the fractions and their decimal equivalents? *Sample answer: When the denominator is 100, there are two numbers after the decimal point. When the denominator is 10, there is one number after the decimal point.*

- Are all your fractions in simplest form? How do you know? *No; I can divide the same number into the numerator and denominator.*

- How do you find an equivalent fraction for a decimal? *Write the number or numbers after the decimal point as the numerator and 10 or 100 as the denominator.*

Connections and Extensions

Number Sense
Play "Decimal Match-Up." Make fraction and decimal cards using ones, tenths, and hundredths. For each decimal card make an equivalent fraction card. Place the cards facedown. Player 1 turns over two cards. If the cards are an equivalent fraction and decimal, Player 1 keeps both cards and tries again. If the cards do not match, Player 1 returns the cards facedown and Player 2 tries to make a match. When all the cards are paired, the player with the most cards wins.

② Apply (30–35 min)

Student Page 49 Guide · · · · ·

Exercises 1–8
Have students share responses with a partner and discuss how the denominator helps them write the decimal number.

How does the denominator relate to the number of places in the decimal number? *If the denominator is 100, there are two decimal places; if the denominator is 10, there is one decimal place.*

Exercises 9–14
Encourage students to write the fraction in simplest form.

How do you know when a fraction is in simplest form? *Sample answer: The only common factor of the numerator and denominator is 1.*

Student Page 50 Guide · · · · ·

Exercises 15–19
For Exercises 15 and 16, encourage students to first write the fraction, then find an equivalent fraction with a denominator of 10 or 100, and then write the decimal number.

In Exercise 18, how did you find the decimal equivalent? *Sample answer: I needed to find a denominator of 10 or 100. So, I multiplied the fraction by $\frac{5}{5}$ and got $\frac{5}{100}$ or 0.05.*

Exercises 20–22
Guide students to first write the decimal as a fraction with a denominator of 10 or 100 and then simplify the fraction.

For Exercise 20, what will the denominator of the fraction equivalent to 0.2 have to be to make it easy to shade the diagram? Explain your choice. *The denominator will be 5; the diagram is divided into 5 equal parts. So, I need to know how many parts out of 5 are equal to 0.2.*

③ Reflect (5–10 min)

- Is it easier to change a decimal to a fraction or a fraction to a decimal? Explain your choice. *Answers will vary. Sample answer: It is easier to change a decimal to a fraction because all I do is put the numbers after the decimal point over 10 or 100, depending on the number of place values in the decimal.*

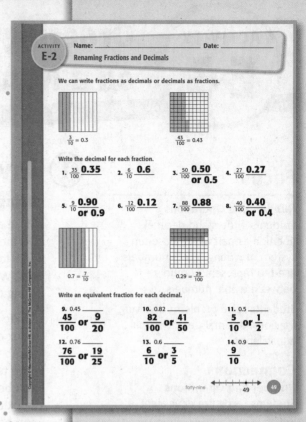

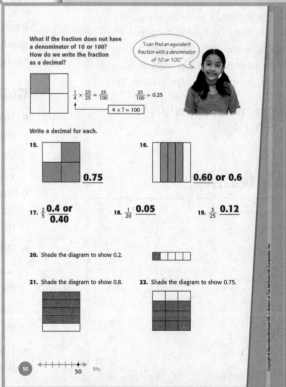

Ordering Fractions and Decimals on a Number Line

Focus

Number and Operations
Students understand decimal notation as part of the base-ten system of writing whole numbers used to represent numbers between whole numbers.

Students solve problems involving fractions, decimals, and decimal equivalents.

Connections

Number and Operations
Students recognize equivalent fractions.

Students' work with models of fractions and multiplication and division facts develops an understanding of equivalent fractions and simplifying fractions.

Review Vocabulary
number line

Materials

index cards
markers
tape

① Investigate (25–30 min)

Using a Number Line

Make a large number line by attaching tape to the board or on the floor. On the left end, tape an index card with the number 0. On the opposite end, tape an index card with the number 1. In the middle, tape an index card with the decimal 0.5 and the fraction $\frac{1}{2}$. Use small pieces of tape along the line to designate tick marks for every tenth.

Divide the students into small groups. Provide each group with two index cards and instruct them to write two decimal numbers. One number should have one decimal place and the other number should have two decimal places. Students should position their cards on the number line using tape. As a class, talk about the placement of their index cards in relationship to the benchmarks. Are their decimal numbers greater than or less than $\frac{1}{2}$?

Invite students to make a list of the decimals in order from least to greatest. Have them look at the numbers and discuss how they can compare the numbers without using the number line.

Guiding Questions

- How do the benchmarks of 0, $\frac{1}{2}$, and 1 help you find the location of the decimals on the number line? *Sample answer: I can compare my decimal to the benchmarks to figure out where my decimal should go on the number line.*

- How do you use a number line to compare two decimal numbers? *Sample answer: I can plot both numbers. The decimal number farther to the right, or closer to 1, is greater.*

- What conclusion can you draw about the decimal numbers that are less than $\frac{1}{2}$? that are greater than $\frac{1}{2}$? *Sample answer: The decimals that have a 0, 1, 2, 3, or 4 in the tenths place are less than $\frac{1}{2}$. The decimals that have a 5, 6, 7, 8, or 9 in the tenths place are greater than $\frac{1}{2}$, except for 0.5 which equals $\frac{1}{2}$.*

- How can you compare and order decimals without using a number line? *Sample answer: Compare place values from left to right.*

Connections and Extensions

Graphing
Have students find the batting averages of baseball players. Instruct them to use four averages, write the numbers to the hundredths place, and display the data in a bar graph. Ask students to order the averages from greatest to least.

② Apply (25–30 min)

Student Page 51 Guide

Exercises 1–5 Have students share answers with a partner and then with the class.	Discuss how a number line is used and remind students that numbers farthest to the left are less than numbers farthest to the right.
Exercise 6 Ask students to share how they changed the number line and what clues they used to help them reposition the fractions and decimals.	Encourage students to use drawings, diagrams, or equivalent fractions to determine if the decimals and fractions are plotted correctly.
Decimal Book	Have students look at the Decimal Book they made in Activity E-1. Have them make a list of the decimals they recorded in order from least to greatest.

Student Page 52 Guide

Exercises 7 and 8 Have students compare their solutions with a partner and then with the class.	What strategies did you use to plot the fractions and decimals? *Answers will vary.*
Exercises 9–11 Explain to students that *per capita* means "per person." Encourage a volunteer to draw his or her number line on the board.	If you did not have a number line, how would you compare and order the data from the table? *Sample answer: I would change all of the numbers to decimals and compare the digits.*

③ Reflect (5–10 min)

- How does knowing benchmark equivalent fractions and decimals such as $0.5 = \frac{1}{2}$ help you compare fractions and decimals? *Sample answer: If I know that a fraction is greater than $\frac{1}{2}$ and that a decimal is less than 0.5, then I know that the fraction is greater than the decimal.*

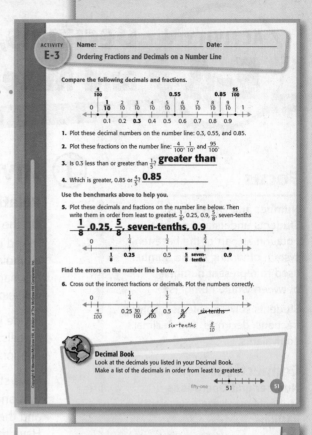

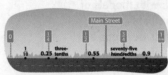

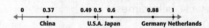

Decimals, Fractions, and Mixed Numbers

Focus

Number and Operations

Students understand decimal notation as part of the base-ten system of writing whole numbers used to represent numbers between whole numbers.

Students solve problems involving fractions, decimals, and decimal equivalents.

Connections

Number and Operations

Students recognize equivalent fractions.

Students' work with models of fractions and multiplication and division facts develops an understanding of equivalent fractions and simplifying fractions.

Vocabulary

mixed number

Materials

paper
play money ($1 bills, dimes, pennies)

① Investigate (20–25 min)

Relating Mixed Numbers and Decimals

On the board, write the mixed number $4\frac{3}{10}$. Explain that a mixed number names a value greater than 1 and is made up of a whole number and a fraction. Ask students if a decimal number can name a value greater than 1. *Yes* Tell students that today they will explore how to write mixed numbers as decimal numbers.

Divide students into pairs and distribute play money consisting of $1 bills, dimes, and pennies to each pair. Review with students the relationship between pennies, dimes, dollars, and decimal numbers.

Have students begin by modeling the mixed number $4\frac{3}{10}$ using the bills and coins. Discuss with students how to model the whole number and the fraction. Guide students to use 3 dimes to model the fraction. Have them record the money amount as a decimal number. *$4.30 or 4.3*

Write the following mixed numbers on the board: $4\frac{5}{100}$, $3\frac{9}{10}$, $4\frac{3}{5}$, $5\frac{1}{2}$ and have students model and record each one. When students are done, have volunteers present their models and have students arrange the models in order from least to greatest.

Guiding Questions

- How did you model the whole number of the mixed number? *I used dollar bills.*

- When you wrote the decimal equivalent of $4\frac{3}{10}$, where did you place the decimal point? Explain. *I placed the decimal point between the 4 and the 3. The decimal point separates the whole number from the parts.*

- How did you model $4\frac{3}{5}$ and $5\frac{1}{2}$? *Sample answer: I first wrote equivalent mixed numbers with denominators of 10. Then I could model the fractions using dimes.*

- List the steps you used to order the decimals. *Sample answer: I first compared the whole numbers to each other and then I compared the digits to the right of the decimal beginning with the tenths.*

Connections and Extensions

Graphing

Give students a sheet of paper with five circle graphs, each divided into ten equal parts. Ask them to color 2.5 of the circles green and 1.5 yellow. Color the remaining circles red. How many are red? *One circle is red.*

Student Page 53 Guide · · · · ·

Exercises 1–3
Have students share responses with a partner and then with the class.

In Exercise 3, why are the two decimals equal? *Sample answer: I can remove the zero from the end of the first decimal number; eighty hundredths is equal to eight tenths.*

Exercises 4–9
Have students focus on changing the fraction to a decimal before comparing.

How did you solve Exercise 9? *Sample answer: I changed $2\frac{51}{100}$ to a decimal. I then compared the tenths. One-tenth is less than five-tenths, so 2.15 is less than 2.51.*

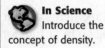 **In Science**
Introduce the concept of density.

Have students compare the density of each item in the table to 1 to determine if the substance would float or sink. Encourage students to check their predictions at home.

Student Page 54 Guide · · · · ·

Exercises 10–12
Have partners share their solutions with the class. Encourage them to draw diagrams to help explain what they did.

In Exercise 12, which shelves could hold more than one size bottle? *The $8\frac{3}{4}$-in. high shelf and the $10\frac{1}{4}$-in. high shelf.*

How did changing fractions to decimals or decimals to fractions help you solve the problems? *Answers may vary.*

(3) **Reflect** (5–10 min)

- When might you need to compare and order fractions and decimals? *Sample answers: to compare prices or distances*

- How is comparing fractions and decimals similar to comparing whole numbers? *Sample answer: In both, I begin comparing the digits in the greatest place value. Then I move right, comparing them until one number is greater than the other.*

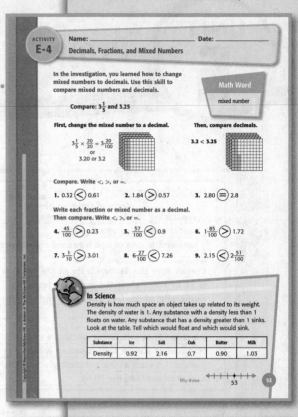

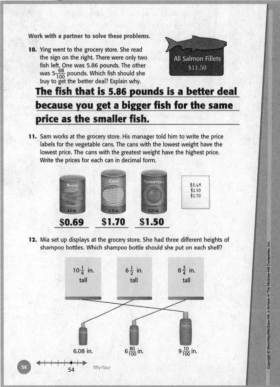

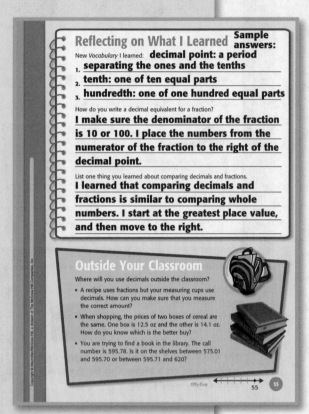

Reflecting on What I Learned

Sample answers:

New *Vocabulary* I learned: **decimal point: a period**

1. **separating the ones and the tenths**

2. **tenth: one of ten equal parts**

3. **hundredth: one of one hundred equal parts**

How do you write a decimal equivalent for a fraction?

I make sure the denominator of the fraction is 10 or 100. I place the numbers from the numerator of the fraction to the right of the decimal point.

List one thing you learned about comparing decimals and fractions.

I learned that comparing decimals and fractions is similar to comparing whole numbers. I start at the greatest place value, and then move to the right.

Outside Your Classroom

Where will you use decimals outside the classroom?

- A recipe uses fractions but your measuring cups use decimals. How can you make sure that you measure the correct amount?
- When shopping, the prices of two boxes of cereal are the same. One box is 12.5 oz and the other is 14.1 oz. How do you know which is the better buy?
- You are trying to find a book in the library. The call number is 595.78. Is it on the shelves between 575.01 and 595.70 or between 595.71 and 620?

fifty-five   55   55

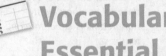

Vocabulary and Essential Learnings

Vocabulary

- Have students discuss in small groups the vocabulary terms and the definitions that they learned or reviewed in this unit.

- Generate a master list of terms on the board or have students create a Foldable®.

- Have students record three terms of their choice, along with a brief definition or picture for each one.

Essential Learnings

Arrange students in pairs. Have partners review the activities on pages 47 through 54 and discuss what they learned.

Allow time for students to share their essential learnings in small groups or as a class.

Outside Your Classroom

You may wish to arrange students into four groups. Then have groups share their responses with the class. Allow time for classmates to extend or enrich the groups' responses.

Possible student responses:

- How can you make sure you measure the correct amount? *I can change the fractions given in the recipe to decimals or the measuring cups into fractions.*

- How do you know which is the better buy? *I need to compare the decimals; the greater decimal is the better buy.*

- How do you know on which library shelves to look for your book? *I need to compare the call number to the decimals on the shelves. My book is on the shelves between 595.71 and 620.*

Spending $100

Materials

catalogs
ads in newspapers
samples of circle graphs and bar graphs

Pacing:
45 min

Introducing the Project

You may wish to have students skim the pages in the unit to refresh their memories.

Show students catalogs and newspaper ads listing items and prices. Talk to students about making a budget. Explain that it is helpful to plan how we will spend our money so that we can calculate the total cost before we spend it. That way we can ensure we have enough money to buy the things we need and want.

Completing the Project

After students have selected their categories and made their lists of items and prices, have them meet with other students. If students believe that another student may exceed the $100 budget, have them suggest alternatives to the plan. Have them recommend deleting items or selecting different items that are priced lower.

Extending the Project

Have students present their spending plans, circle graphs, and bar graphs to the class. Have them share with the class why they chose the items they did and have them explain how they ordered their prices from least to greatest.

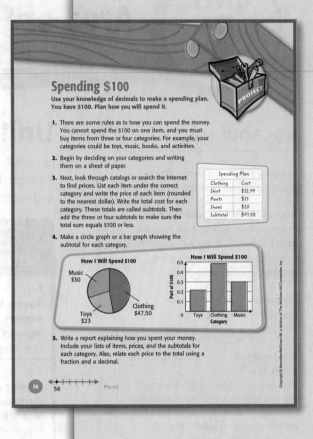

Spending $100

Use your knowledge of decimals to make a spending plan. You have $100. Plan how you will spend it.

1. There are some rules as to how you can spend the money. You cannot spend the $100 on one item, and you must buy items from three or four categories. For example, your categories could be toys, music, books, and activities.

2. Begin by deciding on your categories and writing them on a sheet of paper.

3. Next, look through catalogs or search the Internet to find prices. List each item under the correct category and write the price of each item (rounded to the nearest dollar). Write the total cost for each category. These totals are called *subtotals*. Then add the three or four subtotals to make sure the total sum equals $100 or less.

Spending Plan	
Clothing	Cost
Shirt	$12.99
Pants	$15
Shoes	$20
Subtotal	$47.50

4. Make a circle graph or a bar graph showing the subtotal for each category.

5. Write a report explaining how you spent your money. Include your lists of items, prices, and the subtotals for each category. Also, relate each price to the total using a fraction and a decimal.

56 fifty-six

Suggested Scoring Rubric

4	The student completes the project with accuracy and creativity. The student's report accurately and completely describes the project and is written in clear, concise language including appropriate math terminology.
3	The student completes the project. The student's report has some inaccuracies and uses very little math terminology.
2	The student does not complete all components of the project. The student's report is inaccurate, incomplete, and contains incorrect or no math terminology.
1	The student's project is either incomplete or inaccurate. The student's report is inaccurate, incomplete, and contains incorrect math terminology.

UNIT F

Area of Figures

Vocabulary

complex figure a shape that is made up of two or more shapes

customary system (units) the measurement system that includes units such as foot, pound, quart, and degrees Fahrenheit; also called *standard measurement*

kilometer a metric unit for measuring length
1000 meters = 1 kilometer

line segment
a part of a *line*
between two *endpoints*; the length of the line segment can be measured

metric system (units) the measurement system based on powers of 10 that includes units such as meter, gram, liter, and degrees Celsius

millimeter
a metric unit
for measuring
length
1000 millimeters = 1 meter

Unit-at-a-Glance

In Unit F, students gain understanding of perimeter and area through measuring objects and comparing area sizes in customary and metric units.

Activity	Focus	Student Investigation
F-1 **Square Units: Segments to Squares** (pp. 59–60)	Students find the total number of units of area that cover a shape. Students understand that 1 unit on a side of a square is the standard unit for measuring area.	Students create rectangles with color tiles and find the perimeter and area.
F-2 **Finding Area with Customary and Metric Units** (pp. 61–62)	Students select units and strategies to solve problems involving estimating or measuring area.	Students make paper models of customary and metric square units.
F-3 **Finding Area of Complex Figures** (pp. 63–64)	Students find the total number of units of area that cover a shape. Students understand that 1 unit on a side of a square is the standard unit for measuring area.	Students make a complex figure and find the area.
Unit Project: Pentomino Rectangle Puzzles (p. 66)	Students find the total number of units of area that cover a shape. Students understand that 1 unit on a side of a square is the standard unit for measuring area.	Students create pentomino rectangles and find the perimeter and area of each.

Page Numbers

Each page number in this lesson includes an area or perimeter model as an alternative representation.

- Find the perimeter or area for the figure on each page.
- Compare the two figures. Which area is the largest? Which perimeter is the largest?

Unit Opener

You can open the unit by having students read through the objectives they will accomplish during the unit. Have students restate objectives in their own words to ensure comprehension.

Scaffolding Questions	What tools can we use to measure perimeter and area? *rulers, yard sticks, meter sticks*
	List all of the units of measurement that you know. *Sample answers: inch, foot, mile, pound, ton, meter, gram, centimeter*
Vocabulary WRITING IN MATH	The beginning of the unit is a great time to start a new wall chart.
	Encourage students to write the definitions in their math journals. Writing their own definitions or creating drawings will help internalize the information.

Home Letter	Have students take the Home Letter home.
	Look at the Projects and Discussions throughout the unit to see if any additional opportunities are available for work at home.
ELL	Encourage students to visit the online eGlossary with parents to see vocabulary in 13 languages.
Teacher Works *Plus*	See "Home E-mail" as an alternative for communication. From the Lesson Planner, select the e-mail document for this unit, double-click the file, and edit in the Worksheet Editor.

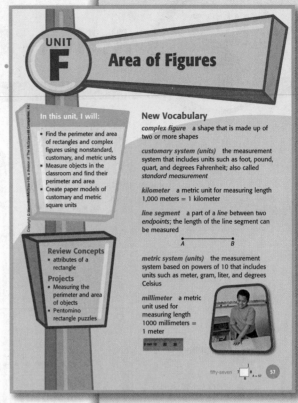

UNIT F — Area of Figures

In this unit, I will:
- Find the perimeter and area of rectangles and complex figures using nonstandard, customary, and metric units
- Measure objects in the classroom and find their perimeter and area
- Create paper models of customary and metric square units

Review Concepts
- attributes of a rectangle

Projects
- Measuring the perimeter and area of objects
- Pentomino rectangle puzzles

New Vocabulary

complex figure a shape that is made up of two or more shapes

customary system (units) the measurement system that includes units such as foot, pound, quart, and degrees Fahrenheit; also called *standard measurement*

kilometer a metric unit for measuring length 1,000 meters = 1 kilometer

line segment a part of a *line* between two *endpoints*; the length of the line segment can be measured

metric system (units) the measurement system based on powers of 10 that includes units such as meter, gram, liter, and degrees Celsius

millimeter a metric unit used for measuring length 1000 millimeters = 1 meter

fifty-seven 57

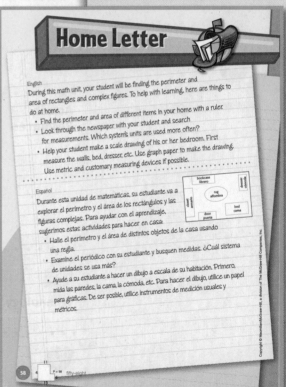

Home Letter

English
During this math unit, your student will be finding the perimeter and area of rectangles and complex figures. To help with learning, here are things to do at home.
- Find the perimeter and area of different items in your home with a ruler.
- Look through the newspaper with your student and search for measurements. Which system's units are used more often?
- Help your student make a scale drawing of his or her bedroom. First measure the walls, bed, dresser, etc. Use graph paper to make the drawing. Use metric and customary measuring devices if possible.

Español
Durante esta unidad de matemáticas, su estudiante va a explorar el perímetro y el área de los rectángulos y las figuras complejas. Para ayudar con el aprendizaje, sugerimos estas actividades para hacer en casa.
- Halle el perímetro y el área de distintos objetos de la casa usando una regla.
- Examine el periódico con su estudiante y busquen medidas. ¿Cuál sistema de unidades se usa más?
- Ayude a su estudiante a hacer un dibujo a escala de su habitación. Primero mida las paredes, la cama, la cómoda, etc. Para hacer el dibujo, utilice un papel para gráficas. De ser posible, utilice instrumentos de medición usuales y métricos.

58 fifty-eight

UNIT F

Activity Planner

KEY

- Real-World Connections
- Projects
- Technology
- CD-ROM
- Math Tool Chest
- Math Adventures

	Activity F-1 (Pacing: 60–80 min)	**Activity F-2** (Pacing: 85–105 min)
Activity/ Objective	**Square Units: Segments to Squares** (pp. 59–60) **Objective** Find the perimeter and area of rectangles using nonstandard units.	**Finding Area with Customary and Metric Units** (pp. 61–62) **Objective** Find the area of rectangles using customary and metric units.
Math Vocabulary	line segment **Review Vocabulary** area perimeter rectangle	customary system (units) kilometer metric system (units) millimeter **Review Vocabulary** area foot meter centimeter inch yard
Activity Resources	**Materials** geoboard dot paper or grid paper rulers, tape measures, string or yarn, scissors, paper clips, rectangular objects **Manipulatives** geoboards—optional color tiles	**Materials** inch grid paper—white, yellow, green cm grid paper—white, pink, blue colored butcher paper—substitute for grid paper yardsticks and rulers metersticks tape and scissors
Technology	**Math Adventures** Number Voyage **Concepts in Motion**	**Math Adventures** Bowl-o-Matic
Real-World Connections		**At Home** Compare the area of newspaper articles with the area of newspaper pictures.
Small Projects	**Measure It!** Find the perimeter and area of rectangular objects using different strategies.	

Activity F-3	Pacing: 55–70 min	Unit Project	Pacing: 45 min	
Finding Area of Complex Figures (pp. 63–64)		**Pentomino Rectangle Puzzles** (p. 66)		Activity/ Objective
Objective Find the area of complex figures.		**Objective** Create pentomino rectangles and find the perimeter and area of each one.		
complex figure **Review Vocabulary** area rectangle				Math Vocabulary
Materials construction paper rulers scissors tape grid paper—optional		**Materials** 1-inch grid paper **Manipulatives** color tiles		Activity Resources
Math Adventures Number Voyage **Concepts in Motion**		**Math Adventures** Bowl-o-Matic		Technology
				Real-World Connections
Finding Area Find a complex figure in the classroom and use color tiles to find the area.				Small Projects

Differentiated Instruction

Below are suggestions on differentiating the materials presented in this unit. Additional modifications should be considered.

Below Level **BL**	Above Level **AL**	English Language Learners **ELL**
ACTIVITY F-1 **Exercises 6–10** You may wish to draw a complex figure on the board and model finding the perimeter and area of the figure.	**Investigate** Have students determine and write formulas to find the perimeter and area of rectangles.	Have students create a poster with vocabulary illustrated. Ask students to create definitions in their own words and draw a diagram to illustrate the meaning.
ACTIVITY F-2 **Investigate** Remind students that when using rulers, yard sticks, or meter sticks, to always line up the end of the object they are measuring with the zero mark.	Have students explain the patterns in the metric system, especially the movement of the decimal point. **Exercise 9** Have students find another rectangle with the same perimeter and a larger area.	**Investigate** Some students may be more familiar with the metric system. Review customary units such as 12 inches = 1 foot, etc.
ACTIVITY F-3 **Investigate** Have the complex figures already made so that students can easily cut the figures into the first 2 ways to find the area. Have a small rectangular cut-out to help with the subtraction method for the 3rd rectangle.	**Challenge** Have students create complex figures. Partners can share their shapes to challenge each other.	

Performance-Based Assessment

Lengthy Rectangles (p. A21)

In *Lengthy Rectangles,* students first draw different rectangles with the same perimeter and identify the one with the largest area. Students then determine for a rectangle the length of a side, given the perimeter and dimension of one of the sides. Finally the students determine the perimeter of a shaded area of a grid.

Connections

Lengthy Rectangles also covers the following skills and concepts:

- Measurement
- Problem solving
- Reasoning
- Division, fact families

Targeting the Task

- **Pretest**–Use Exercises 1–5 on pages A21–A22 to determine understanding of rectangles, perimeter, and area. For those students who do not have this understanding, completing this unit is needed.

- **Formative**–Items can be broken down and administered in sections according to the lessons.

- **Summative**–Administer complete *Lengthy Rectangles* assessment.

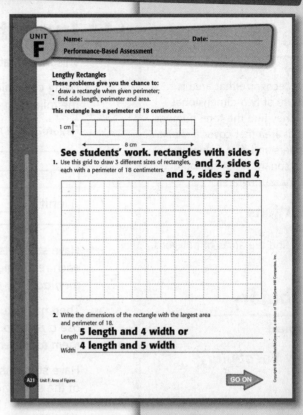

UNIT **F**

Name: _____ Date: _____

Performance-Based Assessment

Lengthy Rectangles

These problems give you the chance to:
- draw a rectangle when given perimeter;
- find side length, perimeter and area.

This rectangle has a perimeter of 18 centimeters.

1 cm ← 8 cm →

See students' work. rectangles with sides 7 and 2, sides 6 and 3, sides 5 and 4

1. Use this grid to draw 3 different sizes of rectangles, each with a perimeter of 18 centimeters.

2. Write the dimensions of the rectangle with the largest area and perimeter of 18.

Length **5 length and 4 width or**
Width **4 length and 5 width**

A21 Unit F: Area of Figures

GO ON →

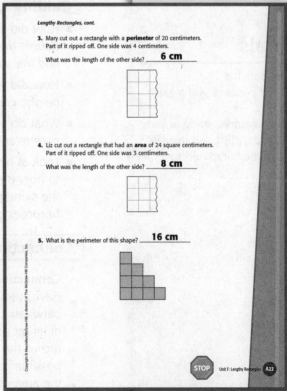

Lengthy Rectangles, cont.

3. Mary cut out a rectangle with a **perimeter** of 20 centimeters. Part of it ripped off. One side was 4 centimeters.

What was the length of the other side? **6 cm**

4. Liz cut out a rectangle that had an **area** of 24 square centimeters. Part of it ripped off. One side was 3 centimeters.

What was the length of the other side? **8 cm**

5. What is the perimeter of this shape? **16 cm**

STOP Unit F: Lengthy Rectangles A22

Square Units: Segments to Squares

Focus

Geometry
Students recognize that area is an attribute of two-dimensional shapes. They find the total number of units of area that cover a shape. They understand that 1 unit on a side of a square is the standard unit for measuring area.

Connections
Geometry
Students find the areas of polygons.

Vocabulary

line segment

Review Vocabulary
area
perimeter
rectangle

Materials

geoboards—optional
geoboard dot paper or grid paper
color tiles
rulers, tape measures, string or yarn, scissors, paper clips, rectangular objects for the Mini Project

① **Investigate** (30–40 min)

This investigation should allow students to explore perimeter and area.

Using color tiles, have students work in pairs to create rectangles with the following dimensions: 1×12; 5×8; 6×7

Organize the rectangles and their perimeters and areas in a table.

Drawing	Perimeter	Area
12 units 1 unit ▭	____ units	____ units^2

Have students discuss ways to find the perimeter, or the distance around each rectangle. *Count each side; use a ruler to measure each side and then add the four measurements together.*

Then have students explain how to measure the area. *Count the tiles; use a ruler to measure the base and the height and then multiply them together.*

Have students find the perimeter and area of each rectangle using one of the strategies they have mentioned.

Guiding Questions

- How did you find the perimeter of each rectangle? *Answers may vary: double the base and height measures and then add them together; find the sum of the four side measures.*

- How did you find the area of each rectangle? *Multiply the base by the height; count the square tiles.*

- What do you notice about the perimeters of the rectangles? *The perimeters are all the same, 26 units.*

- Look at how the rectangles change shape in your chart and compare it to how the areas change. What happens to the area of rectangles with the same perimeter? *As the rectangles become more square, the area becomes greater.*

Connections and Extensions

Connections
Have students work in groups and choose an area measurement between 1 unit^2 and 16 units^2. Instruct them to find figures that have different perimeters but that all have the chosen area. Have them record the figures on paper. Have each group make a chart of all the possible perimeters. Then create a class chart that combines all of the area measurements and the possible perimeters.

② Apply (25–30 min)

Student Page 59 Guide · · · · · ·

Exercises 1–3 Have students compare responses with a partner.	Can you create a complex figure with the same area as these figures? What is the perimeter? *Yes; answers will vary.*
Exercise 5 Lead a class discussion on the changes in perimeter. If time allows, create another set of rectangles with like areas.	How do the perimeters of rectangles with the same area change as the rectangles become more square? *The perimeter decreases as the rectangles become more square.*
Measure It! Place 5–6 objects that are shaped like rectangles or squares in a central location. Provide students with materials to measure the objects.	Have students discuss the different ways to measure the perimeter and area. *Count the number of paper clips that will wrap around an object.* Did anyone get different measurements for the same object? How? *One student used paper clips and another used a ruler.*

Student Page 60 Guide · · · · · ·

Exercises 6–10 Have students work independently.	What strategies did you use to find the area of each figure? *Answers will vary.*
Exercise 11 Engage students in a discussion about when you may want to have a larger perimeter and smaller area or the largest area possible.	Can you think of a situation where you might want a larger perimeter and smaller area? *walls to display art* When would you want a larger area? *when you need to fit more things inside*

③ Reflect (5–10 min)

- How do perimeter and area compare in rectangles? *Perimeter is the border or distance around a figure. Area is the number of square units needed to cover or fill the figure.*

- If you compare a 147 × 65 rectangle with a 637 × 15 rectangle, and they have the same area, what could you say about their perimeters without drawing them or doing any work? *The 637 × 15 rectangle would be longer, skinnier, and have the greater perimeter.*

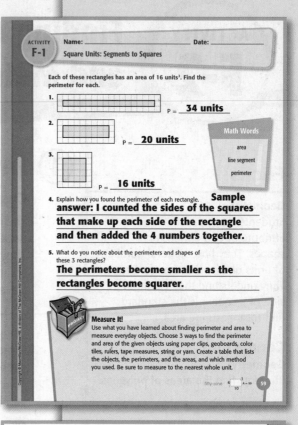

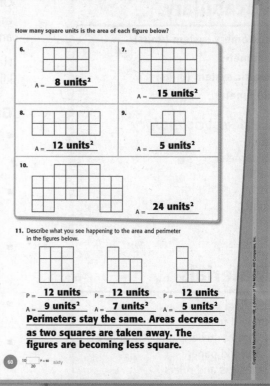

Activity F-1: Square Units: Segments to Squares **T60**

Finding Area with Customary and Metric Units

Focus

Geometry
Students recognize that area is an attribute of two-dimensional shapes. They find the total number of units of area that cover a shape. They understand that 1 unit on a side of a square is the standard unit for measuring area.

Connections
Geometry
Students find the areas of polygons.

Vocabulary

customary system (units)
kilometer
metric system (units)
millimeter

Review Vocabulary
area
centimeter
foot
inch
meter
yard

Materials

inch grid paper
cm grid paper
colored butcher paper—substitute
  for grid paper
yardsticks and rulers
metersticks
tape
scissors

① Investigate (50–60 min)

Customary and Metric Units: Measuring Mania

The objective of this investigation is to have students move from an understanding of non-standard square units to standard square units. They will do this through creating actual *square units*. Students will create paper models for 1 in², 1 ft², 1 yd², 1 cm², 100 cm², and 1 m². Have students work in teams of 2 to 4.

Each team will build each square model using a yardstick or a meterstick for help. It may be easier to tape 3 ft² and 100 cm² sheets of grid paper together to make the 1 yd² and the 1 m² models. Have students label each model.

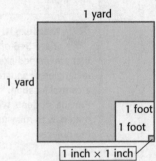

Once created, have students stack the models with the largest unit on the bottom and the smallest unit on top.

Have students discuss and explore other measurements including kilometer and millimeter.

Guiding Questions

- How many inches are on each edge of the square foot? *12 in.* How could you write a math sentence to find the number of square inches in 1 square foot? *12 in. × 12 in. = 1 ft²; 144 in² = 1 ft²*

- Continue this questioning for feet on the side of a square yard, cm on the edge of 100 cm², 100 cm² on the edge of a square meter, and so on. *10 cm × 10 cm = 100 cm²*

- How many inches are on each edge of the square yard? *36 in.* What math sentence could you write to show the number of square inches in 1 square yard? *36 in. × 36 in. = 1 yd², 1,296 in² = 1 yd²*

- Which is larger, the square inch or the square centimeter? *square inch* Why is it larger? *One inch is larger than one centimeter.*

- Which is larger, the square yard, or the square meter? *square meter* Why is it larger? *One meter is larger than one yard.*

Connections and Extensions

You are looking to buy carpet for your bedroom. The paper has ads for the same carpet in the following stores:

- Big Floor Carpet: $10 per ft²

- Carpet Mart: 12¢ per in²

- Which is the better buy? Explain. *The Big Floor Carpet is the better buy. Explanations will vary.*

② Apply (30–35 min)

Student Page 61 Guide · · · · · ·

Exercises 1–4
Have students work with a partner to find the areas.

Encourage students to use the models they made in the Investigation to answer the questions.

How do you know which unit of measure to use when labeling the area? *The area will be labeled with the same unit as the side lengths, but in square units.*

Which figure has the greatest area? Which figure has the least area? *The figure in Exercise 1 has the greatest area. The figure in Exercise 4 has the least area.*

 At Home
Provide students with newspapers or magazines if needed. Help students set up their charts.

Remind students to use the same unit of measure when finding the area of the articles, the pictures, and the headlines.

Student Page 62 Guide · · · · · ·

Exercises 5–8
Have students work with a partner to find the missing side lengths.

What operation do you need to perform to find the missing side lengths? Explain. *Division; I am given the area and one side length, I divide the area by the known side length to find the missing side length.*

Exercises 9 and 10
Encourage students to find what side lengths would equal the given area before drawing their figures.

Is there more than one way to draw a figure with an area of 64 cm²? Explain. *Yes; I could draw a rectangle with a base of 16 cm and a height of 4 cm.*

③ Reflect (5–10 min)

- What did you learn about customary and metric measures that you didn't know before? *Answers will vary.*

- How were the calculations in Activity F-2 different from Activity F-1? *Activity F-1 did not have units of measure.*

- What makes using metric measurements easier than customary measurements? *The metric system is based on powers of 10 which makes converting to smaller or larger units easier.*

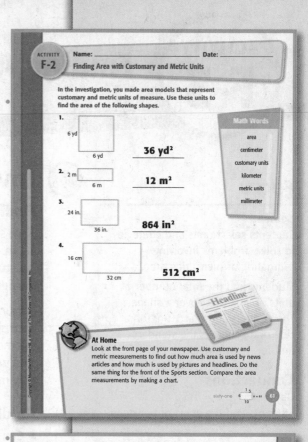

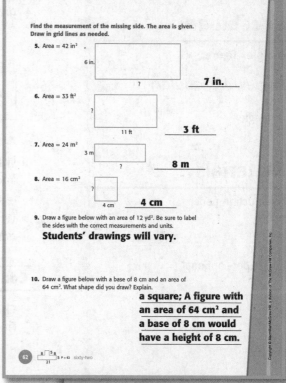

Finding Area of Complex Figures

Focus

Geometry
Students select units and strategies to solve problems involving estimating or measuring area.

Students find the total number of units of area that cover a shape. They understand that 1 unit on a side of a square is the standard unit for measuring area.

Connections
Geometry
Students find the areas of polygons.

Vocabulary

complex figure

Review Vocabulary
area
rectangle

Materials

construction paper
rulers
scissors
tape
grid paper—optional

---

① **Investigate** (30–35 min)

Finding Area of Complex Figures

Have students use construction paper and a ruler to cut out a 6 in.-by-9 in. rectangle and a 5 in.-by-6 in. rectangle. Guide the students to tape the rectangles together to make the figure below.

Instruct students to use the ruler to measure each side of the new figure and then record the measurements. Have students discuss how they would find the area of the complex figure they made.

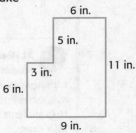

Guiding Questions

- Can you think of a way to find the area of this complex figure? *I can divide the figure into smaller rectangles.*

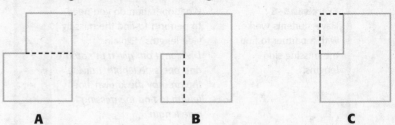

| A | B | C |

- Will the areas of the parts give the same total area? How do you know? *Yes; A = (6 × 5) + (9 × 6) = 84 in²; B = (3 × 6) + (6 × 11) = 84 in²; C = (9 × 11) − (3 × 5) = 84 in²*
- What is different about the third method? *The first two examples are addition methods, but the third is a subtraction method.*

Connections and Extensions

Challenge
Find the area of the shaded complex figure. *12 cm²*

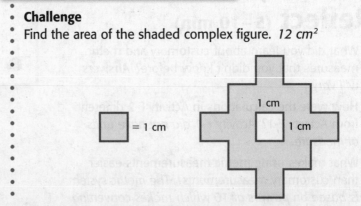

② Apply (20–25 min)

Student Page 63 Guide · · · · ·

Exercises 1 and 2
Have students work with a partner. Guide students to see simple rectangular regions inside each complex shape.

Have students discuss results as a class to draw out different strategies.

How many different rectangular regions are needed to simplify the complex figures?
Figure 1: 3 rectangles; Figure 2: 3 rectangles

Student Page 64 Guide · · · · ·

Exercises 4–7
Have students label the measurements on each figure before solving.

Have students discuss results in pairs and then as a class.

How can you use the measurements to determine which example matches each method? *I can use the measurements to see how the figure is divided for each example.*

 Finding Area

Help students find a complex figure in the classroom to measure. *Examples: a U-shaped desk or L-shaped desk, a door with a window (measure only the door and not the window)*

③ Reflect (5–10 min)

- Is it possible for a shape to have units² as its area? Name two other types of length measures. *yes; ft², mi²*

- What is the advantage to dividing up a complex figure into simpler rectangular shapes? *It is much easier to find the area of rectangles using the base and height.*

- Explain how the subtraction method can be helpful when working with complex figures. *The subtraction method can help by reducing the number of rectangular shapes needed to find the total area.*

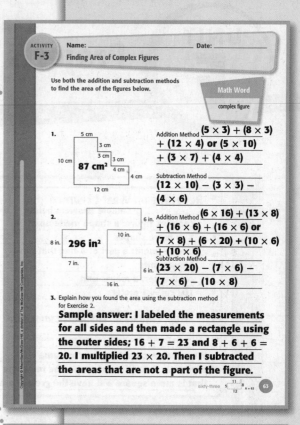

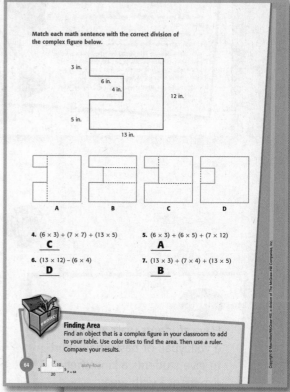

Activity F-3: Finding Area of Complex Figures **T64**

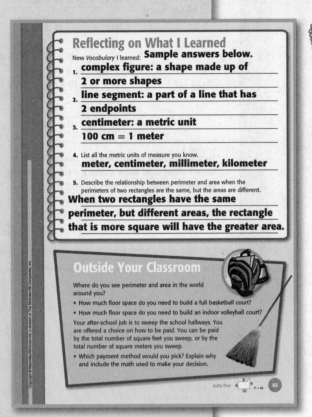

Reflecting on What I Learned

New *Vocabulary* I learned: **Sample answers below.**

1. **complex figure: a shape made up of 2 or more shapes**

2. **line segment: a part of a line that has 2 endpoints**

3. **centimeter: a metric unit**
   100 cm = 1 meter

4. List all the metric units of measure you know.
   meter, centimeter, millimeter, kilometer

5. Describe the relationship between perimeter and area when the perimeters of two rectangles are the same, but the areas are different.
   When two rectangles have the same perimeter, but different areas, the rectangle that is more square will have the greater area.

Outside Your Classroom

Where do you see perimeter and area in the world around you?
- How much floor space do you need to build a full basketball court?
- How much floor space do you need to build an indoor volleyball court?

Your after-school job is to sweep the school hallways. You are offered a choice on how to be paid. You can be paid by the total number of square feet you sweep, or by the total number of square meters you sweep.
- Which payment method would you pick? Explain why and include the math used to make your decision.

sixty-five 65

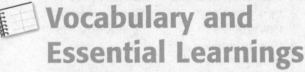
Vocabulary and Essential Learnings

Vocabulary

- Have students discuss in small groups the vocabulary terms and the definitions they learned or reviewed in this unit.
- Generate a master list of terms on the board or have students create a Foldable®.
- Have students record three terms of their choice, along with a brief definition and illustration for each term.

Essential Learnings

Arrange students in pairs. Have partners review the activities on pages 59 through 64 and discuss what they learned. Have each pair create a two-column summary sheet. In the left column, identify the Essential Learning idea/concept/skill. In the right column, write a brief description of the main features or points for the Essential Learning. Include diagrams, charts, or pictures. Allow time for students to share their Essential Learnings in small groups or as a class.

Outside Your Classroom

You may wish to arrange students into four groups. Then have groups share their responses with the class. Allow time for classmates to extend or enrich the groups' responses.

Possible student responses:

- How much floor space do you need for a basketball court? You may want to encourage students to use the internet to find court dimensions. *94 ft × 50 ft*
- How much floor space do you need for an indoor volleyball court? *9 m × 18 m*
- Which payment method would you pick? *Assuming the dollar amount is the same for feet or meters, square feet; square feet are smaller units of measurement; the area swept would be more square feet than square meters.*

BL

Have students walk around a volleyball or basketball court to give students a kinesthetic experience with area.

AL

Have students research and compare the "field" or "court" of 10 sports.

Pentomino Rectangle Puzzles

Materials

color tiles
1-inch grid paper

Pacing:
45 min

Introducing the Project

Review the concepts of perimeter and area taught in the unit. You may wish to have students skim the pages in the unit to refresh their memories.

Ask students to think about puzzles they have put together in the past. Ask them to share any strategies they might use in putting a puzzle together.

Completing the Project

Distribute color tiles. Have students read the questions in Step 1 and give them time to work independently. Then have students partner up to find the 12 pentomino puzzle pieces. Have students complete Step 2 with their partner.

Extending the Project

Have students create other shapes with their puzzle pieces and draw diagrams.

If time permits, allow students to share their puzzles with other students.

Students could also time each other to see who can put their puzzle together the fastest.

Pentomino Rectangle Puzzles

Use your knowledge of perimeter and area to create pentomino puzzle pieces and then use the puzzle pieces to make pentomino rectangles.

Pentominos are shapes made from 5 squares. The five squares must lie flat, and whole sides of squares must touch. Corner to corner connections are not allowed.

This is a pentomino.   This is not a pentomino.

1. Using five color tiles, find the 12 possible pentomino shapes.

   ▪ Trace the 12 pentomino shapes that you created onto a clean piece of grid paper and cut them out. These will become the puzzle pieces for the next part of the project.

2. Create two different rectangles using all 12 pentomino puzzle pieces. Trace the rectangles onto your piece of grid paper and record the area and perimeter of each rectangle puzzle. Use a table to organize your work.

Sketch of Rectangle	Perimeter	Area

   ▪ Can you create any other shapes with the puzzle pieces? If so, draw a diagram.

66   20   13   sixty-six
P = 66

Suggested Scoring Rubric

4	The student completes the project with accuracy and creativity. All pentomino puzzles are shown and the chart of pentomino rectangle puzzles is complete. Student's report accurately and completely describes the project and is written in clear, concise language including appropriate math terminology.
3	The student completes the project. The majority of pentomino puzzles are shown. The chart of pentomino rectangle puzzles is not complete. The student's report describes the project, but it is somewhat inaccurate or incomplete.
2	The student partially completes the project. Less than 10 pentomino puzzles are shown. The chart of pentomino rectangle puzzles is not complete and less than 7 possible types are shown. The student's report describes some parts of the project, but is mostly inaccurate or incomplete.
1	The student does not complete the project. The student's report is inaccurate, incomplete, and contains incorrect or no math terminology.

Time and Temperature

Vocabulary

Celsius (°C) the unit used to measure temperature in the metric system

elapsed time the difference in time between the start and the end of an event

Fahrenheit (°F) the unit used to measure temperature in the customary system

half past 30 minutes past the hour

2:30

hour a unit of time equal to 60 minutes

1 hour = 60 minutes 4:00
1 minute = 60 seconds

minute a unit used to measure time

quarter past 15 minutes past the hour

8:15

quarter to 15 minutes before the hour

1:45

temperature a measure of how hot or how cold something is

thermometer a tool used to measure temperature

Unit-at-a-Glance

In Unit G, students gain understanding of ways to measure time and temperature.

Activity	Focus	Student Investigation
G-1 **Days, Hours, Minutes** (pp. 69–70)	Students' work with models of fractions and multiplication and division facts develops an understanding of equivalent fractions and simplifying fractions.	Students make a circle graph based on the time they spend doing different activities in a day.
G-2 **Parts of an Hour** (pp. 71–72)	Students identify, describe, and extend numeric patterns.	Students find fractions of an hour in minutes using a clock model.
G-3 **Elapsed Time** (pp. 73–74)	Students select methods and apply them to estimate or calculate products mentally.	Students use the benchmark of 10 seconds to estimate what can be done in 1 minute and in 1 hour.
G-4 **Temperature: Fahrenheit and Celsius** (pp. 75–76)	Students expand their understanding of place value and ways of representing numbers to 100,000.	Students measure temperatures of water and make a paper thermometer.
Unit Project: Make A Perfect-Day Timeline (p. 78)	Students relate the concepts and skills they have learned to the real world.	Students make a timeline of daily activities.

Page Numbers

Each page number is represented by two digital clocks in which the page number is the elapsed time in minutes.

Guiding Questions

- What time would it be (page number) minutes from now?
- What time was it (page number) minutes ago?
- What is the page number expressed in hours and minutes? seconds?

Unit Opener

You can open the unit by having students read through the objectives they will accomplish during the unit. Have students restate objectives in their own words to ensure comprehension.

Scaffolding Questions

What are some equivalent fractions for $\frac{1}{2}$? $\frac{2}{4}, \frac{3}{6}, \frac{12}{24}$
What are some equivalent fractions for $\frac{1}{3}$? $\frac{2}{6}, \frac{3}{9}, \frac{8}{24}$ for $\frac{1}{4}$? $\frac{2}{8}, \frac{3}{12}, \frac{6}{24}$
On a horizontal number line, are numbers to the right or left greater? *Numbers to the right are greater.*

On a vertical number line, are higher or lower numbers greater? *Numbers that are higher are greater.*

Vocabulary

The beginning of the unit is a great time to start a new wall chart.

 WRITING IN MATH

Encourage students to write the definitions in their math journals. Writing their own definitions or creating drawings will help internalize the information.

Student Page 68 Guide

 Home Letter

Have students take the Home Letter home.

Look at the Projects and Discussions throughout the unit to see if any additional opportunities are available for work at home.

ELL

Encourage students to visit the online eGlossary with parents to see vocabulary in 13 languages.

TeacherWorks *Plus*

See "Home E-mail" as an alternative for communication. From the Lesson Planner, select the e-mail document for this unit, double-click the file, and edit in the Worksheet Editor.

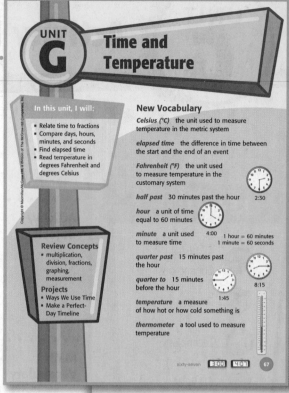

UNIT G Time and Temperature

In this unit, I will:
- Relate time to fractions
- Compare days, hours, minutes, and seconds
- Find elapsed time
- Read temperature in degrees Fahrenheit and degrees Celsius

Review Concepts
- multiplication, division, fractions, graphing, measurement

Projects
- Ways We Use Time
- Make a Perfect-Day Timeline

New Vocabulary

Celsius (°C) the unit used to measure temperature in the metric system

elapsed time the difference in time between the start and the end of an event

Fahrenheit (°F) the unit used to measure temperature in the customary system

half past 30 minutes past the hour   2:30

hour a unit of time equal to 60 minutes   4:00

minute a unit used to measure time
1 hour = 60 minutes
1 minute = 60 seconds

quarter past 15 minutes past the hour

quarter to 15 minutes before the hour   8:15

temperature a measure of how hot or how cold something is   1:45

thermometer a tool used to measure temperature

sixty-seven   **3:00 4:01**   67

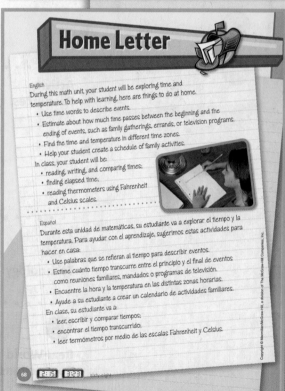

Home Letter

English
During this math unit, your student will be exploring time and temperature. To help with learning, here are things to do at home.
- Use time words to describe events.
- Estimate about how much time passes between the beginning and the ending of events, such as family gatherings, errands, or television programs.
- Find the time and temperature in different time zones.
- Help your student create a schedule of family activities.

In class, your student will be:
- reading, writing, and comparing times;
- finding elapsed time;
- reading thermometers using Fahrenheit and Celsius scales.

Español
Durante esta unidad de matemáticas, su estudiante va a explorar el tiempo y la temperatura. Para ayudar con el aprendizaje, sugerimos estas actividades para hacer en casa:
- Use palabras que se refieran al tiempo para describir eventos.
- Estime cuánto tiempo transcurre entre el principio y el final de eventos como reuniones familiares, mandados o programas de televisión.
- Encuentre la hora y la temperatura en las distintas zonas horarias.
- Ayude a su estudiante a crear un calendario de actividades familiares.

En clase, su estudiante va a:
- leer, escribir y comparar tiempos;
- encontrar el tiempo transcurrido;
- leer termómetros por medio de las escalas Fahrenheit y Celsius.

68   **2:15 5:23**   *sixty-eight*

UNIT G

Activity Planner

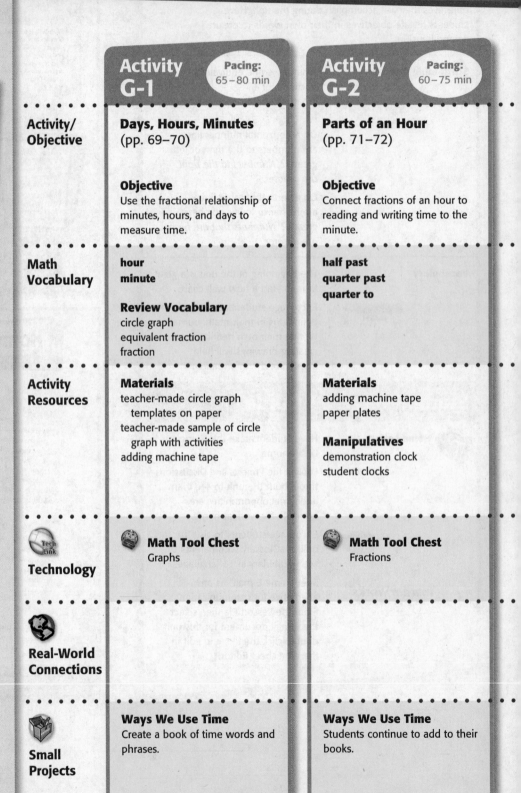
	Activity G-1 Pacing: 65–80 min	**Activity G-2** Pacing: 60–75 min
Activity/ Objective	**Days, Hours, Minutes** (pp. 69–70) **Objective** Use the fractional relationship of minutes, hours, and days to measure time.	**Parts of an Hour** (pp. 71–72) **Objective** Connect fractions of an hour to reading and writing time to the minute.
Math Vocabulary	hour minute **Review Vocabulary** circle graph equivalent fraction fraction	half past quarter past quarter to
Activity Resources	**Materials** teacher-made circle graph templates on paper teacher-made sample of circle graph with activities adding machine tape	**Materials** adding machine tape paper plates **Manipulatives** demonstration clock student clocks
Technology	**Math Tool Chest** Graphs	**Math Tool Chest** Fractions
Real-World Connections		
Small Projects	**Ways We Use Time** Create a book of time words and phrases.	**Ways We Use Time** Students continue to add to their books.

Activity G-3	Pacing: 70–85 min	Activity G-4	Pacing: 55–70 min	Unit Project	Pacing: 45–50 min	
Elapsed Time (pp. 73–74)		**Temperature: Fahrenheit and Celsius** (pp. 75–76)		**Make a Perfect-Day Timeline** (pp. 78)		**Activity/ Objective**
Objective Calculate elapsed time.		**Objective** Read and write temperature in degrees Fahrenheit and degrees Celsius.		**Objective** Create a timeline of daily activites.		
elapsed time		**Celsius (°C)** **Fahrenheit (°F)** **temperature** **thermometer** **Review Vocabulary** scale				**Math Vocabulary**
Materials stopwatches or other time-keeping devices with seconds **Manipulatives** demonstration clock student clocks		**Materials** cups ice teacher-made outline of thermometer thermometers water U.S. map of time zones		**Materials** adding machine tape or paper sheets taped together samples of timelines		**Activity Resources**
Math Tool Chest Fractions						**Technology**
At Home Make a schedule of family activities and elapsed times.		**In Science** Compare and record water temperatures and experiment with the effects on temperature from environmental changes.				**Real-World Connections**
Ways We Use Time Students continue to add to their books.		**Ways We Use Time** Make a poster with one of the time sayings.				**Small Projects**

Differentiation and Assessment

Differentiated Instruction

Below are suggestions on differentiating the materials presented in this unit. Additional modifications should be considered.

Below Level **BL**	Above Level **AL**	English Language Learners **ELL**

ACTIVITY G-1

Exercise 1
Review fractions and equivalent fractions. For example, 8 hours equals $\frac{8}{24}$, $\frac{4}{12}$, or $\frac{1}{3}$ of a day.

Present Roman numerals and their values. For example, XII = 12 and IX = 9. Have students make a clock face using Roman numerals.

Exercises 8–11
Remind students of the meanings of *greater than* (>) and *less than* (<) by using whole numbers. Explain that the open side of the symbol points to the greater number.

ACTIVITY G-2

Exercises 6–8
Under each clock, have students write the time. Then, encourage them to look for the numbers in the time that change to help them find the pattern.

Exercises 1–3
Give students examples of clocks with shaded fractional parts that do not start at 12. For example, $\frac{1}{6}$ (10 minutes) could be a clock face shaded between 5 and 7.

Explain the meanings of *quarter* and *half*. Draw a line down the center of a paper clock from 12 to 6. Explain that we read time in the right half as minutes *past the hour* and the left half as minutes *to the hour*. Then draw a line from 3 to 9 for quarters.

ACTIVITY G-3

Exercises 2–5
Have students use a clock or diagram to find the elapsed time.

Exercises 6–8
Have students find elapsed times that span across A.M. and P.M. For example, 9:15 A.M. to 10:15 P.M. is 13 hours of elapsed time.

To provide further reinforcement of the meaning of elapsed time, show students time on a number line.

ACTIVITY G-4

Exercises 6-8
Have students divide a paper thermometer into fourths. Color the top fourth red for hot temperatures. Color the next fourth, the warm temperatures, orange. Color the next fourth, the cool temperatures, green. Color the bottom fourth, the cold temperatures, blue.

Have students play "What's My Temperature?" Partners take turns giving clues and guessing the temperatures. For example: I am a Celsius degree. I am about the same temperature as 50 degrees Fahrenheit. What temperature am I? *10°C*

Exercises 1–5
Have students look at pictures from a magazine or newspaper. Have them describe the temperature portrayed in the photographs. Is it cold? cool? warm? hot?

Performance-Based Assessment

The School Bus (p. A25)

In *The School Bus,* students first determine the time that students get on the bus and then how long it takes for the bus to arrive at school. Students then explain how they figured this out.

Connections

The School Bus also covers the following skills and concepts:

- Time
- Addition
- Subtraction
- Reasoning

Targeting the Task

- **Pretest** – Use Exercises 1–6 in *The School Bus* assessment to determine foundational understanding of time. For those students who do not have this understanding, completing this unit is needed.

- **Formative** – *The School Bus* assessment can be administered in sections according to the lessons.

- **Summative** – Administer the complete *The School Bus* performance-based assessment.

Differentiation

Build a word wall with the vocabulary related to time, e.g., hours, minutes, seconds, half hour, quarter hour, noon, and midnight. Have students identify what usually happens at certain times and when they would use words like "half hour" or "quarter hour."

Review how many minutes are in an hour, how many half hours are in an hour, and how many quarter hours are in an hour.

Provide opportunities for students to review units of time. For example: George takes 120 minutes to do his homework. How many hours is that? Samantha went on a 3-hour bike ride. How many minutes is that?

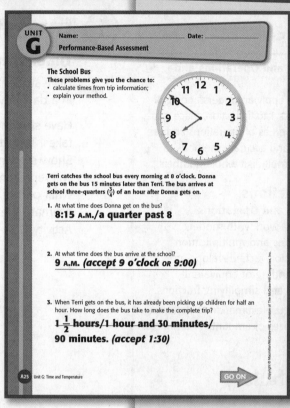

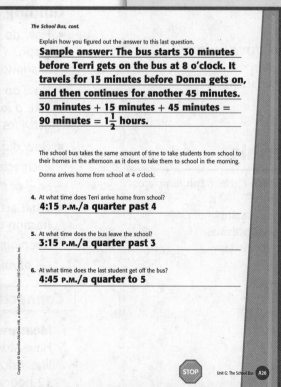

Days, Hours, Minutes

Focus

Number and Operations and Algebra
Students apply an understanding of models for multiplication, place value, and properties of operations and use efficient and accurate methods to multiply multidigit whole numbers.

Connections

Number and Operations
Students' work with models of fractions and multiplication and division facts develops an understanding of equivalent fractions and simplifying fractions.

Students use estimation to determine relative sizes of amounts or distances.

Vocabulary

hour
minute

Review Vocabulary
circle graph
equivalent fraction
fraction

Materials

teacher-made circle graph templates on paper
teacher-made sample of circle graph with activities
adding machine tape

① Investigate (35–40 min)

Time: What Fraction of Your Day?

Have students brainstorm in small groups things they spend time doing in a day. Have groups share their lists with the class.

Have students select a few activities and write how long each activity takes. Tell students they will use these times to make a circle graph. Show students a sample circle graph and tell them that their circle graph will represent one day, or 24 hours. Help students divide it up to show what part of the day they spend doing each activity, and then have them estimate the fraction of the day each activity takes. Keep circle graphs for Activity G-3.

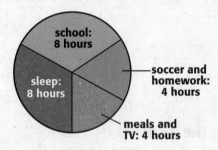

Guiding Questions

- How do you know into how many parts you should divide your circle graph? *I should divide the graph into the number of activities I want to show.*

- How do you know what size each part should be? *The activities that take a longer time will be the larger parts on the graph, and the activities that take a shorter time will be smaller parts on the graph.*

- How did you figure out what fraction of the day you spend doing each activity? *A day is 24 hours. If I sleep 8 hours, that is $\frac{8}{24}$ or $\frac{1}{3}$ of the day.*

- What activity do you spend the most/least time doing and what fraction of the day is it? *Sample answer: I spend the most time sleeping, $\frac{1}{3}$ of my day. I spend the least time playing with a friend, $\frac{1}{24}$ of my day.*

Connections and Extensions

Measurement
Have students use adding machine tape to make a 24-hour number line. Ask them to label the first 12 hours as A.M. and the second 12 hours as P.M. Also, have them label 12 as noon. On the number line, have students mark what they are doing at specific hours.

Student Page 69 Guide · · · · ·

Exercise 1 Have students meet in pairs to compare their graphs.	How is your new graph different from your first graph? Use time words and fractions in your description. *Answers will vary.*
Exercises 2 and 3 Make a class chart listing activities that take about 1 hour and about 1 minute.	What fraction of the day is 1 hour? $\frac{1}{24}$ *of the day* What fraction of an hour is 1 minute? $\frac{1}{60}$ *of an hour*
Ways We Use Time Have fun recalling familiar sayings that use time phrases. For example, "See you later alligator," "How time flies!" and "A day late and a dollar short."	Brainstorm with students different ways we use time throughout the day. Then talk about time words, such as *before, later, yesterday, next year,* and so on.

Student Page 70 Guide · · · · ·

Exercises 4–11 Have students discuss results in small groups and then as a class.	In Exercise 6, how did you find the number of weeks that equal $\frac{1}{2}$ of a year? *Sample answer: There are 52 weeks in one year, so I divided 52 by 2 to get 26.*
Exercises 12–15 Have students explain how they solved the problems.	How does your knowledge of equivalent fractions help you solve these problems? *Sample answer: In Exercise 13, $\frac{3}{24}$ is the fraction of time Brian spent eating. $\frac{3}{24}$ is equivalent to $\frac{1}{8}$.*

③ **Reflect** (5–10 min)

- How can fractions and time be related? *Sample answer: I can describe the number of hours it takes to do something as a fraction of a day.*

- Describe the time it takes you to do something in both hours and in a fraction of a day. *Sample answer: I eat meals 3 hours, or $\frac{1}{8}$, of the day.*

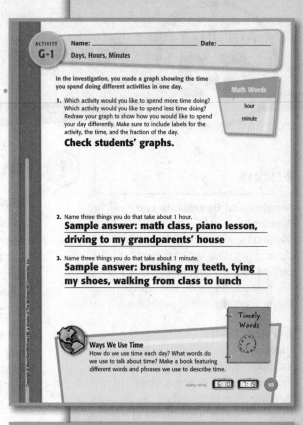

ACTIVITY G-1 Name: _____ Date: _____
Days, Hours, Minutes

In the investigation, you made a graph showing the time you spend doing different activities in one day.

Math Words
hour
minute

1. Which activity would you like to spend more time doing? Which activity would you like to spend less time doing? Redraw your graph to show how you would like to spend your day differently. Make sure to include labels for the activity, the time, and the fraction of the day.
Check students' graphs.

2. Name three things you do that take about 1 hour.
Sample answer: math class, piano lesson, driving to my grandparents' house

3. Name three things you do that take about 1 minute.
Sample answer: brushing my teeth, tying my shoes, walking from class to lunch

Timely Words

Ways We Use Time
How do we use time each day? What words do we use to talk about time? Make a book featuring different words and phrases we use to describe time.

sixty-nine 6:10 1:19 69

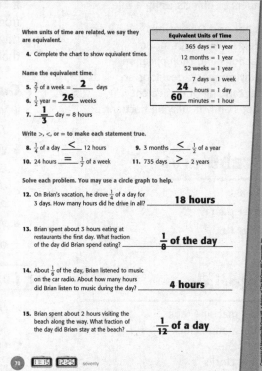

When units of time are related, we say they are equivalent.

4. Complete the chart to show equivalent times.

Equivalent Units of Time
365 days = 1 year
12 months = 1 year
52 weeks = 1 year
7 days = 1 week
24 hours = 1 day
60 minutes = 1 hour

Name the equivalent time.

5. $\frac{2}{7}$ of a week = **2** days
6. $\frac{1}{2}$ year = **26** weeks
7. $\frac{1}{3}$ day = 8 hours

Write >, <, or = to make each statement true.

8. $\frac{1}{4}$ of a day **<** 12 hours   **9.** 3 months **<** $\frac{1}{2}$ of a year
10. 24 hours **=** $\frac{1}{7}$ of a week   **11.** 735 days **>** 2 years

Solve each problem. You may use a circle graph to help.

12. On Brian's vacation, he drove $\frac{1}{4}$ of a day for 3 days. How many hours did he drive in all? **18 hours**

13. Brian spent about 3 hours eating at restaurants the first day. What fraction of the day did Brian spend eating? **$\frac{1}{8}$ of the day**

14. About $\frac{1}{6}$ of the day, Brian listened to music on the car radio. About how many hours did Brian listen to music during the day? **4 hours**

15. Brian spent about 2 hours visiting the beach along the way. What fraction of the day did Brian stay at the beach? **$\frac{1}{12}$ of a day**

70 1:15 12:25 seventy

ACTIVITY G-2

Parts of an Hour

Focus

Number and Operations and Algebra
Students solve problems by developing skills with efficient procedures, understanding why the procedures work, and using the procedures in real problems.

Connections

Algebra
Students identify, describe, and extend numeric patterns. They develop an understanding of how to describe a sequence of numbers or objects using a rule.

Number and Operations
Students' work with models of fractions and multiplication and division facts develops an understanding of equivalent fractions and simplifying fractions.

Vocabulary

half past
quarter past
quarter to

Materials

adding machine tape
demonstration clock
paper plates
student clocks

---

① Investigate (30–35 min)

Time: What Fraction of an Hour?

Give students clocks and display a demonstration clock at the front of the room. Review the minute and hour hands, the number of minutes in an hour, and the movement of the minute hand around the clock beginning at the 12. Tell students that today they will find fractions of an hour and their equivalent time in minutes. Help students make a chart similar to the one shown to record their findings.

Have students show each fraction of an hour using their clocks. Note the patterns relating a fraction of an hour and the number of minutes. Then talk about fractions with numerators other than 1.

If time permits, have students make a clock from a paper plate and shade the number minutes. Discuss the fraction of the circle that is shaded.

Fraction	Minutes
$\frac{1}{60}$	1 minute
$\frac{1}{20}$	3 minutes
$\frac{1}{15}$	4 minutes
$\frac{1}{12}$	5 minutes
$\frac{1}{10}$	6 minutes
$\frac{1}{6}$	10 minutes

Guiding Questions

- What fractions of an hour have a numerator of 1? *Sample answer: The fractions that represent minutes are factors of 60.*

- What patterns do you see between the fractions of an hour and the equivalent numbers of minutes? *Sample answers: As the denominators decrease, the numbers of minutes increase. If you multiply the number of minutes by the denominator, the product is 60.*

- What are some fractions of an hour that have numerators greater than one? *Sample answers: $\frac{3}{4}$ of an hour is 45 minutes; $\frac{6}{12}$ is 30 minutes.*

Connections and Extensions

Money
Ask students how money relates to time. Discuss how 4 quarters equal $1, and how 4 quarters of an hour equal 1 hour.

Measurement
Explain to students that a clock face is similar to a measuring tape or a number line. Have them mark off numbers 1 through 12 equally spaced on adding machine tape. Then have them mark off five marks equally spaced between each "hour." Ask students to find fractions on the number line. Encourage students to wrap the number line in a circle and compare it to a clock face. How are they the same? How are they different?

② Apply (25–30 min)

Student Page 71 Guide · · · · ·

Exercises 1–3
Have students meet with partners and share their responses. Allow students to use their clocks to model the times shown.

How did you figure out the number of minutes shaded in Exercise 3? *Sample answer: I counted by 5s from the 12 to the 9 and got 45 minutes.*

Exercises 4 and 5
Discuss the connection between 30 minutes being halfway around the clock and the meaning of *half past*.

In Exercise 5, how do you know that the time is past, or after, 1 and not before 1? *The hour hand is between the 1 and the 2, so the time is past, or after, the 1 and before the 2.*

Student Page 72 Guide · · · · ·

Exercises 6–8
Have students share their answers with the class. Talk about the patterns they found.

In Exercise 6, what pattern do you see? *The minute hand moves 10 minutes, or $\frac{1}{6}$ of an hour, each time.*

In Exercise 8, what fraction of an hour does the minute hand move? *The minute hand moves $\frac{1}{12}$ of an hour.*

Exercises 9–11
Have students share their responses with partners and then with the class.

In Exercise 10, what did you write as the time the train left Clarksville? What is another way to say this time? *3:50; 50 minutes past 3*

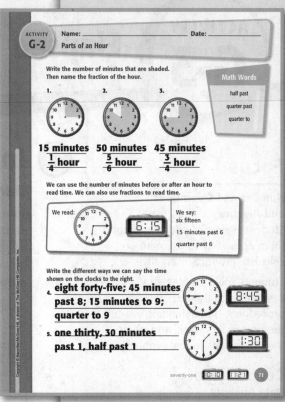

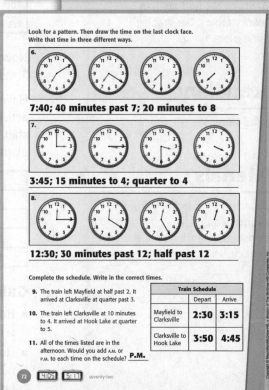

③ Reflect (5–10 min)

- How are fractions of an hour and the number of minutes in an hour related? *Sample answer: An hour is divided into equal parts called minutes. A fraction of an hour can equal a number of minutes.*

- How is it helpful to talk about time either before or after the hour? Give an example of when it is helpful. *Sample answer: Sometimes you want to know how many more minutes you have until the next hour. For example, if math class starts at 9:00 and it is 10 minutes to 9, you know you have 10 minutes until math class.*

Elapsed Time

Focus

Number and Operations and Algebra

Students select methods and apply them accurately to estimate or calculate products mentally.

Students solve problems by developing skills with efficient procedures, understanding why the procedures work, and using the procedures in real problems.

Connections
Data Analysis
Students create and analyze frequency tables, bar graphs, and line plots.

Vocabulary

elapsed time

Materials

stopwatches or watches with
    second hands
demonstration clock
student clocks

(1) Investigate (40–45 min)

Duration: How Much Time Has Passed?

Time can be measured in hours and minutes. It can also be measured in seconds. One minute equals 60 seconds. Demonstrate the movement of the second hand on an analog clock. Point out that the second hand moves around the clock using the minute marks as second marks. The movement of the second hand around the clock one time is 1 minute.

About how many times can you do an activity in 10 seconds? Have students work with a partner to try out the following activities.

10 Seconds	1 Minute	1 Hour
Write my first and last name _____ times.		
Turn _____ pages in a book.		
Walk _____ steps.		

Now, estimate how many times you could do the same activity in 1 minute and in 1 hour. Record your estimates in the chart.

Have students discuss the circle graphs created in Activity G-1 showing activities in their day. Create a chart that lists each activity along with the start and end times. Then have students calculate how much time elapses during each activity.

Activity	Start Time	End Time	Elapsed Time
School			
Sleep			
Soccer			
Homework			

Guiding Questions

- How many 10-second time periods equal 1 minute? Explain. *6; 60 seconds equal 1 minute and 10 × 6 = 60.*

- How did you estimate the number of times you could write your name in 1 minute? *Sample answer: I multiplied the number of times I wrote my name in 10 seconds, 2, by 6; 2 × 6 = 12.*

- How many 10-second time periods equal 1 hour? Explain. *360; There are six 10-second time periods in 1 minute, and 60 minutes equal 1 hour; 6 × 60 = 360.*

- How did you estimate how many steps you could walk in an hour? *Sample answer: I multiplied the number of steps I walked in 10 seconds by 360.*

② Apply (25–30 min)

Student Page 73 Guide

Exercise 1 Have students share their ways of finding the elapsed time with a small group and then with the class.	Did you use skip counting to find the elapsed time? If so, how? *Sample answer: Yes; I counted by 10s from 4:10 to 5:10. Then I added 5 more minutes.*
Exercises 2–5 Have students share how they found the elapsed time. Invite them to use the demonstration clock to show their strategies.	What is one way to solve Exercise 5? *Sample answer: I counted by 5s to 5:05. Then I added the hours: 6:05, 7:05, 8:05, and 9:05, or 4 hours. The elapsed time is 4 hours and 20 minutes.*
Exercises 6–8 Have students share how they found the times using the demonstration clock.	How is Exercise 8 different from Exercises 6 and 7? *We are given the end time and must work backward to get the start time.*

Student Page 74 Guide

Exercises 9–15 Have students share how they completed the schedule.	In Exercise 12, why did the lunch time span from A.M. to P.M.? *Sample answer: 12:00 noon starts the P.M. times.*
At Home	Encourage students to share with their families what they have learned about making schedules and finding elapsed time. Ask students to bring their family schedules in to share with the class.

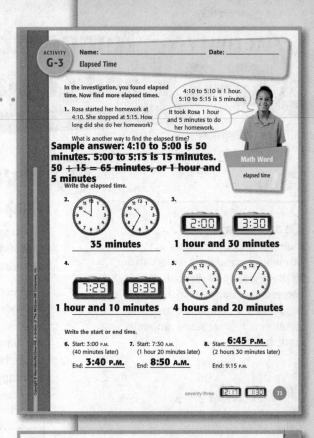

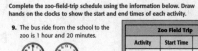

③ Reflect (5–10 min)

- How can you use start and end times to find an elapsed time? *Sample answer: I can find the length of time between the start and end time by counting the number of hours and minutes between the two times.*

- When might you need to know the elapsed time of something? *Sample answers: when you want to know how long a class is, how long a party is, or how long a movie or show is*

Temperature: Fahrenheit and Celsius

Focus

Connections
Number and Operations
Students expand their understanding of place value and ways of representing numbers to 100,000. Students use estimation to determine relative sizes, amounts, or distances.

Vocabulary

Celsius (°C)
Fahrenheit (°F)
temperature
thermometer

Review Vocabulary
scale

Materials

cups
ice
teacher-made outline of thermometer with Celsius and Fahrenheit scales
thermometers
water
U.S. map of time zones

① Investigate (30–35 min)

Temperature: How Hot and How Cold?

When we measure temperature, we use either customary units of measure (Fahrenheit) or metric units of measure (Celsius). To measure degrees Fahrenheit or degrees Celsius, we use a thermometer.

Give each pair of students a cup of ice water, a cup of warm water, and a thermometer. Have students predict which temperature will be higher. Have students measure and record the temperatures of the ice water and the warm water in both degrees Fahrenheit and degrees Celsius periodically throughout the day. What will happen to the ice throughout the day? What will happen to the temperature as the ice melts? Record findings in a chart.

Time	Temperature (Fahrenheit)	Temperature (Celsius)
10:00 A.M.	30°	-1°
10:30 A.M.	39°	4°

Between measurements, have students make a paper thermometer using degrees Fahrenheit and degrees Celsius. When finished with the thermometers, invite students to compare the two temperature scales.

Guiding Questions

- What happens to the temperature of the ice water throughout the day? *The temperature increases.* Is the temperature getting cooler or warmer? *warmer* Are the warmer temperatures higher or lower on the scales? *higher*

- What do you notice when you compare the degrees Fahrenheit and the degrees Celsius scales? *Sample answer: The scale for degrees Fahrenheit is a greater number than degrees Celsius.*

- What are some "common" temperatures you know? *98.6°F, body temperature; 32°F, freezing; 212°F, boiling*

- What numbers are these equivalent to on the Celsius scale? *37°C, 0°C, 100°C*

Connections and Extensions

Graphing Time Zones and Temperature
Give students a map of the United States with time-zone boundaries noted. Explain that there are different time zones based upon the rotation of Earth around the Sun. Have students make a list of four states in four different time zones. Then have students use the newspaper or other weather resources to find and graph the temperatures at these locations on a specific day.

② Apply (20–25 min)

Student Page 75 Guide · · · · · ·

Exercises 1–5
Have students work with partners to answer the questions. Then discuss responses as a class.

In Exercises 4 and 5, how did you know which temperatures to write? *Sample answer: I know what the approximate temperatures are on a hot day and cold day in degrees Fahrenheit, so I looked across the thermometer to find temperatures at the same heights for degrees Celsius.*

In Science
Encourage students to think of other environmental factors that might impact the temperatures of large water bodies such as ponds, lakes, or rivers.

Encourage students to predict temperature changes before they record them. Make sure they compare temperature increases and decreases when exposed to different environmental factors.

Student Page 76 Guide · · · · ·

Exercises 6–8
Have students share their responses with partners and then with the class.

How did you know what clothing suggestions to make for each temperature? *Sample answer: I thought about what to wear in warm and cold temperatures.*

Exercises 9 and 10
Have students share their responses with partners.

Between which two times was there the greatest temperature rise? How many degrees did it rise? *between 10:00 A.M. and 12:00 P.M.; 13°F*

③ Reflect (5–10 min)

- How do you read a temperature on a thermometer? *Sample answer: by comparing the height of the shaded bar to the numbers on the Fahrenheit and Celsius scales*

- Why is it helpful to know how to read a thermometer? *Sample answer: If I know how to read a thermometer, I can find the temperature of the air, water, or other things.*

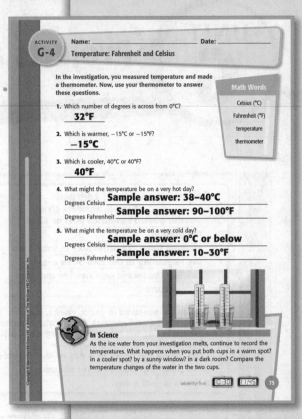

ACTIVITY G-4

Name: _____ Date: _____

Temperature: Fahrenheit and Celsius

In the investigation, you measured temperature and made a thermometer. Now, use your thermometer to answer these questions.

Math Words
Celsius (°C)
Fahrenheit (°F)
temperature
thermometer

1. Which number of degrees is across from 0°C?
   32°F

2. Which is warmer, −15°C or −15°F?
   −15°C

3. Which is cooler, 40°C or 40°F?
   40°F

4. What might the temperature be on a very hot day?
   Degrees Celsius **Sample answer: 38–40°C**
   Degrees Fahrenheit **Sample answer: 90–100°F**

5. What might the temperature be on a very cold day?
   Degrees Celsius **Sample answer: 0°C or below**
   Degrees Fahrenheit **Sample answer: 10–30°F**

In Science
As the ice water from your investigation melts, continue to record the temperatures. What happens when you put both cups in a warm spot? in a cooler spot? by a sunny window? in a dark room? Compare the temperature changes of the water in the two cups.

seventy-five **10:30** **11:45** 75

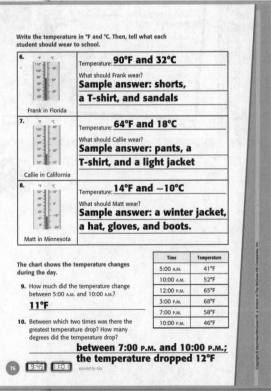

Write the temperature in °F and °C. Then, tell what each student should wear to school.

6. Frank in Florida
   Temperature: **90°F and 32°C**
   What should Frank wear?
   Sample answer: shorts, a T-shirt, and sandals

7. Callie in California
   Temperature: **64°F and 18°C**
   What should Callie wear?
   Sample answer: pants, a T-shirt, and a light jacket

8. Matt in Minnesota
   Temperature: **14°F and −10°C**
   What should Matt wear?
   Sample answer: a winter jacket, a hat, gloves, and boots.

The chart shows the temperature changes during the day.

Time	Temperature
5:00 A.M.	41°F
10:00 A.M.	52°F
12:00 P.M.	65°F
3:00 P.M.	68°F
7:00 P.M.	58°F
10:00 P.M.	46°F

9. How much did the temperature change between 5:00 A.M. and 10:00 A.M.?
   11°F

10. Between which two times was there the greatest temperature drop? How many degrees did the temperature drop?
    between 7:00 P.M. and 10:00 P.M.; the temperature dropped 12°F

76 **9:45** **10:01** seventy-six

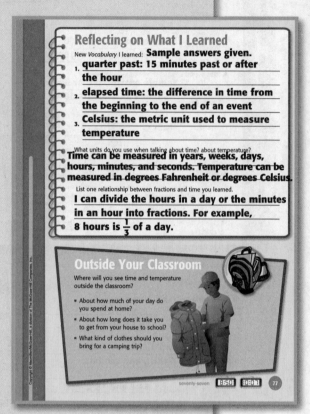

Reflecting on What I Learned

New *Vocabulary* I learned: **Sample answers given.**

1. **quarter past: 15 minutes past or after the hour**

2. **elapsed time: the difference in time from the beginning to the end of an event**

3. **Celsius: the metric unit used to measure temperature**

What units do you use when talking about time? about temperature?
Time can be measured in years, weeks, days, hours, minutes, and seconds. Temperature can be measured in degrees Fahrenheit or degrees Celsius.

List one relationship between fractions and time you learned.
I can divide the hours in a day or the minutes in an hour into fractions. For example, 8 hours is $\frac{1}{3}$ of a day.

Outside Your Classroom

Where will you see time and temperature outside the classroom?

- About how much of your day do you spend at home?
- About how long does it take you to get from your house to school?
- What kind of clothes should you bring for a camping trip?

seventy-seven 77

Vocabulary and Essential Learnings

Vocabulary

- Have students discuss in small groups the vocabulary terms and the definitions that they learned or reviewed in this unit.

- Generate a master list of terms on the board or have students create a Foldable®.

- Have students record three terms of their choice, along with a brief definition or picture for each one.

Essential Learnings

Arrange students in pairs. Have partners review the activities on pages 69 through 76 and discuss what they learned.

Allow time for students to share their essential learnings in small groups or as a class.

Outside Your Classroom

You may wish to arrange students into four groups. Then have groups share their responses with the class. Allow time for classmates to extend or enrich the groups' responses.

Possible student responses:

- About how much of your day do you spend at home? *Sample answer: I spend about 16 hours at home. That is about $\frac{2}{3}$ of a day.*

- About how long does it take you to get to school? *Sample answer: I leave for school about 8:15 and get there about 8:45. It takes about $\frac{1}{2}$ hour, or 30 minutes.*

- How do you choose the kind of clothes you would bring for a camping trip? *Sample answer: I need to find the high- and low-temperature forecast for the location where I will be camping. If the temperature will be warm, I will bring more shorts than pants; if it will be cold, I will bring a heavy coat, sweaters, and gloves.*

Make A Perfect-Day Timeline

Materials

adding machine tape or sheets of paper taped together to form a long strip
samples of timelines

Pacing: 45–55 min

Introducing the Project

Show students timeline samples or have them find samples in reference books. Ask students to describe the timelines. Note the different ways times are noted and how symbols are used to indicate events.

Explain to students that they will be making a timeline of activities they do in one day. Ask students to list some of their favorite activities and record their responses on chart paper.

Completing the Project

Distribute paper. Have students read the questions in Step 1 and respond to them with a partner. Tell students to use their responses to guide the creation of their timeline. Then have students complete Steps 2 and 3 independently.

Extending the Project

To bring in connections with graphing, you could have students graph the amount of time they spend doing certain activities. You could also connect the timeline with story line events and have students make a timeline of events in a book they are reading.

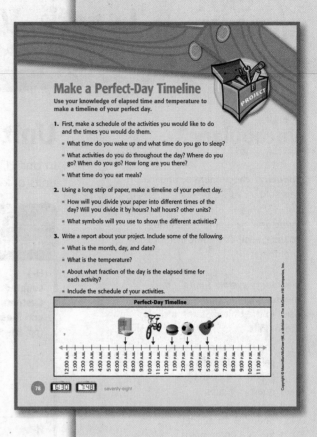

Suggested Scoring Rubric

4	The student completes the project with accuracy and creativity. The student's report accurately and completely describes the project and is written in clear, concise language including appropriate math terminology.
3	The student completes the project. The student's report has some inaccuracies and uses little math terminology.
2	The student does not complete all the components of the project. The student's report has some inaccuracies and uses very little math terminology.
1	The student's project is either incomplete or inaccurate. The student's report is inaccurate, incomplete, and contains incorrect or no math terminology.

UNIT H

Length, Volume, and Weight/Mass

Vocabulary

capacity   the amount a container can hold

cubic unit   a unit for measuring volume, such as a cubic inch or cubic centimeter

customary system (units)   the measurement system that is most used in the United States; includes these units:

   1 cup = 8 ounces
   1 gallon = 16 cups
   1 gallon = 4 quarts
   1 quart = 4 cups
   1 pint = 2 cups
   1 pound = 16 ounces
   1 ton = 2,000 pounds
   1 foot = 12 inches
   1 yard = 3 feet

mass   measure of the amount of matter in an object

metric system (units)   the measurement system based on powers of 10; includes these units:

   1 liter = 1,000 milliliters
   1 meter = 100 centimeters
   1 kilogram = 1,000 grams

volume   the number of cubic units needed to fill a three-dimensional figure or solid figure

weight   a measurement that tells how heavy an object is

Unit-at-a-Glance

In Unit H, students gain understanding of customary and metric units of length, volume, and weight/mass.

Activity	Focus	Student Investigation
H-1 Length: Customary and Metric (pp. 81–82)	Students solve problems involving fractions, decimals, and decimal equivalents.	Students use measuring tools such as a yardstick, ruler, and meterstick to measure body parts. Students will also use fractions and decimals to convert customary measurements into metric measurements.
H-2 Capacity: Customary and Metric (pp. 83–84)	Students determine the relative sizes of amounts (or distances) using estimation.	Students use centimeter cubes to find the volume of rectangular prisms and relate volume to length, width, and height measurements.
H-3 Weight/Mass: Customary and Metric (pp. 85–86)	Students apply an understanding of models for multiplication, place value, and properties as they use efficient and accurate methods to multiply multidigit whole numbers.	Students use a balance to find the weight/mass of objects.
Unit Project: Sandbox Builder (p. 88)	Students relate the concepts and skills they have learned to the real world.	Students use concepts of customary and metric units of length, volume, and weight to design a sandbox.

Page Numbers

Each page number is represented by a conversion equation.

Guiding Questions

- What is the equivalent fraction or decimal for the measurement?
- Convert the measurement into a customary or metric unit.

Unit Opener

Student Page 79 Guide

You can open the unit by having students read through the objectives they will accomplish during the unit. Have students restate objectives in their own words to ensure comprehension.

Scaffolding Questions	What are some units you know for measuring the length of an object? *Sample answers: inch, centimeter, foot, yard, mile, kilometer*
	What is the difference between a two-dimensional figure and a three-dimensional figure? *A two-dimensional figure has length and width; a three-dimensional figure has length, width, and height.*
Vocabulary WRITING IN MATH	The beginning of the unit is a great time to start a new wall chart.
	Encourage students to write the definitions in their math journals. Writing their own definitions or creating drawings will help internalize the information.

Student Page 80 Guide

Home Letter	Have students take the Home Letter home.
	Look at the Projects and Discussions throughout the unit to see if any additional opportunities are available for work at home.
ELL	Encourage students to visit the online eGlossary with parents to see vocabulary in 13 languages.
TeacherWorks *Plus*	See "Home E-mail" as an alternative for communication. From the Lesson Planner, select the e-mail document for this unit, double-click the file, and edit in the Worksheet Editor.

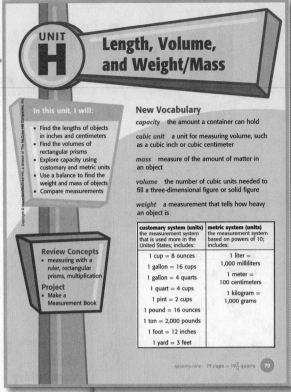

UNIT H

Length, Volume, and Weight/Mass

In this unit, I will:
- Find the lengths of objects in inches and centimeters
- Find the volumes of rectangular prisms
- Explore capacity using customary and metric units
- Use a balance to find the weight and mass of objects
- Compare measurements

Review Concepts
- measuring with a ruler, rectangular prisms, multiplication

Project
- Make a Measurement Book

New Vocabulary

capacity the amount a container can hold

cubic unit a unit for measuring volume, such as a cubic inch or cubic centimeter

mass measure of the amount of matter in an object

volume the number of cubic units needed to fill a three-dimensional figure or solid figure

weight a measurement that tells how heavy an object is

customary system (units) the measurement system that is used more in the United States; includes:	metric system (units) the measurement system based on powers of 10; includes:
1 cup = 8 ounces	1 liter = 1,000 milliliters
1 gallon = 16 cups	
1 gallon = 4 quarts	1 meter = 100 centimeters
1 quart = 4 cups	
1 pint = 2 cups	1 kilogram = 1,000 grams
1 pound = 16 ounces	
1 ton = 2,000 pounds	
1 foot = 12 inches	
1 yard = 3 feet	

seventy-nine   79 cups = $19\frac{3}{4}$ quarts   **79**

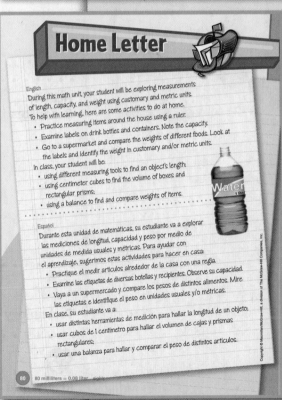

Home Letter

English

During this math unit, your student will be exploring measurements of length, capacity, and weight using customary and metric units. To help with learning, here are some activities to do at home.
- Practice measuring items around the house using a ruler.
- Examine labels on drink bottles and containers. Note the capacity.
- Go to a supermarket and compare the weights of different foods. Look at the labels and identify the weight in customary and/or metric units.

In class, your student will be:
- using different measuring tools to find an object's length;
- using centimeter cubes to find the volume of boxes and rectangular prisms;
- using a balance to find and compare weights of items.

Español

Durante esta unidad de matemáticas, su estudiante va a explorar las mediciones de longitud, capacidad y peso por medio de unidades de medida usuales y métricas. Para ayudar con el aprendizaje, sugerimos estas actividades para hacer en casa:
- Practique el medir artículos alrededor de la casa con una regla.
- Examine las etiquetas de diversas botellas y recipientes. Observe su capacidad.
- Vaya a un supermercado y compare los pesos de distintos alimentos. Mire las etiquetas e identifique el peso en unidades usuales y/o métricas.

En clase, su estudiante va a:
- usar distintas herramientas de medición para hallar la longitud de un objeto;
- usar cubos de 1 centímetro para hallar el volumen de cajas y prismas rectangulares;
- usar una balanza para hallar y comparar el peso de distintos artículos.

80   80 milliliters = 0.08 liter   eighty

Activity Planner

	Activity H-1 Pacing: 65–80 min	**Activity H-2** Pacing: 55–75 min
Activity/ Objective	**Length: Customary and Metric** (pp. 81–82) **Objective** Find lengths using customary and metric units.	**Capacity: Customary and Metric** (pp. 83–84) **Objective** Explore volume of rectangular prisms and capacity in customary and metric units.
Math Vocabulary	centimeter (cm) customary system (units) inch (in.) metric system (units) **Review Vocabulary** length width	capacity milliliter (mL) cubic unit pint (pt) cup (c) quart (qt) gallon (gal) volume liter (L) **Review Vocabulary** rectangular prism
Activity Resources	**Materials** yardstick meterstick string of various lengths **Manipulatives** flexible rulers (centimeter and inch)	**Materials** boxes or plastic containers cup, pint, quart, gallon, and liter containers water or sand food and drink containers yardstick **Manipulatives** centimeter cubes flexible rulers (centimeter and inch)
Technology	**Personal Tutor Concepts in Motion**	**Personal Tutor Games** Bowl-O-Matic
Real-World Connections	**In Science** Use string to relate the width of fists to the length of feet.	
Small Projects	**Measurement Book** Make a measurement book to record lengths in centimeters and inches.	**Measurement Book** Students add capacity to their measurement books.

Activity H-3	**Pacing:** 60–75 min	Unit Project	**Pacing:** 45 min	

Weight/Mass: Customary and Metric (pp. 85–86)	**Sandbox Builder** (p. 88)	**Activity/ Objective**
Objective Find the weight/mass of objects in customary and metric units.	**Objective** Use concepts of length, volume, weight, and mass to design a sandbox.	

gram (g) pound (lb) kilogram (kg) ton (T) mass weight ounce (oz)		**Math Vocabulary**

Materials items of various sizes and weights measuring cup rice and flour	**Materials** dot or grid paper markers	**Activity Resources**
Manipulatives balance scales centimeter cubes	**Manipulatives** flexible rulers centimeter cubes	

Personal Tutor	**Games** Bowl-O-Matic	Tech Link **Technology**

		Real-World Connections

Measurement Book Students add weight/mass to their measurement books.		**Small Projects**

Differentiated Instruction

Below are suggestions on differentiating the materials presented in this unit. Additional modifications should be considered.

Below Level **BL**	Above Level **AL**	English Language Learners **ELL**

ACTIVITY H-1

Exercises 1–4
Have students work with a partner to measure and draw each line. Then they can check each other's work.

Have students practice converting measurements to different units. Students can also measure to the nearest millimeter.

Students may need assistance with customary units. Have the students make a chart for the customary units of length and include an example and the abbreviation for each.

ACTIVITY H-2

Exercises 1 and 2
Have students work in small groups to make different rectangular prisms.

Exercises 3–8
Have students research the capacity of other items and make a matching test for their classmates to solve.

Review with students the words *length*, *width*, and *height*. Encourage students to describe the prisms they made using these terms.

ACTIVITY H-3

Exercises 1–5
Have students work in small groups to make each list.

Challenge students to make a game that involves units of weight. Students can play the game with classmates.

Review the terms *greater than*, *less than*, and *equal to*. Check students' understanding by showing objects of different sizes and having students use the terms to compare the items.

Performance-Based Assessment

Rectangle (p. A30)

In *Rectangle,* students first measure the length and width of a rectangle. Students then determine its area and perimeter and show how they figured it out.

Connections

Rectangle also covers the following skills and concepts:

- Measurement
- Area
- Perimeter
- Multiplication and addition

Targeting the Task

- **Pretest**—Exercises 1–3 in the assessment *Rectangle* can be used to determine a foundational understanding of area and perimeter. For those students who do not have this understanding, completing this unit is needed.

- **Formative**—Exercise 1 of *Rectangle* may be used first to determine students' skill in measuring. Exercises 2 and 3 may be used according to the lesson.

- **Summative**—Administer complete *Rectangle* performance-based assessment.

Differentiation

Having students make their own rulers may help to eliminate misunderstandings about how rulers work. Students can measure items with one-inch color tiles cut from construction paper, and then glue them to paper strips to emphasize the connection between the spaces on a ruler and the actual units. For more accurate measures, have students find the halfway point of each tile to begin measuring to the nearest half inch.

When measuring perimeter, give students linear-type materials such as toothpicks, paper clips, string, or straws to measure rectangles.

Area measures space. Give students a chance to cover rectangular and non-rectangular shapes with color tiles or pattern blocks. Students who are comfortable with area can be challenged to create different shapes with equal area using color tiles or tangrams.

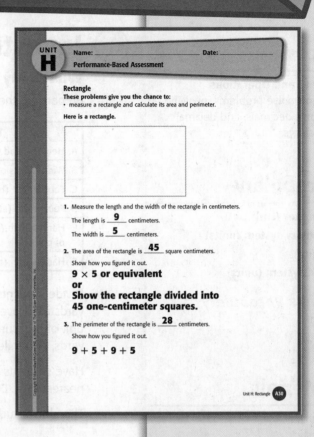

ACTIVITY H-1

Length: Customary and Metric

Focus

Number and Operations
Students solve problems involving fractions, decimals, and decimal equivalents.

Vocabulary

centimeter (cm)
customary system (units)
inch (in.)
metric system (units)

Review Vocabulary
length
width

Materials

yardstick
meterstick
string of various lengths
flexible rulers (centimeter and inch)

① Investigate (40–45 min)

What's My Size?

Prepare for the activity by copying this table on the board.

To Be Measured	Customary (in.)	Metric (cm)
A. Height (head to heel)		
B. Width (arms out to sides, finger tip to finger tip)		
C. Foot length (heel to toe)		
D. Foot width (at widest part)		
E. Hand length (tip of middle finger to bottom of palm)		
F. Hand width (at widest part)		

Divide students into pairs. Provide each pair with an inch ruler and a yardstick. Have students examine the measuring tools and discuss the unit of measure on each. Customary units of length are inches, feet, yards, and miles.

Have students use the measuring tools to measure their partner to the nearest inch. Discuss and complete the table.

Then have students measure using metric units to the nearest centimeters.

Guiding Questions

- Look at the measuring tools. How are inches, feet, and yards related? *12 inches in 1 foot; 36 inches or 3 feet in 1 yard*

- Could you use a different unit other than inches for any of your measurements? Explain. *Sample answer: Yes; if something is shorter than 12 inches, I can measure it in centimeters. If it is longer than 36 inches, I can measure it in yards.*

- Look at your height measurement in inches and in centimeters. Which is greater? What does this tell you about inch and centimeter units? *The centimeter measurement is greater; inches are larger than centimeters.*

- Why is it important to record the unit you used to measure? *Sample answer: Units are different lengths, so my measurement will be different in different units.*

Connections and Extensions

Graphing
Have students make graphs displaying their heights and the heights of three or four of their classmates.

② Apply (20–25 min)

Student Page 81 Guide · · · · · ·

Exercise 1 Have students examine an inch ruler prior to completing the exercise.	Look at the ruler on the page. How many tick marks are between each inch? *4* What does each tick mark represent? $\frac{1}{4}$ *of an inch*
Exercises 2–6 Encourage students to check their work with a partner.	How do you use the ruler to draw a line with a given length? *Sample answer: Place the ruler on the paper. Begin at the zero mark and draw a line until you reach the given length.*
In Science Provide students with string of different lengths to test the trick.	Did the string length match the length of your foot? *Answers will vary.*

Student Page 82 Guide · · · · ·

Exercises 7–12 Have students work with a partner to list items with the given measurement.	What are some benchmarks to help you list the different objects? *Sample answers: I am about 4 ft tall; a penny is about 2 cm long; a paper clip is about 1 in. long.*
Exercises 13 and 14 Guide students to discover the relationship between inches and centimeters.	How many centimeters do you think equal 1 inch? *Sample answer: A line that is 1 in. long is about $2\frac{1}{2}$ cm.*
Measurement Book	Have students make a book with 16–20 pages. Have students use 6–7 pages to record items with different measurements. Instruct students to record the lengths in customary and metric units.

③ Reflect (5–10 min)

- How are inches and centimeters the same? How are they different? *Both are units of length. Inches are customary units and centimeters are metric units. An inch is larger than a centimeter.*

- Which is longer, an item that measures 12 inches or an item that measures 3 feet? Explain. *The item that measures 3 feet is longer; 12 inches equals 1 foot and 3 feet is longer than 1 foot.*

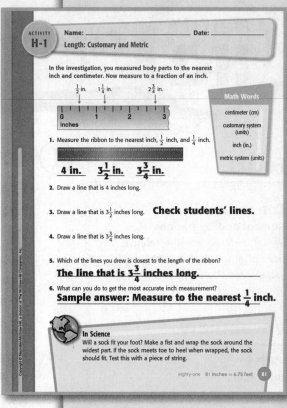

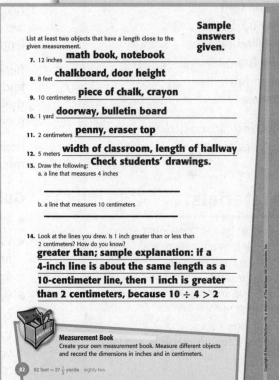

Capacity: Customary and Metric

Focus

Connection
Number and Operations
Students determine the relative sizes of amounts (or distances) using estimation.

Vocabulary

capacity
cubic unit
cup (c)
gallon (gal)
liter (L)
milliliter (mL)
pint (pt)
quart (qt)
volume

Review Vocabulary
rectangular prism

Materials

boxes or plastic containers
cup, pint, quart, gallon, and
 liter containers
water or sand
food and drink containers
yardstick
centimeter cubes
flexible rulers (centimeter and inch)

① Investigate (30–40 min)

Exploring Capacity and Volume

Introduce the activity by showing a gallon container and a liter container. Have students share what they know about capacity. Tell students that capacity is the amount a container can hold and is related to volume, which is the amount of space a three-dimensional figure takes up. Make a list of capacity words on the board, such as gallon, quart, pint, cup, liter, and milliliter. Show examples of each.

Provide small groups with centimeter cubes and a clear plastic box. Instruct students to fill the box with the centimeter cubes. Guide them to place the cubes in rows, columns, and layers. Have students record the number of cubes used.

Have students use a centimeter ruler to measure the length, width, and height of the box. Ask students to determine how these measurements are connected to the number of cubes filling the box. *The product of the length, width, and height equals the number of centimeter cubes.*

Repeat with different-sized boxes. Then ask students how they could find the volume of the classroom. Have them first estimate the volume, then measure the length, width, and height and multiply to find the room's volume in cubic feet.

Point out that capacity can be measured using both customary and metric units of length.

Guiding Questions

- Which capacity is greater, a gallon or a liter? *gallon*
- What are some things that have capacity or volume? *Sample answers: juice or milk containers, water bottles, boxes, any three-dimensional figure*
- What do you notice about the length, width and height of the centimeter cubes? *each equals 1 centimeter*
- What is the relationship between the dimensions of a box and its volume? *The volume is equal to the length times width times height.*

Connections and Extensions

Measurement
Have students explore the relationship between cups, pints, quarts, and gallons. Provide students with water (or sand) and a cup, a pint, a quart, and a gallon container. Have them use the water and containers to find how many cups equal 1 pint, how many pints equal 1 quart, and how many quarts equal 1 gallon.

② Apply (20–30 min)

Student Page 83 Guide · · · · ·

Exercises 1 and 2
Have students compare responses with a partner.

How can you use factors to check your work? *I can find combinations of three factors that equal the given volume.*

Student Page 84 Guide · · · · ·

Exercises 3–8
Have students work independently and then discuss their answers as a class.

How can you use the benchmarks to help you determine the capacity of each container? *Sample answer: I can think about the size of the container and use the benchmarks to decide which unit would be used to measure the capacity.*

Which item has the greatest capacity? the least? *greatest: the swimming pool; least: the medicine dropper*

 Measurement Book

Bring in food and drink containers and show students where the measurements are found. Students can draw pictures or cut out and paste the labels into their measurement books. Students should use six to seven pages for capacity measurements.

③ Reflect (5 min)

- What is the difference between volume and capacity? *Volume is the amount of space an object takes up; capacity is the amount a container can hold.*

- List two ways you can find the volume of a box. *Sample answer: Fill the box with cubes in rows, columns, and layers and then count the number of cubes used; measure the length, width, and height of the box and multiply the measurements together.*

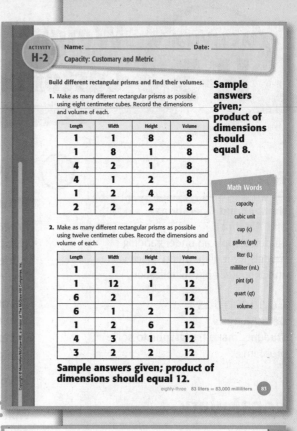

ACTIVITY H-3

Weight/Mass: Customary and Metric

Focus

Number and Operations and Algebra
Students apply an understanding of models for multiplication, place value, and properties of multiplication.

Connections

Data Analysis
Students make bar graphs to solve problems.

Vocabulary

gram (g)
kilogram (kg)
mass
ounce (oz)
pound (lb)
ton (T)
weight

Materials

items of various sizes and weights
measuring cup
rice and flour
balance scales
centimeter cubes

① Investigate (30–35 min)

How Much Does It Weigh?

Prepare for the activity by placing five different items on a table (e.g., paper clip, marker, small book, calculator, box of crayons). Instruct students to make a chart with rows for each item and columns labeled "estimated weight" and "actual weight".

Demonstrate how to use the balance. Place centimeter cubes on one side and a pencil on the other side. Determine the weight of the pencil in centimeter cubes. Explain to students that the centimeter cubes are nonstandard units for weight.

Have students estimate the weight of the other items in centimeter cubes and record their estimates in their charts. Then, have students work in small groups to weigh the items on the balance to find the actual weights.

Ask students to list some units of weight that are familiar to them. Write their responses in two columns on the board: customary (ounce, pound, ton) and metric (gram, kilogram).

Guiding Questions

- How do you use a balance to find the weight of an item in centimeter cubes? *Sample answer: Place the item on one side and place centimeter cubes on the other side until both sides are the same level.*

- How close were your estimates to the actual weights? *Answers will vary.*

- Which item had the greatest weight? the least weight? *Answers dependent on items chosen.*

- How could you find the weight of each item in a standard unit like ounces? *Sample answer: Place the item on one side of the balance and place items that weigh 1 ounce on the other side until the balance is even.*

Connections and Extensions • • • • • • • • • • • •

Relate Weight and Volume
Compare a cup of rice to a cup of flour. Which has the greater weight? *the flour* Why do you think this is so? *Responses will vary. Students may allude to the idea of density or the number of rice grains compared to the number of flour particles that can fit in both containers.*

Graphing
Have students make a bar graph of the weights of the five items from the investigation.

② Apply (25-30 min)

Student Page 85 Guide · · · · ·

Exercises 1–5
Have students work with a partner. Encourage students to look around the classroom or through books to help them think of items. Discuss the items as a class.

List the customary units in order from lightest to heaviest. *ounces, pounds, tons*

Student Page 86 Guide · · · · ·

Exercises 6–9
Remind students how to use a balance and what it means when one side of the balance is higher than the other side.

Encourage students to use the terms *less than* and *greater than* when making their comparisons.

How do you know if two items on a balance are the same weight? *The balance is even.*

How do you know if one item is heavier than another item on a balance? *The heavier item is lower than the other side of the balance.*

Two items are placed on a balance. How do you know which item weighs less? *The item that is higher weighs less.*

Exercises 10–15
Have students use the information given on page 85 to help them determine the greater weight/mass.

How many ounces are in 1 pound? *16 ounces*

How many pounds equal 1 ton? *2,000 pounds*

What is the relationship between grams and kilograms? *1 kilogram = 1,000 grams*

 Measurement Book
Have students add weight and mass measurements to their books.

Encourage students to use a balance to weigh items or to utilize research materials to find things that weigh different amounts.

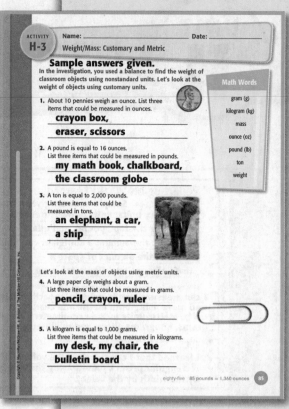

Copyright © Macmillan/McGraw-Hill, a division of The McGraw-Hill Companies, Inc.

ACTIVITY H-3
Name: _____ Date: _____

Weight/Mass: Customary and Metric

Sample answers given.

In the investigation, you used a balance to find the weight of classroom objects using nonstandard units. Let's look at the weight of objects using customary units.

1. About 10 pennies weigh an ounce. List three items that could be measured in ounces.
crayon box, eraser, scissors

2. A pound is equal to 16 ounces. List three items that could be measured in pounds.
my math book, chalkboard, the classroom globe

3. A ton is equal to 2,000 pounds. List three items that could be measured in tons.
an elephant, a car, a ship

Let's look at the mass of objects using metric units.

4. A large paper clip weighs about a gram. List three items that could be measured in grams.
pencil, crayon, ruler

5. A kilogram is equal to 1,000 grams. List three items that could be measured in kilograms.
my desk, my chair, the bulletin board

Math Words
gram (g)
kilogram (kg)
mass
ounce (oz)
pound (lb)
ton
weight

eighty-five 85 pounds = 1,360 ounces **85**

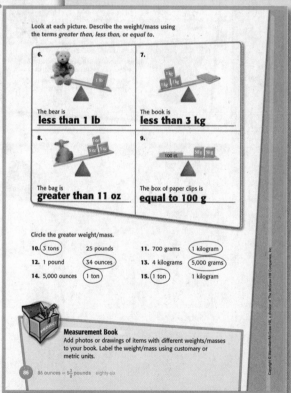

Look at each picture. Describe the weight/mass using the terms *greater than, less than,* or *equal to.*

6. The bear is **less than 1 lb**

7. The book is **less than 3 kg**

8. The bag is **greater than 11 oz**

9. The box of paper clips is **equal to 100 g**

Circle the greater weight/mass.

10. (3 tons)   25 pounds
11. 700 grams   (1 kilogram)
12. 1 pound   (34 ounces)
13. 4 kilograms   (5,000 grams)
14. 5,000 ounces   (1 ton)
15. (1 ton)   1 kilogram

Measurement Book
Add photos or drawings of items with different weights/masses to your book. Label the weight/mass using customary or metric units.

86 86 ounces = 5⅜ pounds eighty-six

Copyright © Macmillan/McGraw-Hill, a division of The McGraw-Hill Companies, Inc.

③ Reflect (5-10 min)

- When might you need to compare customary units to metric units? *when comparing the cost of items measured in different units*

- Give an example of an item whose mass you would find in kilograms. *Answers will vary.*

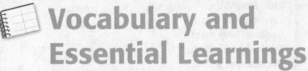

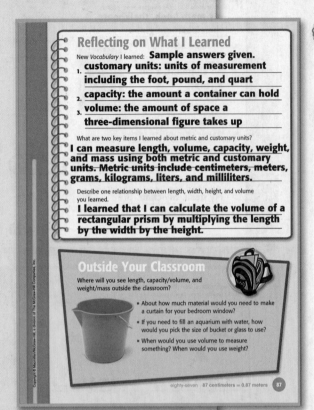

Reflecting on What I Learned

New *Vocabulary* I learned: **Sample answers given.**

1. **customary units: units of measurement including the foot, pound, and quart**

2. **capacity: the amount a container can hold**

3. **volume: the amount of space a three-dimensional figure takes up**

What are two key items I learned about metric and customary units?
I can measure length, volume, capacity, weight, and mass using both metric and customary units. Metric units include centimeters, meters, grams, kilograms, liters, and milliliters.

Describe one relationship between length, width, height, and volume you learned.
I learned that I can calculate the volume of a rectangular prism by multiplying the length by the width by the height.

Outside Your Classroom

Where will you see length, capacity/volume, and weight/mass outside the classroom?

- About how much material would you need to make a curtain for your bedroom window?
- If you need to fill an aquarium with water, how would you pick the size of bucket or glass to use?
- When would you use volume to measure something? When would you use weight?

eighty-seven 87 centimeters = 0.87 meters **87**

Vocabulary and Essential Learnings

Vocabulary

- Have students discuss in small groups the vocabulary terms and the definitions that they learned or reviewed in this unit.

- Generate a master list of terms on the board or have students create a Foldable®.

- Have students record three terms of their choice, along with a brief definition or picture for each one.

Essential Learnings

Arrange students in pairs. Have partners review the activities on pages 81 through 86 and discuss what they learned.

Allow time for students to share their essential learnings in small groups or as a class.

Outside Your Classroom

You may wish to arrange students into four groups. Then have groups share their responses with the class. Allow time for classmates to extend or enrich the groups' responses.

Possible student responses:

- About how much material would you need to make a curtain for your bedroom window? *Measure the length and width of the window. Cut the material to fit.*

- How could you find how much water you need to fill an aquarium? *Measure the length, width, and height. Multiply the dimensions to find the volume.*

- When would you use volume to measure something? When would you use weight? *If something like a box is being filled, I would use volume. If the item is a solid, such as fruit, I would use weight.*

Sandbox Builder

Materials

dot or grid paper   centimeter cubes

markers   flexible rulers

Pacing: 45 min

Introducing the Project

Ask students to think about sandboxes they have seen at playgrounds or in backyards. Encourage students to discuss basic shapes, the depth, and then discuss the materials needed to build a sandbox.

Completing the Project

Distribute centimeter cubes, rulers, and grid or dot paper. Have students read the questions in Step 1 and use them as a guide in building a model of a sandbox. In Step 2, students transfer their three-dimensional model to a two-dimensional drawing on dot or grid paper. Students may work in pairs to complete Step 3.

Extending the Project

Have students explore how changing one of the dimensions affects the volume. Encourage discussion relating the perimeter and area of the sandbox to its volume. Have students use the same number of centimeter cubes and arrange them to answer the following questions: Which combination of dimensions results in the greatest perimeter? the greatest area? the greatest volume?

Extend the activity to include money by having students find the cost of supplies to build their sandbox. They can make a shopping list and create a budget.

Sandbox Builder

In this unit, you measured length, volume, and weight/mass in both customary and metric units. Use this knowledge to design a sandbox.

1. Use the centimeter cubes to plan your sandbox. Explore different shapes and sizes.
   - What shape is your sandbox?
   - What will be the length and width of your sandbox?
   - How high will your sandbox be?

2. Let each cube represent 1 cubic foot.
   - Draw a diagram of your sandbox on grid or dot paper.
   - Label the dimensions in feet.

3. You need sand for your sandbox.
   One bag of sand covers 1 cubic foot.
   Each bag of sand weighs 50 pounds.

   Use the math in this unit and the information above to answer these questions:
   - How much sand will you need?
   - How much will the sand weigh altogether?

4. Write a report on your project. Include some of the following.
   - What are the dimensions of your sandbox? Did you use customary or metric units?
   - How much wood do you need to buy at the hardware store to build the sandbox?
   - What measurements did you use to calculate how many bags of sand to buy?

88   88 pints = 44 quarts   eighty-eight

Suggested Scoring Rubric

4	The student completes the project with accuracy and creativity. The student's report accurately and completely describes the project and is written in clear, concise language including appropriate math terminology.
3	The student completes the project. The student's report has some inaccuracies and uses some math terminology.
2	The student does not complete all components of the project. The student's report is inaccurate, incomplete, and contains incorrect or no math terminology.
1	The student's project is either incomplete or inaccurate. The student's report is inaccurate, incomplete, and contains incorrect math terminology.

UNIT I

Graphs: Creating and Interpreting

Vocabulary

bar graph a graph that compares data by using bars of different lengths or heights to show the values

data numbers or symbols, sometimes collected from a survey or experiment, to show information; datum is singular; data is plural

double bar graph a bar graph that compares two related groups of data

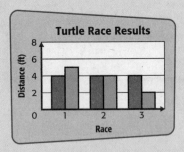

line graph a graph that uses points connected by line segments to represent data

point an exact location in space

survey a method of collecting data

tally chart a way to keep track of data using tally marks to record the number of responses or occurrences

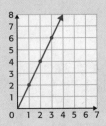

Unit-at-a-Glance

In Unit I, students gain understanding of bar graphs and line graphs.

Activity	Focus	Student Investigation
I-1 Bar Graphs (pp. 91–92)	Students make frequency tables, bar graphs, picture graphs, and line plots to solve problems.	Students conduct a short survey and record the data.
I-2 Double Bar Graphs (pp. 93–94)	Students make frequency tables, bar graphs, picture graphs, and line plots to solve problems.	Students create bar graphs to represent and compare data collected in a survey.
I-3 Line Graphs (pp. 95–96)	Students identify, describe, and extend numeric patterns involving operations. Students make frequency tables, bar graphs, picture graphs, and line plots to solve problems.	Students interpret and complete a line graph.
Unit Project: Design a New School Room (p. 98)	Students relate the concepts and skills they have learned to the real world.	Students conduct a survey, create a graph, and apply the data to the design of a new school room.

Page Numbers

Each page number is represented by coins.

Guiding Questions

- How many more coins do we need to make $1.00? $5.00?
- How much would we have if we added all the page numbers in this unit?

Unit Opener

Student Page 89 Guide · · · · · · · ·

You can open the unit by having students read through the objectives they will accomplish during the unit. Have students restate objectives in their own words to ensure comprehension.

Scaffolding Questions

When have you used a chart to record data? *Sample answers: I have made charts or tables to list number pairs, equivalent measurements, equivalent times, and equivalent fractions. I have also made function tables.*

What kinds of graphs have you seen or created? *Answers will vary; real graphs, picture graphs, circle graphs, bar graphs*

Vocabulary

 WRITING IN MATH ▶

The beginning of the unit is a great time to start a new wall chart.

Encourage students to write the definitions in their math journals. Writing their own definitions or creating drawings will help internalize the information.

Student Page 90 Guide · · · · · · · ·

 Home Letter

Have students take the Home Letter home.

Look at the Projects and Discussions throughout the unit to see if any additional opportunities are available for work at home.

ELL

Encourage students to visit the online eGlossary with parents to see vocabulary in 13 languages.

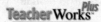 Teacher Works *Plus*

See "Home E-mail" as an alternative for communication. From the Lesson Planner, select the e-mail document for this unit, double-click the file, and edit in the Worksheet Editor.

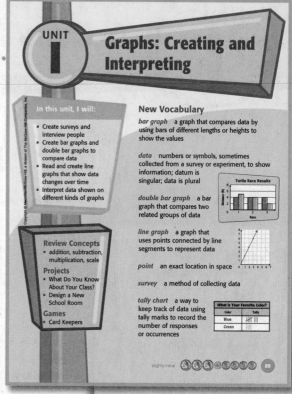

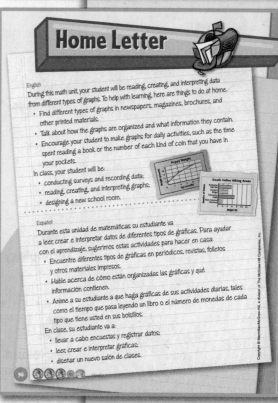

Activity Planner

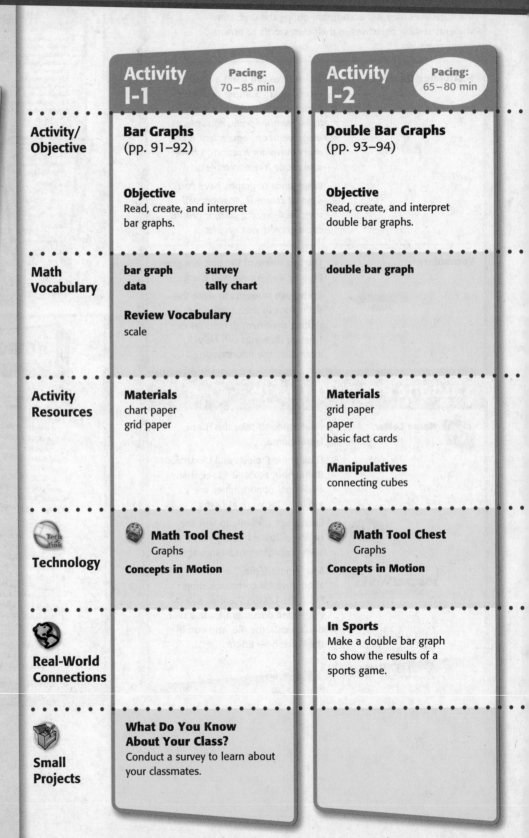

KEY

- Real-World Connections
- Projects
- Technology
- CD-ROM
- Math Tool Chest
- Math Adventures

	Activity 1-1 **Pacing: 70–85 min**	Activity 1-2 **Pacing: 65–80 min**
Activity/ Objective	**Bar Graphs** (pp. 91–92) **Objective** Read, create, and interpret bar graphs.	**Double Bar Graphs** (pp. 93–94) **Objective** Read, create, and interpret double bar graphs.
Math Vocabulary	bar graph survey data tally chart **Review Vocabulary** scale	double bar graph
Activity Resources	**Materials** chart paper grid paper	**Materials** grid paper paper basic fact cards **Manipulatives** connecting cubes
Technology	**Math Tool Chest** Graphs **Concepts in Motion**	**Math Tool Chest** Graphs **Concepts in Motion**
Real-World Connections		**In Sports** Make a double bar graph to show the results of a sports game.
Small Projects	**What Do You Know About Your Class?** Conduct a survey to learn about your classmates.	

Activity I-3 Pacing: 60–75 min	**Unit Project** Pacing: 45 min	
Line Graphs (pp. 95–96)	**Design a New School Room** (p. 98)	**Activity/ Objective**
Objective Read, create, and interpret line graphs.	**Objective** Create a survey, record data, and use the data collected to design a school room.	
line graph point	**Review Vocabulary** bar graph double bar graph line graph survey	**Math Vocabulary**
Materials teacher-made recording sheets teacher-made line graphs stopwatches or watch with a second hand	**Materials** grid paper crayons, markers, or colored pencils	**Activity Resources**
Math Tool Chest Graphs	**Concepts in Motion**	**Technology**
		Real-World Connections
		Small Projects

Differentiated Instruction

Below are suggestions on differentiating the materials presented in this unit. Additional modifications should be considered.

Below Level **BL**	Above Level **AL**	English Language Learners **ELL**

ACTIVITY I-1

Exercises 1–4
Have students work with their partner from the Investigation to complete the exercises and make their bar graphs.

Exercises 5–12
Have students create a line plot and a picture graph showing the same data represented on the bar graph.

Exercises 3 and 4
Talk about different kinds of *scales.* Provide samples or pictures of scales on a ruler, balance, or thermometer.

ACTIVITY I-2

Exercises 5–7
Students may have difficulty keeping track of which color bar represents each group. Have students write *adults* or *children* on the corresponding bars.

Find the high and low temperatures for four days. Make a double bar graph showing these temperatures. What conclusions can you make about the temperature changes throughout the four days?

Exercises 5–7
Define *double*—two of the same item or number. Have students give examples of things that come in doubles such as a double-scoop ice-cream cone or a double-decker bus. A double bar graph means there are two bars for each category.

ACTIVITY I-3

Exercises 1–3
To help students read the graphs, explain that the data to the right is later in time than the data to the left.

Exercises 1–3
Have students create a chart with data that represents a graph where data stays about the same.

Exercises 1–3
Review the words *increase* and *decrease.* Discuss times when numbers increase and decrease.

Performance-Based Assessment

Shells (p. A34)

In *Shells,* students first enter data and interpret a bar graph. Students then do further interpretations and explain their reasoning.

Connections

Shells also covers the following skills and concepts:

- Entering data on a graph
- Interpreting data on a graph
- Subtraction
- Addition

Targeting the Task

- **Pretest**–Use Exercises 1–5 in the *Shells* assessment to determine students' foundational understanding of graphs. For those students who do not have this understanding, completing this unit is needed.

- **Formative**–The *Shells* assessment can be administered individually according to the lessons.

- **Summative**–Administer the complete *Shells* performance-based assessment.

Differentiation

Start with a graph that has fewer entries on the *x*-axis. How does a graph help you interpret data or information? What does each bar on the graph represent?

Have students make their own bar graphs with given data. For example, make a bar graph for the lost-and-found department. They have 8 sets of eyeglasses, 14 hats, and 3 scarves.

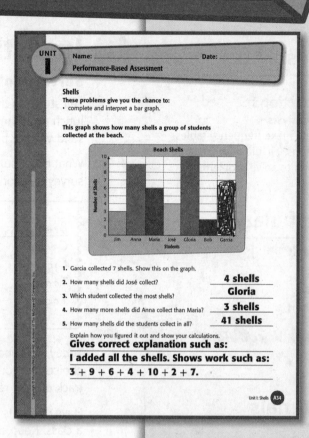

Bar Graphs

Focus

Connections
Data Analysis
Students make frequency tables, bar graphs, picture graphs, and line plots to solve problems.

Vocabulary

bar graph
data
survey
tally chart

Review Vocabulary
scale

Materials

chart paper
grid paper

① Investigate (40–45 min)

Survey: Collecting and Recording Data

Tell students that you will be conducting a survey. Ask them which lunch food they prefer: peanut butter and jelly sandwich, hot dog, turkey sandwich, or pizza. Survey the class and record the results in a tally chart.

What other surveys could you take? Have students brainstorm possible survey categories. Write them on the board or chart paper.

Breakfast	Games	Books	Movies
Cereal	Board games	Fiction	Comedy
Eggs	Ball games	Nonfiction	Action
Toast	Card games	Biography	Drama
Yogurt	Video games	Comic books	Animated (cartoon)

Today, you and your partner will select one category and decide on four choices for your survey. Survey at least 15 people in your class. Keep track of your results in a tally chart.

Have students meet in groups and then discuss the survey results as a class. Keep charts to use for student page 91.

Guiding Questions

- What category and choices did you use for your survey? *Answers will vary.*

- Which choice received the most votes? How do you know? *Sample answer: Cereal; it had the most tally marks.*

- How does the tally chart help you record and understand the data you collected? *Sample answer: Making tally marks is a quick way to record the answers to my survey. I can count the tallies to figure out the number of responses for each choice.*

- What are some other ways you could organize and display the same information? *Sample answer: list, bar graph, picture graph*

Connections and Extensions

Graphing
Introduce an example of a line plot to students. A line plot shows data along a number line. Have students conduct a survey, such as the number of letters in first names, and then create a line plot to show the results. Discuss results as a class and informally discuss mean, mode, and median. Discuss how line and bar graphs differ.

Student Page 91 Guide

Exercises 1–3 Help students determine a title for their graphs.	How did you know what to label the sides? *Sample answer: One side has the choices and the other side has the scale.* How did you decide on the scale? *Sample answer: My bars will range from 3 to 10, so I decided to have a scale of 1.*
Exercise 4 Have students share their bar graphs with a partner.	What question could you ask about the data in your graph? *Answers will vary.*

Student Page 92 Guide

Exercises 5–12 Have students discuss their responses in small groups. Remind students how to read a bar that is between two numbers on the scale.	How are the chart and the graph the same and how are they different? *Sample answer: They have the same title and categories. They are different because the tally chart uses tally marks to show the data and the bar graph uses bars and a number scale. Also, there is no data shown for the color black in the bar graph.*
What Do You Know About Your Class? Have students record their responses in a tally chart.	Have students brainstorm questions they would like to ask their classmates. Be sure students choose a question that has at least three possible answer choices.

③ **Reflect** (5–10 min)

- How is a tally chart helpful when collecting data? *Sample answer: It allows you to quickly record survey results. When you are done recording, you can easily add up the tally marks to find the total amount for each choice.*

- How does a bar graph communicate information? *It uses bar lengths on a number scale to show and compare numbers.*

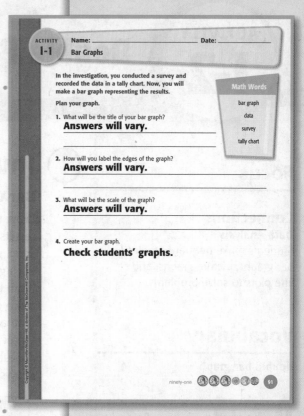

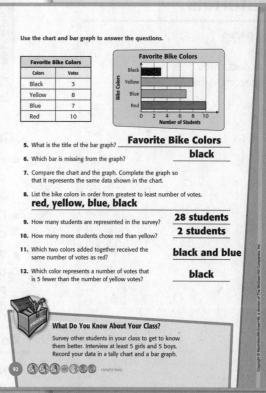

Double Bar Graphs

Focus

Connections
Data Analysis
Students make frequency tables, bar graphs, picture graphs, and line plots to solve problems.

Vocabulary

double bar graph

Materials

grid paper
paper
basic fact cards
connecting cubes

① Investigate (40–45 min)

Bar Graph: Comparing Data

Draw the two bar graphs shown below on the board, one showing the results of a survey for girls and the other showing the results for boys. In small groups, have students use connecting cubes to build the bars for each graph using one color for boys and a different color for girls. Have them line up the cubes for each graph on a sheet of paper. How many more girls like apples than oranges? *1* How many more boys like oranges than apples? *1* Have students move the cubes that represent the second graph next to the appropriate cubes that represent the first graph, creating a double bar graph. Tell students this is called a double bar graph and shows the data from two different groups on the same subject.

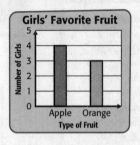

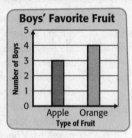

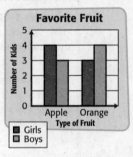

Guiding Questions

- How do you compare the data in both graphs? *Sample answer: I compare the heights of the bars for the same category. The higher bar is the greater number.*

- Do more girls or boys prefer apples? Explain how you know. *Sample answer: more girls; the bar for girls shows 4; the bar for boys shows 3*

- Was it easier to compare the data when there were two graphs or one? Explain. *Sample answer: One graph is easier because each category's bars are next to each other. I just look at the heights of the two different bars to compare the categories.*

Connections and Extensions

Number and Operations
Divide the class into two teams and play the Card Keepers game. Using basic fact cards, have teams name the product or quotient for each card. Each team keeps the card they get correct. Make a class bar graph showing the results of each round.

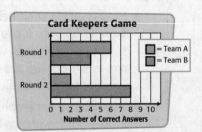

② Apply (20–25 min)

Student Page 93 Guide · · · · ·

Exercises 1–4
Draw students' attention to the key and the number scale. Have students compare responses with a partner.

How is a double bar graph different from a single bar graph? *Sample answer: A double bar graph has a key to show which group each bar stands for and uses two groups of data for each choice.*

In Sports
Give students grid paper to use for their double bar graphs.

Tell students they can use any sporting event. Explain they can get information from a newspaper or the Internet, or they can make up numbers for two teams.

Student Page 94 Guide · · · · ·

Exercises 5–7
Have students discuss the data in the graph in small groups.

Talk about how they can figure out the total number of people interviewed.

In Exercise 5, how do you know how many people were interviewed? *Sample answer: I added the number of adult responses for chewy and crunchy or sweet and salty. I did the same for children. There were 50 adults and 50 children surveyed.*

Exercises 8–10
Have students share their answers in small groups.

What other questions can you answer using the data in the graph? *Answers will vary.*

③ Reflect (5–10 min)

- If you wanted to compare the time it takes four people to run 5 miles, would you use a bar graph or a double bar graph? Explain. *I would use a bar graph because I would want to show the time for each person.*

- If you wanted to compare the number of girls who prefer cats to the number of boys who prefer cats and wanted to compare the number of girls who prefer dogs to the number of boys who prefer dogs, would you use a bar graph or a double bar graph? Explain. *I would use a double bar graph because you are comparing two groups of data.*

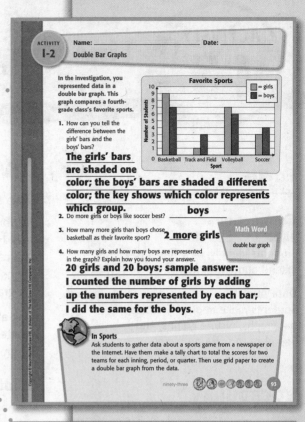

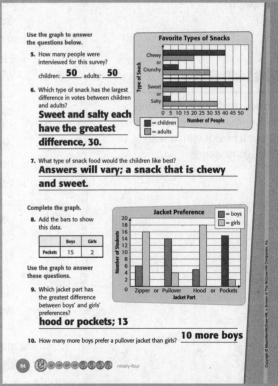

Line Graphs

① **Investigate** (30–35 min)

Line Graph: Changing Data

Distribute recording sheets filled in for Days 1 through 3. Tell students that this data can be shown on a line graph. Line graphs show data over time. Distribute line graphs.

Look at the points on the graph to find a pattern. Use the pattern to complete the graph through Day 6.

Mountain Climbing	
Day	**Distance**
1	5 miles
2	10 miles
3	15 miles
4	
5	
6	

Guiding Questions

- What pattern do you see for the distance climbed per day? *Sample answer: The distance increases 5 miles each day.*

- How do you find the number of miles traveled for a certain day? *Sample answer: I look along the bottom for the day. I follow the line up to the point and move left to find the number of miles.*

- What does the line tell you? *Sample answer: The line connects the points from day to day. It shows the change in distance over several days.*

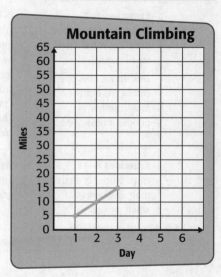

- If the mountain climbers traveled the same distance for the next three days, what would the graph look like? *Sample answer: The points would be at 20, 25, and 30 miles. The line would go diagonally up in a straight line.*

- If the mountain trail is 90 miles long, how many days would it take them to reach the top? *18 days*

Connections and Extensions

Number Sense

Using the data about students' reading times in Exercise 9, have students estimate how many words they will read in five minutes, ten minutes, and one hour. Then ask them to estimate how long it would take them to read five 100-page books, if each page had 100 words.

② Apply (25–30 min)

Student Page 95 Guide · · · · ·

Exercises 1–3 Review with students how to read a line graph.	What does a very steep incline indicate on a line graph? *Sample answer: A very steep incline indicates that there is a significant difference between data points; the data increases significantly over time.*
Exercise 4 Have students share their answers with a partner.	How is this graph different from the graphs above? *Sample answer: This graph has labels and a scale and a line that increases and then decreases.*

Student Page 96 Guide · · · · ·

Exercises 5–8 Have students discuss results in small groups and then as a class.	How did you figure out between which two years the greatest increase in height occurred? *Sample answer: I chose pairs of years that had a steep incline between them and subtracted the numbers to find the greatest difference.*
Exercises 9 and 10 Have students create three questions that can be answered by reading their graphs.	Is there a pattern in the number of words you read each ten-second period? *Answers will vary.*

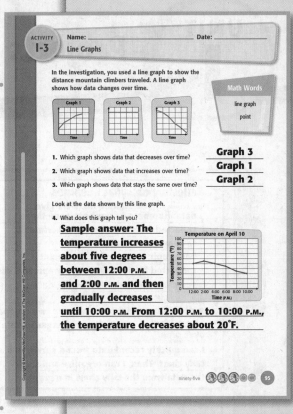

In the investigation, you used a line graph to show the distance mountain climbers traveled. A line graph shows how data changes over time.

Math Words
line graph
point

1. Which graph shows data that decreases over time? **Graph 3**
2. Which graph shows data that increases over time? **Graph 1**
3. Which graph shows data that stays the same over time? **Graph 2**

Look at the data shown by this line graph.

4. What does this graph tell you?
Sample answer: The temperature increases about five degrees between 12:00 P.M. and 2:00 P.M. and then gradually decreases until 10:00 P.M. From 12:00 P.M. to 10:00 P.M., the temperature decreases about 20°F.

ninety-five   95

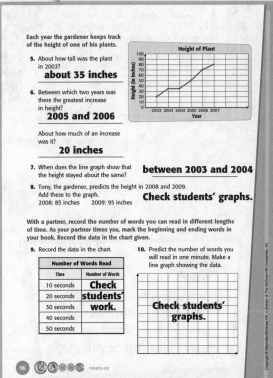

Each year the gardener keeps track of the height of one of his plants.

5. About how tall was the plant in 2003? **about 35 inches**

6. Between which two years was there the greatest increase in height? **2005 and 2006**
   About how much of an increase was it? **20 inches**

7. When does the line graph show that the height stayed about the same? **between 2003 and 2004**

8. Tony, the gardener, predicts the height in 2008 and 2009. Add these to the graph.
   2008: 85 inches   2009: 95 inches   **Check students' graphs.**

With a partner, record the number of words you can read in different lengths of time. As your partner times you, mark the beginning and ending words in your book. Record the data in the chart given.

9. Record the data in the chart.

Number of Words Read	
Time	Number of Words
10 seconds	**Check students' work.**
20 seconds	
30 seconds	
40 seconds	
50 seconds	

10. Predict the number of words you will read in one minute. Make a line graph showing the data.
    Check students' graphs.

96   ninety-six

③ Reflect (5–10 min)

- How is a line graph the same as a bar graph? How is it different? *Sample answer: They are the same because they both have a scale that tells how many; they are different because a line graph uses points and a line to show changes in data over time. A bar graph uses bars to show amounts in different categories so that you can compare the data.*

- If you wanted to show changes in the data, or numbers, over several days, would you use a bar graph or a line graph? Explain why. *I would use a line graph because the lines between the points would show increases or decreases over time.*

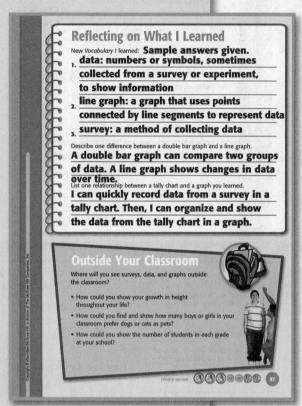

Reflecting on What I Learned

New *Vocabulary* I learned: **Sample answers given.**

1. **data: numbers or symbols, sometimes collected from a survey or experiment, to show information**
2. **line graph: a graph that uses points connected by line segments to represent data**
3. **survey: a method of collecting data**

Describe one difference between a double bar graph and a line graph.

A double bar graph can compare two groups of data. A line graph shows changes in data over time.

List one relationship between a tally chart and a graph you learned.

I can quickly record data from a survey in a tally chart. Then, I can organize and show the data from the tally chart in a graph.

Outside Your Classroom

Where will you see surveys, data, and graphs outside the classroom?

- How could you show your growth in height throughout your life?
- How could you find and show how many boys or girls in your classroom prefer dogs or cats as pets?
- How could you show the number of students in each grade at your school?

ninety-seven 97

AL

Have students conduct one of the surveys discussed in *Outside Your Classroom* and display their results in a graph.

Vocabulary and Essential Learnings

Vocabulary

- Have students discuss in small groups the vocabulary terms and the definitions that they learned or reviewed in this unit.
- Generate a master list of terms on the board or have students create a Foldable®.
- Have students record three terms of their choice, along with a brief definition or picture for each one.

Essential Learnings

Arrange students in pairs. Have partners review the activities on pages 91 through 96 and discuss what they learned.

Allow time for students to share their essential learnings in small groups or as a class.

Outside Your Classroom

You may wish to arrange students into four groups. Then have groups share their responses with the class. Allow time for classmates to extend or enrich the groups' responses.

Possible student responses:

- How could you show your growth in height throughout your life? *I can show my height on a line graph, each point showing the height in inches for each age.*
- How could you find and show how many boys or girls in your classroom prefer dogs or cats as pets? *I can create a survey, make a tally chart to record the results, and organize and show the data in a double bar graph.*
- How could you show the number of students in each grade in your school? *I can show the data in a bar graph with a bar for the number of students in each grade. Or, I could show the girls and boys in each class by making a double bar graph, a bar for girls and a bar for boys in each grade.*

Design a New School Room

Materials

grid paper
crayons, markers, or colored pencils

Pacing: 45 min

Introducing the Project

Review the different rooms in your school (gym, lunchroom, library, etc.). With the students, brainstorm ideas for the use of a new school room and record their ideas on the board.

Completing the Project

Have students read the questions in Step 1 and then invite small groups to react to different survey ideas. Encourage students to use their group's responses to guide them in the creation of their survey. Then have students complete Steps 2 and 3 independently.

Extending the Project

To connect to time, have students create a schedule of times different classes can use the room. To connect to fractions and area, have students determine what fraction of the room is used for different purposes. To connect to money, have students prepare a list of things to buy for the room that meets a specific budget requirement.

To extend the idea even further, encourage students to conduct a survey about a school improvement idea, such as new playground equipment, more computers in the classroom, school uniforms, or more books in the library. Have them use their data to report on the improvement idea.

Design a New School Room

Use your knowledge of graphs and surveys to collect data for a new school room.

1. First, create a survey asking at least ten people what new room they would like in the school. Give them choices for their answers.

   - How will the room be used? (e.g., computer room, game room, art gallery)
   - Who will use the room? (e.g., students, teachers, visitors)
   - What will be in the room? (e.g., games, computers, books, musical instruments)

   How will you record the responses to your survey questions? How will you organize and display the data in a graph?

2. Use grid paper to draw a room design based on the results from your survey.

   - How large will the room be? What is the area and the perimeter?
   - Will the room have computers, play equipment, books, or other items?

3. Write a report on your project including some of the following:

   - What information from your survey and graphs helped you design the room?
   - Include your room design.
   - Include a copy of your graph.

New Room Ideas

- girls
- boys

Number of Students (vertical axis: 0, 2, 4, 6, 8, 10, 12)

Room Types (horizontal axis: Indoor Playground, Theater, Game Room, Computer Room)

98   ninety-eight

Copyright © Macmillan/McGraw-Hill, a division of The McGraw-Hill Companies, Inc.

Suggested Scoring Rubric

4	The student completes the project with accuracy and creativity. The student's report accurately and completely describes the project and is written in clear, concise language including appropriate math terminology.
3	The student completes the project. The student's report has some inaccuracies and uses very little math terminology.
2	The student does not complete all the components of the project. The student's report has some inaccuracies and uses very little math terminology.
1	The student's project is either incomplete or inaccurate. The student's report is inaccurate, incomplete, and contains incorrect or no math terminology.

Transformations

Vocabulary

congruent figures two figures having the same size and the same shape

line of symmetry a line on which a figure can be folded so that its two halves match exactly

point an exact location in space that is represented by a dot

reflection a figure that is flipped over a line to create a mirror image of the figure

rotation rotating a figure about a point

rotational symmetry a figure has rotational symmetry if, after a rotation of the figure about a point, the figure lies in its original position

similar figures that have the same shape but different sizes

transformation a movement of a figure that does not change the size or shape of the figure

translation sliding a figure in a straight line horizontally, vertically, or diagonally

Unit-at-a-Glance

In Unit J, students gain understanding of symmetry, congruence, and transformations.

Activity	Focus	Student Investigation
J-1 Symmetry (pp. 101–102)	Students expand work with symmetry and congruence to include transformations.	Students cut out a figure from construction paper and determine if their figure has line symmetry and/or rotational symmetry.
J-2 Congruence (pp. 103–104)	Students expand work with symmetry and congruence to include transformations.	Students sort figures and explore congruence to find the figure that matches a cutout.
J-3 Rotations, Reflections, and Translations (pp. 105–106)	Students expand work with symmetry and congruence to include transformations.	Students manipulate a figure to explore rotations, reflections, and translations.
Unit Project: Design a Flag (p. 108)	Students relate the concepts and skills they have learned to the real world.	Students use concepts of symmetry, congruence, and transformation to design a flag.

Page Numbers

Each page number is represented by two or three figures that show transformation, congruence, or symmetry.

Guiding Questions

- What transformation do the figures represent?
- Are the figures congruent or similar?
- Do the figures have line or rotational symmetry?

Unit Opener

You can open the unit by having students read through the objectives they will accomplish during the unit. Have students restate objectives in their own words to ensure comprehension.

Scaffolding Questions

What are some ways you can describe a figure? *Sample answers: number of sides, length of sides, number of angles, types of angles*

What is the difference between a rectangle and a square? *A square has 4 sides the same length. A rectangle has 2 pairs of opposite sides the same length.*

Vocabulary

WRITING IN MATH

The beginning of the unit is a great time to start a new wall chart.

Encourage students to write the definitions in their math journals. Writing their own definitions or creating drawings will help internalize the information.

Student Page 100 Guide

Home Letter

Have students take the Home Letter home.

Look at the Projects and Discussions throughout the unit to see if any additional opportunities are available for work at home.

ELL

Encourage students to visit the online eGlossary with parents to see vocabulary in 13 languages.

TeacherWorks *Plus*

See "Home E-mail" as an alternative for communication. From the Lesson Planner, select the e-mail document for this unit, double-click the file, and edit in the Worksheet Editor.

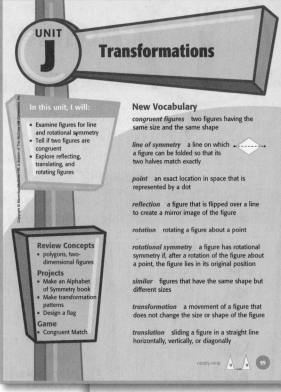

UNIT
J
Transformations

In this unit, I will:
- Examine figures for line and rotational symmetry
- Tell if two figures are congruent
- Explore reflecting, translating, and rotating figures

Review Concepts
- polygons, two-dimensional figures

Projects
- Make an Alphabet of Symmetry book
- Make transformation patterns
- Design a flag

Game
- Congruent Match

New Vocabulary

congruent figures two figures having the same size and the same shape

line of symmetry a line on which a figure can be folded so that its two halves match exactly

point an exact location in space that is represented by a dot

reflection a figure that is flipped over a line to create a mirror image of the figure

rotation rotating a figure about a point

rotational symmetry a figure has rotational symmetry if, after a rotation of the figure about a point, the figure lies in its original position

similar figures that have the same shape but different sizes

transformation a movement of a figure that does not change the size or shape of the figure

translation sliding a figure in a straight line horizontally, vertically, or diagonally

ninety-nine **99**

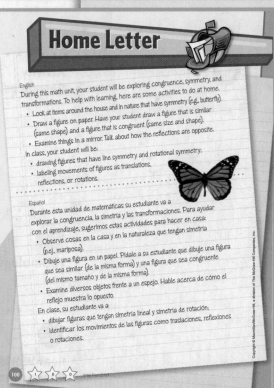

Home Letter

English

During this math unit, your student will be exploring congruence, symmetry, and transformations. To help with learning, here are some activities to do at home.
- Look at items around the house and in nature that have symmetry (e.g., butterfly).
- Draw a figure on paper. Have your student draw a figure that is similar (same shape) and a figure that is congruent (same size and shape).
- Examine things in a mirror. Talk about how the reflections are opposite.

In class, your student will be:
- drawing figures that have line symmetry and rotational symmetry;
- labeling movements of figures as translations, reflections, or rotations.

Español

Durante esta unidad de matemáticas su estudiante va a explorar la congruencia, la simetría y las transformaciones. Para ayudar con el aprendizaje, sugerimos estas actividades para hacer en casa:
- Observe cosas en la casa y en la naturaleza que tengan simetría (p.ej. mariposa).
- Dibuje una figura en un papel. Pídale a su estudiante que dibuje una figura que sea similar (de la misma forma) y una figura que sea congruente (del mismo tamaño y de la misma forma).
- Examine diversos objetos frente a un espejo. Hable acerca de cómo el reflejo muestra lo opuesto.

En clase, su estudiante va a:
- dibujar figuras que tengan simetría lineal y simetría de rotación;
- identificar los movimientos de las figuras como traslaciones, reflexiones o rotaciones.

100 one hundred

UNIT J

Activity Planner

KEY

Real-World Connections	
Projects	
Technology	
CD-ROM	
Math Tool Chest	
Math Adventures	

	Activity J-1 Pacing: 55–75 min	**Activity J-2** Pacing: 50–65 min
Activity/ Objective	**Symmetry** (pp. 101–102) **Objective** Explore line symmetry and rotational symmetry.	**Congruence** (pp. 103–104) **Objective** Determine if two figures are congruent, similar, or neither.
Math Vocabulary	**line of symmetry** **reflection** **rotational symmetry**	**congruent figures** **similar**
Activity Resources	**Materials** construction paper; grid paper; mirrors; scissors; colored pencils; pictures of flags; letter stencils; magazines **Manipulatives** assorted shapes (circles, stars) pattern blocks	**Materials** grid paper construction paper scissors **Manipulatives** pattern blocks
Technology	**Math Tool Chest** Pattern Blocks	**Math Tool Chest** Pattern Blocks **Concepts in Motion**
Real-World Connections		**In Art** Make a picture using congruent and similar figures.
Small Projects	**Alphabet of Symmetry** Make a book to record the letters of the alphabet and determine which letters have symmetry.	

Activity J-3	Pacing: 60–75 min	Unit Project	Pacing: 45 min	
Rotations, Reflections, and Translations (pp. 105–106) **Objective** Explore rotating, reflecting, and translating figures.		**Design a Flag** (p. 108) **Objective** Use concepts learned to solve real-world problems.		**Activity/ Objective**
point transformation rotation translation **Review Vocabulary** flip slide reflection turn				**Math Vocabulary**
Materials construction paper; grid paper or dot paper; rulers or straightedges; scissors; crayons, colored pencils, or markers; tape **Manipulatives** pattern blocks		**Materials** examples of flags; poster board; construction paper; markers; glue; scissors; ruler or straightedge; glitter, string, fabric **Manipulatives** pattern blocks color tiles		**Activity Resources**
Math Tool Chest Pattern Blocks		**Math Tool Chest** Pattern Blocks		**Technology**
				Real-World Connections
Transformation Patterns Make a pattern using transformations.				**Small Projects**

Differentiated Instruction

Below are suggestions on differentiating the materials presented in this unit. Additional modifications should be considered.

Below Level **BL**	Above Level **AL**	English Language Learners **ELL**
ACTIVITY J-1 — **Exercises 7–12** Have students work with an above-level peer to complete these exercises.	**Exercises 7–12** Challenge students to draw figures that have rotational symmetry.	Illustrate the terms *line* and *rotation*. Present items that are in a straight line, such as a yardstick, and items that rotate, such as the hands of a clock.
ACTIVITY J-2 — Have students work in small groups and provide them with tracing paper to help them determine congruency.	**Exercises 8–11** Have students explore other types of polygons. Have them write statements following the forms: "All _____ are similar" or "All _____ are not similar."	Ensure that students understand the terms *congruent* and *similar*. Use illustrations to demonstrate the phrases *same size* and *same shape*.
ACTIVITY J-3 — **Exercises 7–9** Have students work with partners. Provide each pair with tracing paper to trace the original figure and manipulate it. This will help them to determine the transformations shown.	Have one student draw a triangle on a coordinate grid and then translate it to a new location. This student will tell a partner the coordinates of the vertices of the triangle and the translation performed. The partner then works backward to find the original coordinates.	Check students' understanding of direction words, such as *up, down, left, right, vertical,* and *horizontal.* Have students say the word and perform a corresponding action, such as pointing to the right.

Performance-Based Assessment

The Play Area (p. A37)

In *The Play Area,* students first use line symmetry to complete an area. Students then find the area, explain how they figured it out, and draw the shape in different places on the grid.

Connections

The Play Area also covers the following skills and concepts:

- Symmetry
- Area
- Transformational geometry
- Communication

Targeting the Task

- **Pretest** – Use Exercises 1–3 of *The Play Area* to determine students' foundational understanding of line symmetry and area. For those students who do not have this understanding, completing this unit is needed.

- **Formative** – Exercises 1–3 of *The Play Area* may be administered separately during the course of the lessons.

- **Summative** – Administer complete *The Play Area* performance-based assessment.

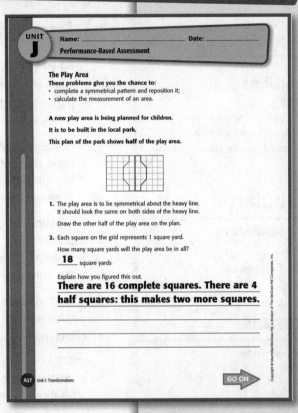

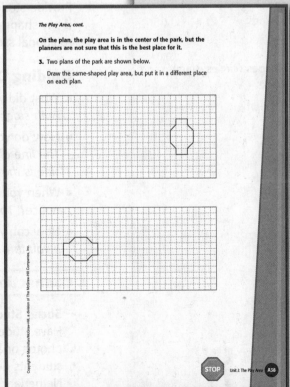

Symmetry

Focus

Connections
Geometry
Students expand work with symmetry and congruence to include transformations.

Vocabulary

line of symmetry
reflection
rotational symmetry

Materials

construction paper
grid paper
mirrors
scissors
colored pencils
pictures of flags
letter stencils
magazines
assorted shapes (circles, stars)
pattern blocks

① **Investigate** (30–40 min)

Exploring Symmetry

Have students work in small groups. Distribute a sheet of construction paper to each student. Ask students how they can use the paper to draw a shape that is the same on the left and right sides.

Guide students to fold the paper in half lengthwise and draw a shape. Have students cut out the shape, ensuring that they do not cut along the fold. After students have unfolded their shapes, discuss their observations. *Both sides are the same.*

Explain that the fold is a line of symmetry and that shapes can have one or more lines of symmetry, or they can have no lines of symmetry. Distribute small mirrors to each group. Have them place the mirror on the line of symmetry and explain what they see.

Next, discuss rotational symmetry. Distribute rectangle pattern blocks. Have students trace the rectangle on grid paper, then turn the rectangle $\frac{1}{4}$ turn (90° angle) and trace the rectangle again. Repeat with a $\frac{1}{2}$ (180°) turn and a $\frac{3}{4}$ (270°) turn. Ask if any of the turned rectangles are the same as the first rectangle. *yes* Explain that the rectangle has rotational symmetry.

Provide students with additional shapes. Have students determine if any shape has more than one line of symmetry, or if any shape has rotational symmetry.

Guiding Questions

- What did you notice about your shape when you unfolded your paper? *Both sides of the fold were the same size and shape.*

- How do you know that a line dividing a shape is a line of symmetry? *The line divides the shape so that both sides are the same, or one side is the mirror image of the other side.*

- When you placed the mirror on the line of symmetry, what did you notice? *The reflection was the same as the half shape.*

- How can you tell if a shape has rotational symmetry? *Sample answer: If you turn the shape and it looks the same, it has rotational symmetry.*

Connections and Extensions

Social Studies
Have students explore state and national flags. Provide students with photos or allow students to use the Internet to locate flags. Have students determine which flags have symmetry (for example, the Netherlands, Germany, France, Japan, and Russia).

② Apply (20–25 min)

Student Page 101 Guide · · · ·

Exercises 1–5
Have students work independently and then share their drawings with the class.

How do you draw a figure that has line symmetry? *Sample answer: Draw half of the figure and then draw the other half to be the mirror image.*

Exercise 6
Have students explore shapes that have rotational symmetry and examine the lines of symmetry the shapes have.

A heart has one line of symmetry. Does it have rotational symmetry? *no*

Draw a figure with two lines of symmetry. Does it also have rotational symmetry? *check students' drawings; yes*

Student Page 102 Guide · · · ·

Exercises 7–12
Have students draw each shape on paper and then cut it out so that they can model each turn.

If a shape has rotational symmetry, what is the least number of positions that would look the same? *2*

Which figures do NOT have rotational symmetry? How do you know? *Exercises 8 and 11; When I turned these figures, they looked different at each $\frac{1}{4}$ (90°) turn.*

 Alphabet of Symmetry
Have students fold and staple together 8 sheets of paper to make a book with 16 pages. Have them title the front cover.

Students should write one letter of the alphabet on the front and back of each page. Use stencils, cutout letters from magazines, or use a computer to print each letter. Have students discuss how handwriting can affect which letters have symmetry.

③ Reflect (5–10 min)

- How do you know if a shape has symmetry? *Sample answer: A shape has symmetry if a line can be drawn that divides the shape into two parts that are mirror images of each other, or if it can be rotated around a point and look the same in at least two positions.*

- Where do you see symmetry around you? Give some examples. *Answers will vary. Sample answers: leaves on trees, faces, flowers, windmills*

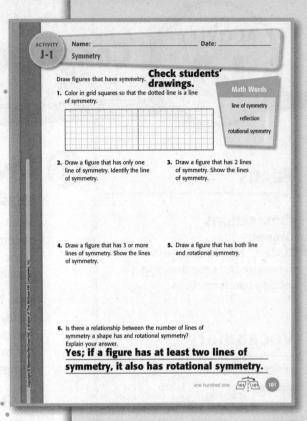

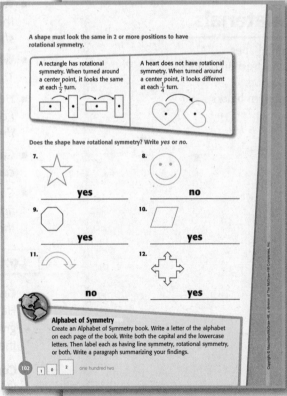

ACTIVITY J-2 Congruence

Focus

Connections
Geometry
Students expand work with symmetry and congruence to include transformations.

Vocabulary

congruent figures
similar

Materials

grid paper
construction paper
scissors
pattern blocks

 Investigate (20–25 min)

Missing Puzzle Piece

Separate students into groups. Provide each group with grid paper and pattern blocks. Have the students trace and cut out a pattern block figure in the center of one of the sheets and then use the other sheets to cut out additional figures that vary in size and shape.

Have the groups switch paper cutouts and figures. The groups sort through the cutouts to find the one that fits the figure. Begin a discussion about how they determined which cutout matched. Relate this to similarity and congruence. Explore congruence and similarity further by examining all the figures.

Guiding Questions

- What did you look for first when trying to find which cutout matched the figure? *Sample answer: I looked for a cutout that was the same shape as the figure.*

- What is true about the matching cutout and figure? *Sample answer: They are congruent. They are the same size and shape.*

- How do you determine if two figures are congruent? *Sample answer: I can place the figures on top of each other. If they match exactly, they are congruent.*

- Can two figures be similar but not congruent? Explain. *Yes; figures can be the same shape but not the same size.*

- Can two figures be congruent but not similar? Explain. *No; if the figures are congruent, then they are also similar, because when they are congruent they are the same size and shape.*

Connections and Extensions · · · · · · · · · · · · · ·

Geometry
Have students work in pairs. Each student draws a polygon with a given number of sides. Then have students examine if the polygons they drew are similar, congruent, or neither.

Congruent Match Game
Have students make a set of 12 number cards that contains 6 pairs of congruent figures. Students shuffle the cards and place them facedown in rows. Players take turns flipping over 2 cards. If the figures drawn on the cards are congruent, the player keeps the cards and flips over 2 more cards. If the figures are not congruent, the cards are turned facedown and the next player takes his or her turn. Play continues until all cards are matched. The player with the most cards wins.

② Apply (25–30 min)

Student Page 103 Guide · · · ·

Exercises 1–4 Have students work independently. Reinforce the definitions of *congruent* and *similar*.	How did you draw a figure that was congruent to the given figure? *Sample answer: I first traced the given figure to make sure the figure I drew was the same size and shape.*
In Art 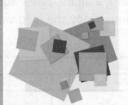	Guide students to first select and draw a figure. Then repeat that figure several times to make a picture. Encourage them to change the size, color, or orientation of the figure to make their designs.

Student Page 104 Guide · · · ·

Exercises 5–7 Have students work with partners and then discuss results in small groups.	In Exercise 5, the first figure is the same size and shape as the figure on the left, but it is positioned differently. Are the two figures congruent? How do you know? *Yes; position does not matter. Two figures are congruent if they are the same size and shape.*
Exercises 8–11 Encourage students to draw pictures to help them answer each question.	Can you draw two triangles that are different shapes? Explain. *Yes; I can draw one triangle with the sides all the same length and another triangle with the sides all different lengths.*

③ Reflect (5–10 min)

- How do you determine if two figures are congruent? similar? *Two figures are congruent if they are the same size and shape. Two figures are similar if they are the same shape.*

- When might it be helpful to know if two figures are congruent? *Sample answers: putting together a puzzle, matching buttons, making a pattern using the same shape, making pictures that are identical*

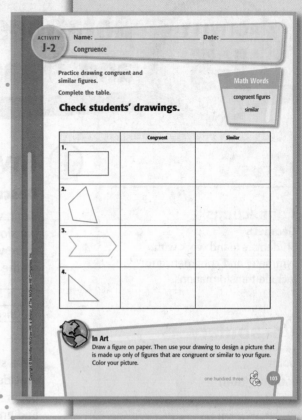

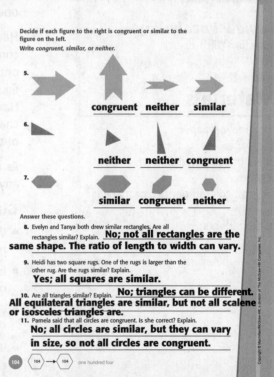

Rotations, Reflections, and Translations

Focus

Connections
Geometry
Students expand work with symmetry and congruence to include transformations.

Vocabulary

point
rotation (turn)
transformation
translation (slide)

Review Vocabulary
reflection (flip)

Materials

construction paper
grid paper
rulers or straightedges
scissors
crayons, colored pencils, or markers
tape
pattern blocks

① Investigate (30–35 min)

Describing Transformations

Begin with a discussion about transformations. Explain to students that transformations are different ways of moving a figure. Have students share what they know about transformations. Copy the following chart on the board.

Transformations			
Original polygon	Rotation (turn)	Reflection (flip)	Translation (slide)

Have students work in groups of 3 or 4. Provide each group with construction paper, pattern blocks, rulers, scissors, and grid paper. Assign each group one of the figures to the right.

Have each group use the pattern blocks to draw their figure on construction paper and then cut it out. Then have them trace the cutout onto grid paper. Students should then rotate, reflect, or translate their figure in different ways and trace the new figures on the same grid paper. Have students tape their transformations in the correct column of the chart. Continue until each group has made at least one of each type of transformation.

As a class, examine the pairs of figures taped in each column. Discuss any patterns students see.

Guiding Questions

- Which type of transformation results in a mirror image of the figure? *reflection or flip*

- How do you describe the direction when rotating a figure? *clockwise or counter-clockwise*

- What changes when you translate (slide) a figure? *the location of the figure*

- What stays the same with all of the transformations? *the size and shape of the figure*

Connections and Extensions ● ● ● ● ● ● ● ● ● ● ● ●

Geometry
Present examples of tessellations. Explain that tessellations are patterns made by transforming a geometric figure or figures. The arrangement made covers a flat surface with no gaps or overlaps. Some figures tessellate while others do not. Have students explore tessellations using pattern blocks. Challenge them to make a tessellation.

Student Page 105 Guide · · · ·

Exercises 1–6
Encourage students to trace the shape and manipulate it to determine the type of transformation.

How can you tell the difference between a reflection and a translation? *Sample answer: A reflection will be a mirror image. In a translation, the figure looks exactly the same, just in a different position.*

Student Page 106 Guide · · · ·

Exercises 7–9
Have students work individually and compare their figures with partners.

Does a vertical reflection line run up and down or side to side? *up and down*

What is different about Exercises 8 and 9 compared to Exercise 7? *I have to make two transformations compared to just one.*

Exercise 10
Provide students with grid paper or dot paper. Have students draw and transform their figures independently and then present their drawings to the class.

Does your figure look the same in any of the transformations? *Answers will vary.*

 Transformation Patterns

Remind students to use only one figure in their patterns. The patterns should be made by reflecting, rotating, or translating their figure.

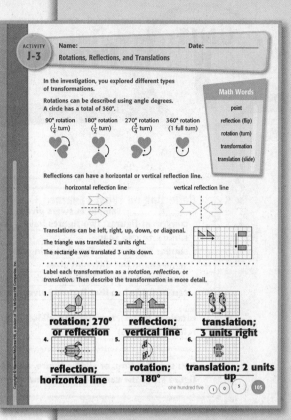

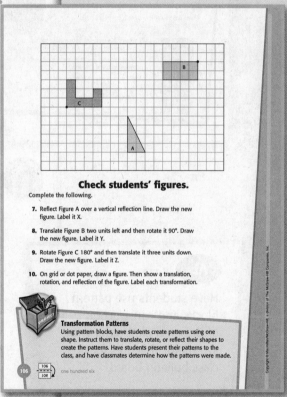

③ **Reflect** (5–10 min)

- What stays the same when you transform a figure? What changes? *The figure's size and shape stay the same; the figure's orientation or position changes.*

- Describe the different types of transformations. *A translation slides a figure in a straight line; a rotation turns a figure around a point; and a reflection flips a figure over a line to make a mirror image.*

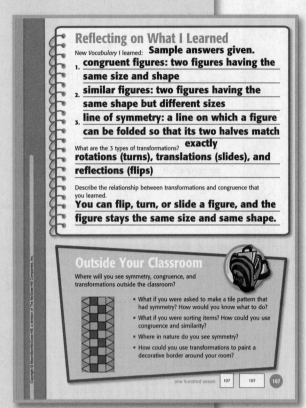

Reflecting on What I Learned

New *Vocabulary* I learned: **Sample answers given.**

1. **congruent figures: two figures having the same size and shape**
2. **similar figures: two figures having the same shape but different sizes**
3. **line of symmetry: a line on which a figure can be folded so that its two halves match exactly**

What are the 3 types of transformations?
rotations (turns), translations (slides), and reflections (flips)

Describe the relationship between transformations and congruence that you learned.
You can flip, turn, or slide a figure, and the figure stays the same size and same shape.

Outside Your Classroom

Where will you see symmetry, congruence, and transformations outside the classroom?

- What if you were asked to make a tile pattern that had symmetry? How would you know what to do?
- What if you were sorting items? How could you use congruence and similarity?
- Where in nature do you see symmetry?
- How could you use transformations to paint a decorative border around your room?

one hundred seven 107 107 107

Vocabulary and Essential Learnings

Vocabulary

- Have students discuss in small groups the vocabulary terms and the definitions that they learned or reviewed in this unit.

- Generate a master list of terms on the board or have students create a Foldable®.

- Have students record three terms of their choice, along with a brief definition or picture for each one.

Essential Learnings

Arrange students in pairs. Have partners review the activities on pages 101 through 106 and discuss what they learned.

Allow time for students to share their essential learnings in small groups or as a class.

Outside Your Classroom

If possible, show examples of a decorative border or nature items that have symmetry or congruence.

Possible student responses:

- *I would make the tile pattern look the same on both sides.*
- *I could put all the items that were similar (the same shape) into one pile and then I could sort the items using congruency. I could group all the items that were the same size and same shape.*
- *Leaves have line symmetry. Flowers have rotational symmetry.*
- *I could make a figure that I want to use in the pattern and then turn it, flip it, or slide it to make the pattern interesting.*

AL

Have students use pattern blocks and construction paper to design a tile border with symmetrical figures for the class bulletin board.

Design a Flag

Materials

examples of flags; poster board; construction paper; markers; glue; scissors; ruler or straightedge; additional craft supplies (glitter, string, fabric); pattern blocks; color tiles

Pacing: 45 min

Introducing the Project

Ask students to think about some flags they have seen. You may wish to have students look at pictures of state flags, country flags, or decorative flags.

Completing the Project

Distribute poster boards and make other materials available to students. Show students photos or actual examples of flags. Have students read the questions in Step 1 and respond to them in small groups.

Encourage students to be creative with their flag designs. Remind them to include the math from the unit. Their flag should have some type of symmetry, have at least one pair of congruent figures, and demonstrate at least one type of transformation.

Extending the Project

Have students make another flag using all of the skills learned in the unit. Have them determine how they can show both types of symmetry, utilize congruent and similar shapes, and incorporate the three types of transformations into their designs. You may also wish to have students analyze flags of other countries and note symmetry, congruence, and transformations on those flags.

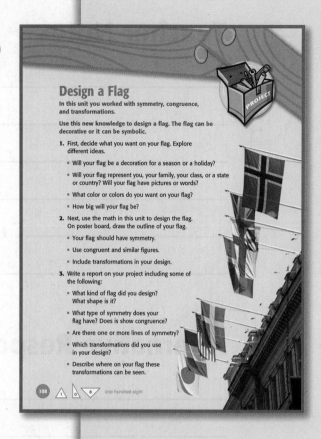

Design a Flag

In this unit you worked with symmetry, congruence, and transformations.

Use this new knowledge to design a flag. The flag can be decorative or it can be symbolic.

1. First, decide what you want on your flag. Explore different ideas.
   - Will your flag be a decoration for a season or a holiday?
   - Will your flag represent you, your family, your class, or a state or country? Will your flag have pictures or words?
   - What color or colors do you want on your flag?
   - How big will your flag be?

2. Next, use the math in this unit to design the flag. On poster board, draw the outline of your flag.
   - Your flag should have symmetry.
   - Use congruent and similar figures.
   - Include transformations in your design.

3. Write a report on your project including some of the following:
   - What kind of flag did you design? What shape is it?
   - What type of symmetry does your flag have? Does is show congruence?
   - Are there one or more lines of symmetry?
   - Which transformations did you use in your design?
   - Describe where on your flag these transformations can be seen.

108 one hundred eight

Suggested Scoring Rubric

4	The student completes the project with accuracy and creativity. The student's report accurately and completely describes the project and is written in clear, concise language including appropriate math terminology.
3	The student completes the project. The student's report has some inaccuracies and uses very little math terminology.
2	The student does not complete all the components of the project. The student's report has some inaccuracies and uses very little math terminology.
1	The student's project is either incomplete or inaccurate. The student's report is inaccurate, incomplete, and contains incorrect or no math terminology.

Teacher Notes

_____

_____

_____

_____

_____

_____

Alternative Responses to Rubric

_____

_____

_____

_____

_____

_____

Ways to Modify or Extend Assessments

_____

_____

_____

_____

_____

Visiting a Theme Park
These problems give you the chance to:
- apply numbers to a practical situation.

Thirteen children and five adults plan to visit a theme park.

**They decide to travel in cars.
Each car takes up to five people.**

1. How many cars will be needed?

_____

Explain how you figured it out.

_____

_____

_____

_____

· ·

John buys two cans of soda for each of the thirteen children and the five adults.

The cans are sold in packs of twelve.

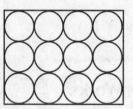

2. How many packs of soda should John buy?

_____

Tell how you figured it out.

_____

_____

_____

_____

Rubric: *Visiting a Theme Park*

The core element of performance required by this task is:

■ apply numbers to a practical situation.

Based on this, credit for specific aspects of performance should be assigned as follows:

Exercises	Points	Section Points
1. Gives correct answer as: **4** cars	2	
Gives an explanation which includes:		
A consideration of **18** people.	1	
Attempts to find the number of cars: divides **18** by **5**.	1	
Accept repeated addition. *Accept alternative correct solutions including diagrams.*		4
2. Gives correct answer as: **3** packs	1	
Shows work which includes:		
Attempts to find the correct number of cans: multiplies the number of people by 2.	1	
Finds the correct number of cans: **36** cans	1	
Attempts to find the correct number of packs: **number of cans ÷ 12.** *Accept alternative correct work.*	1	
		4
Total Points		8

Sample Student Papers

Additional scored sample student work available.

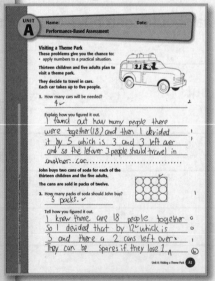

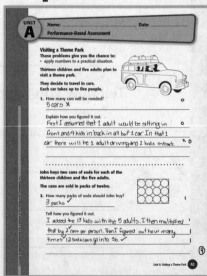

Data-Driven Decision Making

Exercises	Objective	What's the Math?	Error Analysis	Next Steps
1	Apply math to a practical problem	Students use division (or repeated addition).	Students give a whole number and part of a car.	Discuss reasonableness of results.
2	Apply math to a practical problem	Students use multiplication and division.	Students provide number of cans but not packs.	Remind students to read problem carefully.

Transitioning Students to Standardized Test Format

Once the students have mastered the concept of division in the Performance-Based Assessment, you may want to ensure they are familiar with different presentations of the same concept that may appear on a standardized test.

- In division problems, students may drop the remainder when they should add it instead.

- With multi-step problems, students may skip a step or read the problem incorrectly. Drawing a diagram may help students diagnose the problem correctly.

Avoiding Common Errors

- Look at the reasonableness of the answers. Mathematics makes sense and their answers need to as well. Students should be encouraged to read the question carefully and provide an answer that would work to transport 18 people.

- Check the solution to be sure it answers the question asked. This is important in two-step problems where multiplication is needed to work toward the answer but division is needed to answer the question the problem asked. For example: Ten students each need 4 crayons to complete their projects. The crayons come in packages of 8. How many packages of crayons are needed?

Penny has 125 photos. Her photo album has slots for 6 photos on a page. How many pages will she need for her photo album?

A 19 pages

B 20 pages

C 21 pages

D 22 pages

Ms. Rodriguez has 24 students in her homeroom. She has 2 books for each student. The books are in boxes of 6. How many boxes of books will she need?

F 4 boxes

G 8 boxes

H 24 boxes

J 6 boxes

See Chapter Resource Masters for more sample practice test questions.

What's My Rule?

These problems give you the chance to:
- find relationships between two sets of related numbers.

Try to guess my rule.

Ben and Sue are playing a number game.

Sue thinks of a multiplication or division rule. Ben gives Sue a number.

Sue uses her rule and gives Ben the answer. Ben tries to guess Sue's rule.

In Exercises 1–3:

(a) **figure out the missing numbers in the table**

(b) **and write down Sue's rule in words.**

1. a.

Ben's Number	1	2	3	4	10	25		
Sue's Reply	3	6	9	12			24	27

b. _____

_____

2. a.

Ben's Number	2	14	8	22	12	4		
Sue's Reply	1	7	4	11			8	14

b. _____

_____

GO ON

3. a.

Ben's Number	3	10	5	8	9	1		
Sue's Reply	12	40	20	32			28	8

b. _____

_____

4. Write down a multiplication rule or a division rule for Sue to use.

a. _____

_____

b. Fill in the correct numbers in the table below using your rule.

Ben's Number	1	7	4	8	11
Sue's Reply					

STOP

Rubric: *What's My Rule?*

The core element of performance required by this task is:

■ find relationships between two sets of related numbers.

Based on this, credit for specific aspects of performance should be assigned as follows:

Exercises	Points	Section Points
1. a. Gives correct answers: **30, 75**	1	
Gives correct answers: **8, 9**	1	
b. Gives correct answer such as: **Multiply by 3.**	1	
		3
2. a. Gives correct answers: **6, 2**	1	
Gives correct answers: **16, 28**	1	
b. Gives correct answer such as: **Divide by 2.**	1	
		3
3. a. Gives correct answers: **36, 4**	1	
Gives correct answers: **7, 2**	1	
b. Gives correct answer such as: **Multiply by 4.**	1	
		3
4. a. Gives correct rule.	1	
b. Gives correct answers.	2	
Partial credit Gives three correct answers.	(1)	
		3
	Total Points	12

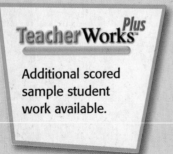

Additional scored sample student work available.

Sample Student Papers

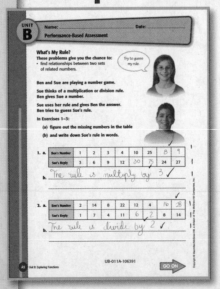

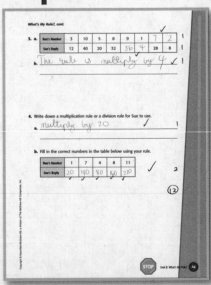

Data-Driven Decision Making

Exercises	Objective	What's the Math?	Error Analysis	Next Steps
1	Exploring relationship between two sets of numbers	Students use multiplication.	Students do not find rule or make mistakes in multiplication.	Make an input/output table for rules such as "multiply by 5," "multiply by 4," or "multiply by 6."
2	Exploring relationship between two sets of numbers	Students use division.	Students do not find rule or make mistakes in division.	Make an input/output table for rules such as "divide by 5," "divide by 4," or "divide by 6."
3	Exploring relationship between two sets of numbers	Students use multiplication.	Students do not find rule or make mistakes in multiplication.	Provide tables for students to complete that show a multiplicative relationship between the numbers.
4	Exploring relationship between two sets of numbers	Students create a relationship between two sets of numbers.	Students do not write a rule or they follow their rule incorrectly.	Have students work in pairs to write a rule and then develop an input/output table. Pairs can exchange tables and find the rule for the other pair's table.

Transitioning Students to Standardized Test Format

Once the students have mastered the concept of finding relationships between two sets of numbers in the *What's My Rule?* assessment, you may want to ensure they are familiar with different presentations of the same concept that may appear on a standardized test.

- Given a table with two sets of numbers, find the relationship.
- Find pairs of numbers to complete an equation (rule).

Avoiding Common Errors

Some students may be able to find the rule and complete the table but have difficulty writing or expressing the rule. Start with tables where the rule is easy to find and have students volunteer to tell what the rule is. Do this several times and then move to writing the rule.

Look at the table below. What rule does the table follow as it moves numbers from "Input" to "Output"?

RULE: ?	
Input	**Output**
1	6
3	18
5	30
7	42

A add 5

B multiply by 12

C add 12

D multiply by 6

Which pair of numbers correctly completes this equation?

$$\bigcirc \times 10 = \square$$

F 5 and 50

G 6 and 9

H 2 and 200

J 3 and 15

See Chapter Resource Masters for more sample practice test questions.

Teacher Notes

_____

_____

_____

_____

_____

_____

Alternative Responses to Rubric

_____

_____

_____

_____

_____

_____

Ways to Modify or Extend Assessments

_____

_____

_____

_____

_____

Brick Wall

This problem gives you a chance to:
- choose a good strategy to estimate a number.

The picture shows a brick wall partly hidden by a car parked in front of it.

1. Estimate how many bricks there are in the wall.

_____

Explain how you got your answer.

_____

_____

_____

_____

Rubric: *Brick Wall*

The core element of performance required by this task is:

■ choose a good strategy to estimate a number.

Based on this, credit for specific aspects of performance should be assigned as follows:

Exercises	Points	Section Points
1. Gives an acceptable estimate between **1,000** and **2,000**.	2	
Partial credit: Gives an estimate more than **500** and less than **1,000**.	(1)	
or Gives an estimate more than **2,000** and less than **2,500**.	**or** (1)	2
Gives a correct explanation such as: Uses a multiplication method, for example: There are about 40 bricks in a row	1	
and about 40 rows	1	
so there are about 40 × 40 = 1,600 bricks. *Accept repeated addition.*	1	
or Uses a systematic grouping and counting. For example: Divides the wall into a number of equal groups	**or** 1	
and finds the number in each group.	1	
Multiplies the number in each group by the number of groups.	1	
		3
Total Points		5

Sample Student Papers

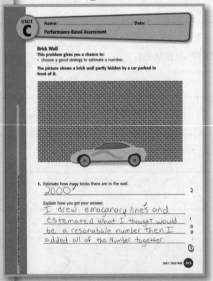

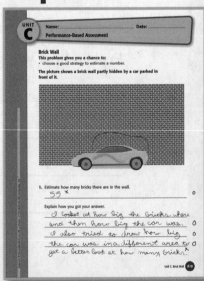

Data-Driven Decision Making

Exercises	Objective	What's the Math?	Error Analysis	Next Steps
1	Use strategy to estimate.	Students should use estimation.	Students try to calculate exactly.	Practice multiplying by multiples of 10.

Transitioning Students to Standardized Test Format

Once the students have demonstrated strategies for estimation in the *Brick Wall,* you may want to ensure they are familiar with different presentations of estimation that may appear on a standardized test.

- Make an estimate based on time. Student may estimate the number provided in the problem.
- Make an estimate in different contexts.

Avoiding Common Errors

- It's important for students to know that every answer to a mathematics problem does not have to be exact. Give students practice estimating to the highest place value, determining if the number is more or less than half way to the next rounded number. For example, 73 is between 70 and 80. 75 is half way. Since 73 is less than half, it is closer to 70.
- Secondly, multiplying by multiples of ten becomes extremely important when rounding to the highest place. Practice for this skill can take the form of building arrays with base-ten blocks or playing games that involve multiplying tens or hundreds.

A roller coaster at an amusement park runs 21 times every half hour. About how many times does the ride run each hour?

- **A** 20 times
- **B** 30 times
- **C** 40 times
- **D** 50 times

Linda has 443 pennies. She wants to put them into rolls of 50 each. About how many rolls will she need?

- **F** 9 rolls
- **G** 10 rolls
- **H** 11 rolls
- **J** 12 rolls

See Chapter Resource Masters for more sample practice test questions.

Teacher Notes

_____

_____

_____

_____

_____

Alternative Responses to Rubric

_____

_____

_____

_____

_____

Ways to Modify or Extend Assessments

_____

_____

_____

_____

_____

Fractions

These problems give you the chance to:

- work with fractions, with equivalence, and with comparison of size.

Tom has four number cards.

1. He arranges his four cards to make fractions less than 1. Using each number card only once, make two fractions that have the same value.

2. Find a way to use two of the number cards to make a fraction less than $\frac{1}{2}$.

3. Find two ways to use two of the numbers cards to make a fraction between $\frac{1}{2}$ and 1.

Rubric: *Fractions*

The core element of performance required by this task is:

- work with fractions, with equivalence and comparison of size.

Based on this, credit for specific aspects of performance should be assigned as follows:

Exercises	Points	Section Points
1. Gives correct answer as: $\dfrac{3}{6}$ and $\dfrac{4}{8}$ or $\dfrac{3}{4}$ and $\dfrac{6}{8}$	2 or 2	
		2
2. Gives correct answer as: $\dfrac{3}{8}$	1	
		1
3. Gives two of the three possible correct answers below: $\dfrac{3}{4}, \dfrac{4}{6}, \dfrac{6}{8}$ *Allow 1 point for each correct response up to a maximum of 2 points.*	2×1	2
	Total Points	5

Sample Student Papers

Additional scored sample student work available.

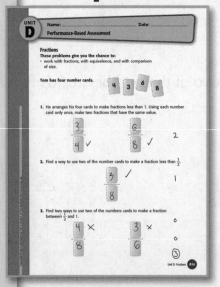

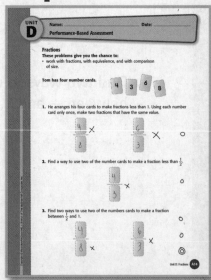

Data-Driven Decision Making

Exercises	Objective	What's the Math?	Error Analysis	Next Steps
1	Exploring fractions less than 1	Students should find equivalent fractions.	Students make fractions less than 1 but not equal to each other. Students do not make a fraction less than 1.	Sort fraction pieces into groups of less than 1 and equal to 1. Have students draw two rectangles (the same size) on grid paper. Shade fractional amounts to show equivalence.
2	Exploring fractions less than $\frac{1}{2}$	Students should identify fractions less than $\frac{1}{2}$.	Students do not make a fraction less than $\frac{1}{2}$.	Sort fraction pieces into groups of less than $\frac{1}{2}$, equal to $\frac{1}{2}$, and greater than $\frac{1}{2}$. Have students fold paper in $\frac{1}{2}$ and then again and again to find examples of fractions less than $\frac{1}{2}$.
3	Exploring fractions between $\frac{1}{2}$ and 1	Students should find equivalent fractions between $\frac{1}{2}$ and 1.	Students make fractions equal to $\frac{1}{2}$, less than $\frac{1}{2}$, or greater than 1.	Create fractions with manipulatives that are in between $\frac{1}{2}$ and 1.

Transitioning Students to Standardized Test Format

Once the students have mastered the concepts of fractions less than 1 and equivalence of fractions in the *Fractions* assessment, you may want to familiarize them with a different presentation of the same concepts that may appear in a standardized test.

- Find the equivalent fraction with a shaded diagram.
- Determine equivalence from a model.

Avoiding Common Errors

- Start with fractions that can easily be created by paper folding or that may be part of a manufactured kit so that students can connect the symbol to the quantity.
- Have students sort fractions into groups of less than $\frac{1}{2}$, exactly $\frac{1}{2}$, between $\frac{1}{2}$ and 1, exactly 1, and more than 1. Pay attention to the patterns these numbers make and generalize them to fractions outside the kit.
- Use a number line to show fractions less than 1 and equivalent fractions.

Santos answered 8 out of 10 questions on a quiz correctly. Which fraction is equivalent to $\frac{8}{10}$?

A $\frac{4}{5}$ B $\frac{3}{4}$

C $\frac{5}{6}$ D $\frac{2}{3}$

Which expression is shown by the model?

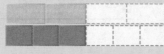

F $\frac{2}{4} = \frac{3}{6}$ G $\frac{2}{4} > \frac{3}{6}$

H $\frac{2}{4} < \frac{3}{6}$ J $\frac{2}{4} + \frac{3}{6}$

See Chapter Resource Masters for more sample practice test questions.

Teacher Notes

_____

_____

_____

_____

_____

Alternative Responses to Rubric

_____

_____

_____

_____

_____

Ways to Modify or Extend Assessments

_____

_____

_____

_____

_____

Name: _____ Date: _____

Performance-Based Assessment

On the Line

These problems give you the chance to:
- represent simple fractions and decimals on a number line;
- explain the meaning of a decimal digit.

Here is a number line.

1. Draw arrows to show where each value in the box should go.
   Three of the boxes have already been done for you.

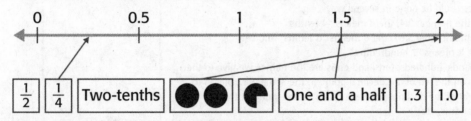

2. Your friend finds it hard to understand decimals.
   She asks, "In a number like 2.4, what does the 4 really mean?"
   Write a note that will help her .

   _____

   _____

   _____

   _____

   _____

   _____

Rubric: *On the Line*

The core elements of performance required by this task are:

- represent simple fractions and decimals on a number line;
- explain the meaning of a decimal digit.

Based on these, credit for specific aspects of performance should be assigned as follows:

Exercises	Points	Section Points
1.  *Allow one point for each correct arrow up to a maximum of 5 points.*	5 × 1	
		5
2. This could be done in several ways, e.g.: In the number 2.4, the 4 means "4 tenths." In the number 3.67, the 6 means "6 tenths" and the 7 means "7 hundredths." Thousands, hundreds, tens, and ones are the names we give to the places on the left of the decimal point. In the same way, places to the right of the decimal point are called tenths, hundredths, thousandths, etc.	1	
		1
	Total Points	6

. . . .

Sample Student Papers

Teacher Works™ Plus

Additional scored sample student work available.

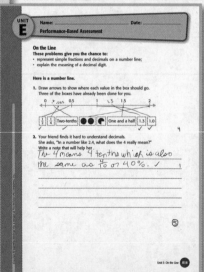

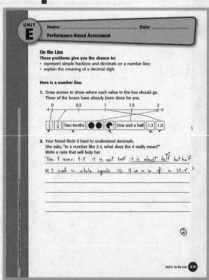

Data-Driven Decision Making

Exercises	Objective	What's the Math?	Error Analysis	Next Steps
1	Exploring fractions and decimal numbers	Students should place fractions and decimal numbers on a number line.	Students can't convert fractions to decimals.	Use manipulatives to practice placing benchmark fractions and decimals on a number line.
2	Explaining a decimal number	Students should interpret the number to the right of the decimal point.	Students misinterpret place value of the decimal.	Use base blocks to build decimals to reinforce place value.

Transitioning Students to Standardized Test Format

Once the students have mastered the meaning and relationship of fractions and decimal numbers in the *On the Line* assessment, you may want to familiarize them with different presentations of the same concepts that may appear on a standardized test.

- Find a point on a number line.
- Find a decimal representation of a point on the number line.

Avoiding Common Errors

- Use base-ten blocks and a place-value mat to build decimals and connect to decimal words and symbols.
- For fraction-to-decimal conversions, use paper folding to practice putting benchmark fractions of 0, $\frac{1}{4}$ (0.25), $\frac{1}{2}$ (.5), $\frac{3}{4}$ (0.75), and 1 (1.00) on a number line.
- Practice drawing and building multiple representations of fractions and decimals, including number words, pictures, and symbols.

Megan's dog is $3\frac{1}{2}$ years old. Which point best represents $3\frac{1}{2}$ on the number line?

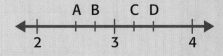

A Point A

B Point B

C Point C

D Point D

On the number line below, what number does point M represent?

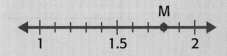

F 1.8

G 1.2

H 1.88

J 1.6

See Chapter Resource Masters for more sample practice test questions.

Lengthy Rectangles

These problems give you the chance to:
- draw a rectangle when given perimeter;
- find side length, perimeter and area.

This rectangle has a perimeter of 18 centimeters.

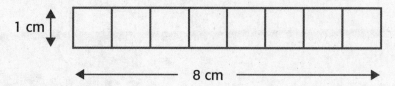

1 cm

8 cm

1. Use this grid to draw 3 different sizes of rectangles, each with a perimeter of 18 centimeters.

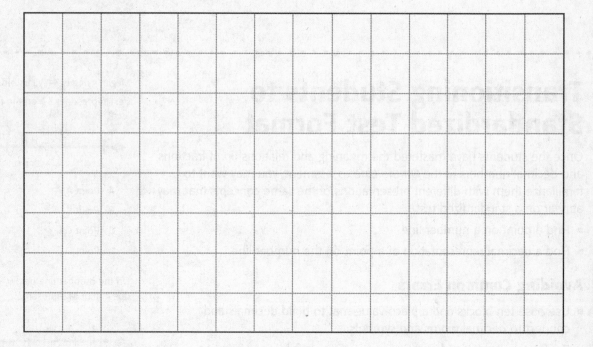

2. Write the dimensions of the rectangle with the largest area and perimeter of 18.

Length _____

Width _____

GO ON

3. Mary cut out a rectangle with a **perimeter** of 20 centimeters. Part of it ripped off. One side was 4 centimeters.

What was the length of the other side? _____

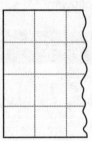

4. Liz cut out a rectangle that had an **area** of 24 square centimeters. Part of it ripped off. One side was 3 centimeters.

What was the length of the other side? _____

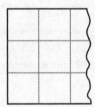

5. What is the perimeter of this shape? _____

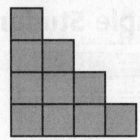

STOP

Rubric: *Lengthy Rectangles*

The core elements of performance required by this task are:

- draw a rectangle when given perimeter;
- find side length, perimeter and area.

Based on these, credit for specific aspects of performance should be assigned as follows:

Exercises	Points	Section Points
1. Draws correct rectangles: sides **7** and **2**	1	
sides **6** and **3**	1	
sides **5** and **4**	1	
with no extras.		
		3
2. Gives correct answer: **5, 4** or **4, 5**	1	1
3. Gives correct answer: **6** cm	1	1
4. Gives correct answer: **8** cm	1	1
5. Gives correct answer: **16** cm	1	1
	Total Points	7

Sample Student Papers

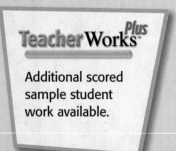

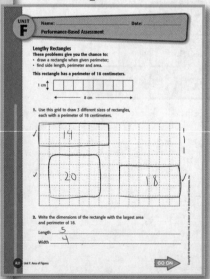

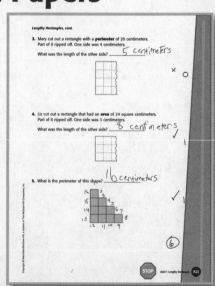

Data-Driven Decision Making

Exercises	Objective	What's the Math?	Error Analysis	Next Steps
1	Exploring perimeter	Students should create different rectangles with the same perimeter.	Students create rectangles with the same area and/or various perimeters.	Review meaning of perimeter and area. Use vocabulary in context.
2	Exploring relationship between perimeter and area	Students should find the rectangle with the largest area.	Students find area but not the largest.	Review finding area of rectangles on a grid.
3	Exploring perimeter	Students should find the length of a side knowing the perimeter and one side.	Students indicate twice the length of the side.	Review properties of rectangles and meaning of perimeter.
4	Exploring perimeter	Students should find the perimeter of a shape on a grid.	Students indicate twice the length of the side.	Review properties of rectangles and meaning of area.
5	Exploring perimeter	Students should find the perimeter of a shape on a grid.	Students find area or do not count the 2 sides of the squares in the corners.	Review meaning of perimeter and area.

Transitioning Students to Standardized Test Format

Once the students have mastered the concept of perimeter in the *Lengthy Rectangles* performance-based assessment, you many want to ensure they are familiar with different presentations of the same concept that may appear on a standardized test.

- Length is indicated in the labeling and students must determine perimeter. Understanding of the meaning of perimeter is needed to answer the question.

- The perimeter and the length of one side is provided. Students must find the length of the side not given.

Avoiding Common Errors

- Use tiles to have students build rectangles. Demonstrate how to count perimeter, paying special attention to the corners.

- Use string to measure around rectangles or faces of prisms to illustrate that perimeter is length (around) and not area.

- Encourage students to devise a way to keep track of counting perimeter on paper, such as making tick marks on the edges or highlighting each side with a colored pencil.

- Help students be organized in finding solutions, perhaps in a T or rate table, so they see the pattern (as length increases, width decreases).

Mr. Johnson bought 84 ft of fencing for his rectangular garden. What are the dimensions of his garden if one side is 12 ft?

A 12 ft by 30 ft

B 12 ft by 7 ft

C 7 ft by 8 ft

D 12 ft by 8 ft

What is the area of the room with dimensions shown below?

24 ft

13 ft

F 37 ft

G 312 ft

H 74 ft

J 288 ft

See Chapter Resource Masters for more sample practice test questions.

The School Bus
These problems give you the chance to:
- calculate times from trip information;
- explain your method.

Terri catches the school bus every morning at 8 o'clock. Donna gets on the bus 15 minutes later than Terri. The bus arrives at school three-quarters ($\frac{3}{4}$) of an hour after Donna gets on.

1. At what time does Donna get on the bus?

_____

2. At what time does the bus arrive at the school?

_____

3. When Terri gets on the bus, it has already been picking up children for half an hour. How long does the bus take to make the complete trip?

_____

GO ON

Explain how you figured out the answer to this last question.

_____

_____

_____

_____

_____

The school bus takes the same amount of time to take students from school to their homes in the afternoon as it does to take them to school in the morning.

Donna arrives home from school at 4 o'clock.

4. At what time does Terri arrive home from school?

_____

5. At what time does the bus leave the school?

_____

6. At what time does the last student get off the bus?

_____

STOP

Rubric: *The School Bus*

The core elements of performance required by this task are:

- calculate times from trip information;
- explain your method.

Based on these, credit for specific aspects of performance should be assigned as follows:

Exercises	Points	Section Points
1. Gives correct answer as: **8:15 A.M./a quarter past 8**	1	
		1
2. Gives correct answer as: The bus arrives at school at **9 A.M.** *(accept 9 o'clock or 9:00)*	1	
		1
3. Gives correct answer as: $1\frac{1}{2}$ **hours/1 hour and 30 minutes /90 minutes.** *(accept 1:30)*	1	
Gives explanation such as: The bus starts 30 minutes before Terri gets on the bus at 8 o'clock. It travels for 15 minutes before Donna gets on, and then continues for another 45 minutes. 30 minutes + 15 minutes + 45 minutes = 90 minutes = $1\frac{1}{2}$ hours.	2	
Partial credit: Allow 1 point for a partially correct explanation.	(1)	3
4. Gives correct answer as: **4:15 P.M./a quarter past 4**	1	
		1
5. Gives correct answer as: **3:15 P.M./a quarter past 3**	1	
		1
6. Gives correct answer as: **4:45 P.M./a quarter to 5**	1	
		1
	Total Points	8

Sample Student Papers

Additional scored sample student work available.

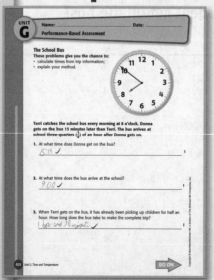

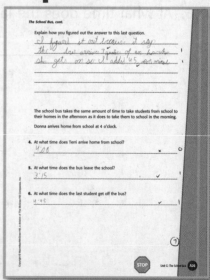

Data-Driven Decision Making

Exercises	Objective	What's the Math?	Error Analysis	Next Steps
1	Exploring time	Students add times.	Students subtract 15 minutes.	Demonstrate with clock face time 8:00, 8:15, etc.
2	Exploring time	Students add times.	Students add 45 minutes to 8 A.M.	Have students make a table with a column for time and a column for events. Use the table to keep track of when events occur.
3	Exploring time	Students determine elapsed times.	Students do not include time for bus before picking up students.	Identify the starting point for keeping track of time.
4	Exploring time	Students determine arrival time home (addition).	Students subtract 15 minutes.	Distinguish between going back in time and going forward in time.
5	Exploring time	Students determine start time.	Students add an hour.	Find the starting point going back in time.
6	Exploring time	Students determine end time.	Students miscalculate.	Review use of quarter hours.

Transitioning Students to Standardized Test Format

Once the students understand the meaning of operations in *The School Bus* assessment, you may want to familiarize them with some presentations that they may see on a standardized test.

- Find what additional information is needed to answer a time-related question.
- Find the time for a prior event given the time for a current event.

Avoiding Common Errors

Students may confuse "quarter hour" with 25 cents (a quarter) and want to say a "quarter hour" is 25 minutes. Have students draw a circle and divide it into quarters. Mark 12, 3, 6, and 9 to show the quarter hours. Ask how could you find the number of quarter hours in 8 hours? How could you find the number of half hours in 8 hours?

Percy is flying to his grandparent's house. It takes 25 minutes to drive to the airport. He needs to arrive at least 1 hour before his plane leaves. What other information is needed for Percy to arrive at the airport on time?

- **A** the time the plane leaves
- **B** how fast he drives
- **C** the distance he will fly
- **D** the amount of time he will fly

Hannah's reading class begins at the time shown. This is 1 hour 30 minutes after school begins. At what time does school begin?

- **F** 8:30
- **G** 8:45
- **H** 9:00
- **J** 9:15

See Chapter Resource Masters for more sample practice test questions.

Teacher Notes

_____

_____

_____

_____

_____

_____

Alternative Responses to Rubric

_____

_____

_____

_____

_____

_____

Ways to Modify or Extend Assessments

_____

_____

_____

_____

_____

Name: _____ Date: _____

Performance-Based Assessment

Rectangle
These problems give you the chance to:
- measure a rectangle and calculate its area and perimeter.

Here is a rectangle.

1. Measure the length and the width of the rectangle in centimeters.

The length is _____ centimeters.

The width is _____ centimeters.

2. The area of the rectangle is _____ square centimeters.

Show how you figured it out.

3. The perimeter of the rectangle is _____ centimeters.

Show how you figured it out.

Rubric: *Rectangle*

The core element of performance required by this task is:

- measure a rectangle and calculate its area and perimeter.

Based on this, credit for specific aspects of performance should be assigned as follows:

Exercises	Points	Section Points
1. Gives the correct length and width of the rectangle as: Length = **9** centimeters (± 0.5 centimeters)	1	
Width = **5** centimeters (± 0.5 centimeters)	1	
		2
2. Gives correct answer as: **45** square centimeters	2	
Shows work such as: **9 × 5** or equivalent.	1	
or Shows the rectangle divided into 45 one-centimeter squares.	**or** 1	
		3
3. Gives correct answer as: **28** centimeters	1	
Shows work such as: **9 + 5 + 9 + 5**	1	
		2
	Total Points	7

- -

Sample Student Papers

Additional scored sample student work available.

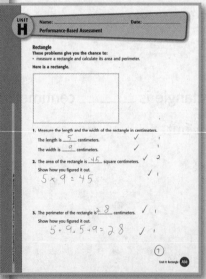

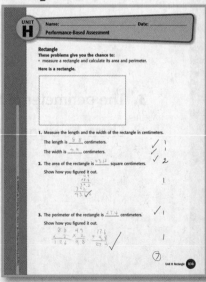

Data-Driven Decision Making

Exercises	Objective	What's the Math?	Error Analysis	Next Steps
1	Using a ruler	Students should understand measurement.	Students measure incorrectly. Students use wrong unit to measure.	Remind students to measure from 0, not from the edge of the ruler. Give students more practice with centimeters and inches.
2	Exploring area	Students should understand how to find area.	Students find perimeter.	Use color tiles to cover various shapes and find the area.
3	Exploring perimeter	Students should understand how to find perimeter.	Students find area.	Use string to go around shapes and then measure the length of the string on a ruler.

Transitioning Students to Standardized Test Format

Once the students have mastered using rulers to find area and perimeter in the *Rectangle* assessment, you may want to ensure that they are familiar with different presentations of the same concepts that may appear on a standardized test.

- Find the area of a shape on a grid.
- Find the perimeter when the dimensions are given.

Avoiding Common Errors

- A common cause for measuring incorrectly is misuse of the ruler. Students need to know to start at zero, not necessarily at the end of the ruler. Measuring takes practice. Provide several cutouts of construction paper and have students measure the length and width with a ruler. Cover the shapes with color tiles to practice finding area; lay string around the sides to estimate perimeter.

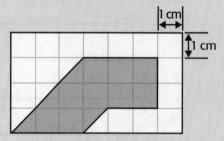

What is the area of the shaded figure?

A 9 square centimeters

B 11 square centimeters

C 13 square centimeters

D 14 square centimeters

Sam is building a deck behind his house. When completed, the deck will be 16 feet long and 21 feet wide. What is the perimeter of the deck?

F 58 feet

G 42 feet

H 37 feet

J 74 feet

See Chapter Resource Masters for more sample practice test questions.

Teacher Notes

_____
_____
_____
_____
_____
_____
_____

Alternative Responses to Rubric

_____
_____
_____
_____
_____
_____
_____

Ways to Modify or Extend Assessments

_____
_____
_____
_____
_____
_____

Name: _____ Date: _____

Performance-Based Assessment

Shells

These problems give you the chance to:
• complete and interpret a bar graph.

This graph shows how many shells a group of students collected at the beach.

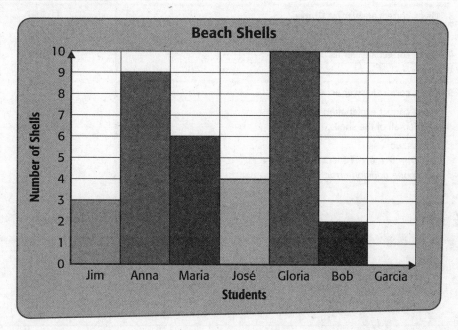

1. Garcia collected 7 shells. Show this on the graph.

2. How many shells did José collect? _____

3. Which student collected the most shells? _____

4. How many more shells did Anna collect than Maria? _____

5. How many shells did the students collect in all? _____

Explain how you figured it out and show your calculations.

_____

_____

_____

Rubric: *Shells*

The core element of performance required by this task is:

■ complete and interpret a bar graph.

Based on this, credit for specific aspects of performance should be assigned as follows:

Exercises	Points	Section Points
1. Fills in a bar height of 7 above the name Garcia.	1	
		1
2. Gives correct answer as: **4 shells**	1	
		1
3. Gives correct answer as: **Gloria**	1	
		1
4. Gives correct answer as: **3 shells**	1	
		1
5. Gives correct answer as: **41 shells**	1	
Gives correct explanation such as: I added all of the shells.	1	
Shows work as: $3 + 9 + 6 + 4 + 10 + 2 + 7$ *Allow one addition error.*	1	
		3
	Total Points	7

- -

Sample Student Papers

TeacherWorks™ *Plus*

Additional scored sample student work available.

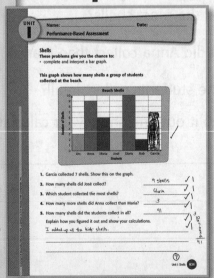

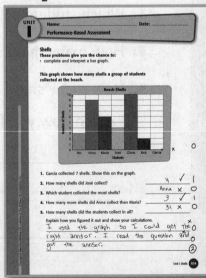

Data-Driven Decision Making

Exercises	Objective	What's the Math?	Error Analysis	Next Steps
1	Exploring graphs	Students make an entry.	Students add information to another student's entry.	Review how to record data on a graph.
2	Exploring graphs	Students interpret a graph.	Students read a different student's entry.	Distinguish between the *y*-axis and the *x*-axis and their labels.
3	Exploring graphs	Students interpret a graph.	Students select entry that is not the "most."	Identify what data the graph communicates.
4	Exploring graphs	Students interpret a graph and subtract.	Students use incorrect data or subtract incorrectly.	Review what data the bars on a graph represent.
5	Exploring graphs	Students interpret a graph and add.	Students omit one or more entries and/or add incorrectly.	Estimate answers to check for reasonableness.

Transitioning Students to Standardized Test Format

Once the students have mastered the concept of completing and interpreting a bar graph in the *Shells* assessment, you may want to ensure they are familiar with different presentations of the same concept that may appear on a standardized test.

- Interpret the information displayed in a graph.
- Solve a problem with information gathered from interpreting a graph.

Avoiding Common Errors

Review vocabulary and meaning for graphs (e.g., *x*-axis, *y*-axis, and bar graphs). Have students build their own bar graphs on grid paper. For example, in Mr. Smith's class 12 students have a dog as a pet, 9 students have a cat as a pet, and 4 students have a hamster. Show the number of students on the *y*-axis and kinds of pets on the *x*-axis.

Ray made a bar graph to show how many pies have been sold at a bake sale. How many more apple pies have been sold than pumpkin pies?

A 1 pie

B 3 pies

C 12 pies

D 14 pies

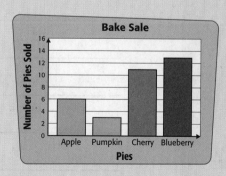

See Chapter Resource Masters for more sample practice test questions.

Name: _____   **Date:** _____

Performance-Based Assessment

The Play Area
These problems give you the chance to:
- complete a symmetrical pattern and reposition it;
- calculate the measurement of an area.

A new play area is being planned for children.

It is to be built in the local park.

This plan of the park shows half of the play area.

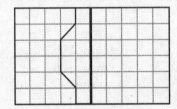

1. The play area is to be symmetrical about the heavy line.
   It should look the same on both sides of the heavy line.

   Draw the other half of the play area on the plan.

2. Each square on the grid represents 1 square yard.

   How many square yards will the play area be in all?

   _____ square yards

   Explain how you figured this out.

   _____

   _____

   _____

   _____

GO ON

On the plan, the play area is in the center of the park, but the planners are not sure that this is the best place for it.

3. Two plans of the park are shown below.

Draw the same-shaped play area, but put it in a different place on each plan.

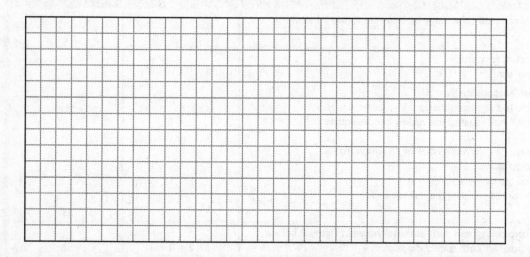

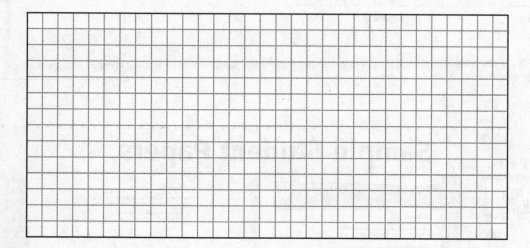

Rubric: *The Play Area*

The core elements of performance required by this task are:

- complete a symmetrical pattern and reposition it;
- calculate the measurement of an area.

Based on these, credit for specific aspects of performance should be assigned as follows:

Exercises	Points	Section Points
1. Correctly completes the shape as shown in Figure 1 below.	2	
		2
2. Gives correct answer as: **18** square yards	1	
Gives explanations such as: There are 16 complete squares. There are 4 half squares: this makes 2 more squares. **or** *Dependent on a correct answer of 18 square yards,* *the student states:* I counted the whole squares. Makes sense of counting the half squares.	2 **or** 2	
		3
3. Draws correct diagrams such as those shown in Figure 2 below. *Allow 1 point for each correct diagram.*	2 × 1	2
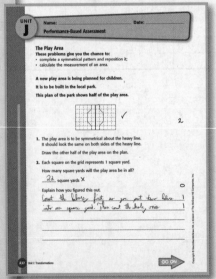 **Figure 1** **Figure 2**		
	Total Points	7

Sample Student Papers

Additional scored sample student work available.

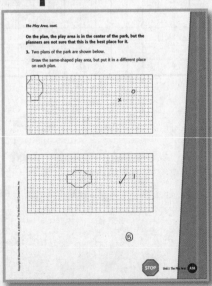

Data-Driven Decision Making

Exercises	Objective	What's the Math?	Error Analysis	Next Steps
1	Explore symmetry	Students complete a shape given half the shape.	Students draw picture incorrectly.	Have students use pattern blocks to make simple shapes and practice building the other half of the design.
2	Explore area	Students determine area.	Students do not count half spaces, or count them as one whole space.	Have students practice cutting squares and rectangles into triangles to see they're one-half.
3	Explore transformations	Students locate shape in different places on the grid.	Students draw play area in the same place as in the example.	Have students practice with transformations other than reflection.

Transitioning Students to Standardized Test Format

Once the students have mastered the concepts of symmetry and area in *The Play Area,* you may want to ensure they are familiar with different presentations of the same concepts that may appear on a standardized test.

- Find the lines of symmetry for a given shape.
- Determine the area of a shape given the dimensions.

Avoiding Common Errors

- Transformational symmetry includes: translations (slides), reflections (flips), and rotations (turns). Provide students with hands-on experience or dynamic software experience with sliding, flipping, and turning shapes and designs.

- Have students build small designs with pattern blocks on their desks, then replicate the designs on sheets of paper. Have them slide their papers to different locations on their desks. What changes? What doesn't? Have them turn their papers 90 degrees to see the rotation. How do their designs look different from the ones built on their desks?

- Reflections can be illustrated by each student making a "mirror" partner. Be sure students notice that everything they do is the OPPOSITE in the mirror partner.

- Paper folding or the use of reflective mirrors can assist in understanding reflection.

How many lines of symmetry does this shape have?

A 2 lines

B 3 lines

C 4 lines

D 5 lines

A vegetable garden is 9 yards long and 35 yards wide. What is the area of the garden in square yards?

F 98 sq yd

G 305 sq yd

H 315 sq yd

J 630 sq yd

See Chapter Resource Masters for more sample practice test questions.

Notes

_____

_____

_____

_____

_____

_____

_____

_____

_____

_____

_____

_____

_____

_____

_____

_____

_____

_____

_____

_____

_____

_____

_____

_____

UNIT A

Multiplication and Division

In this unit, I will:

- Use area models and lattice multiplication
- Find the relationship between factors and multiples
- Use multiplication to check division
- Interpret the remainder

Review Concepts
- multiplication, division, area

Projects
- Rolling a Divisor
- Planning a Bowling Party

Game
- "Buzz" Multiple Game

New Vocabulary

divide (division)   an operation on two numbers in which the first number is split into the same number of equal groups as the second number

$$
\begin{array}{r}
\text{quotient} \longrightarrow\ 6\ \text{R1} \longleftarrow \text{remainder} \\
\text{divisor} \longrightarrow 3\overline{)19} \longleftarrow \text{dividend} \\
-18 \\
\hline
1
\end{array}
$$

factor   a number that divides a whole number evenly; a number that is multiplied by another number

multiple   a multiple of a number is the *product* of that number and any whole number; 15 is a multiple of 5 because $3 \times 5 = 15$

multiply (multiplication)   an operation on numbers to find their product; it can be thought of as repeated addition

product   the answer to or result of a multiplication problem; it also refers to expressing a number as the product of its factors

Home Letter

English

During this math unit, your student will be exploring different strategies to solve multiplication and division problems. To help with learning, here are things to do at home.

- Talk about how you know whether to divide or multiply in everyday situations (for example: when grocery shopping, you would divide to find out how much one yogurt costs in a pack of 6 yogurts; when ordering pizza, you would multiply the number of slices everyone wants by the number of people).
- Talk about situations in which it is necessary to interpret a remainder (for example: sharing a pizza, deciding how many cars are needed for a family trip, dividing money).

Español

Durante esta unidad de matemáticas, su estudiante va a explorar distintas estrategias para resolver problemas de multiplicación y división. Para ayudar con el aprendizaje, sugerimos estas actividades para hacer en casa:

- Hable de cómo se sabe si hay que dividir o multiplicar en situaciones comunes de la vida diaria (por ejemplo: cuando se compran alimentos, hay que dividir para saber cuánto cuesta un yogurt en un paquete de seis; cuando se pide pizza, hay que multiplicar el número de rebanadas que cada persona desea por el número de personas que hay).
- Hable acerca de situaciones en las que es necesario interpretar un residuo (por ejemplo: al compartir una pizza, al decidir cuántos automóviles se necesitan para un viaje familiar, al dividir dinero).

Name: _____ Date: _____

Multiplication Strategies

In the investigation, you learned how to use an area model and lattice multiplication to find products. Use these new strategies to find more products.

Math Words

area

multiply
(multiplication)

product

Use an area model to solve. Then check using lattice multiplication.

1. 5 × 13

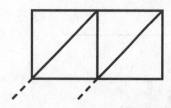

2. 2 × 17

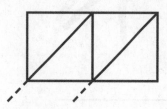

Use lattice multiplication to solve. Check using an area model.

3. 6 × 14

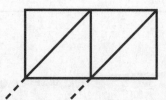

4. 4 × 14

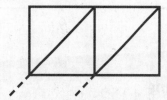

Sarah works in a toy factory. She makes shoes for different toy animals and dolls. How many shoes does she make for each group below? Draw an area model or use lattice multiplication to solve.

5. 15 giraffes

_____

6. 18 dolls

_____

7. 11 spiders

_____

8. 14 ladybugs

_____

9. How many shoes are in your classroom right now? Use what you know about multiplication strategies to find out.

_____

_____

At Home

About how big is your favorite room at home? Use your feet to measure the distance from one end of the room to the other. Be sure to find both the length and width of your room. Use lattice multiplication to find the area of the room.

Name: _____ Date: _____

Factors and Multiples

In the investigation, you learned the relationship between factors and multiples. Let's explore how to find more factors and multiples.

All multiples of 6 have 6 as a factor.

24 is a multiple of 6, so 6 is a factor of 24.

Math Words

factor

multiple

Choose six of the numbers below. List the factors of the numbers. Use counters to help you.

5	8	10	14	15
16	18	20	21	24

1. _____

   Factors:

2. _____

   Factors:

3. _____

   Factors:

4. _____

   Factors:

5. _____

   Factors:

6. _____

   Factors:

Choose two numbers for which you found factors.
Find the first four multiples of each number.
Circle the number in your list of multiples.

7. My number is _____. Its multiples are _____.

8. My number is _____. Its multiples are _____.

five   **5**

Solve the following riddles.

factor   multiple   factor

9. I am _____. • greater than 10 • less than 20 • a multiple of 7	**10.** I am _____. • between 20 and 30 • a multiple of 9	**11.** I am _____. • a multiple of 8 • less than 30 • greater than 20
12. I am _____. • a factor of 18 • between 5 and 8	**13.** I am _____. • greater than 10 • less than 20 • a multiple of 9	**14.** I am _____. • between 4 and 8 • a factor of 15
15. I am _____. • greater than 5 • less than 10 • a multiple of 2 • a factor of 12	**16.** I am _____. • greater than 10 • less than 20 • a multiple of 3 • a factor of 30	**17.** I am _____. • between 6 and 12 • a multiple of 4 • a factor of 32

18. Write your own riddles for any two numbers. Challenge a
classmate to find your numbers.

I am _____.   I am _____.

• _____   • _____

• _____   • _____

• _____   • _____

Name: _____ Date: _____

Relating Multiplication and Division

Remainder in division?
Add it in when you check!

**Use what you have learned about
to examine patterns in division.**

Use multiplication to check the division.

1.
$$\begin{array}{r} 26 \\ 2\overline{)\ 52} \\ -4 \\ \hline 12 \\ -12 \\ \hline 0 \end{array}$$

2.
$$\begin{array}{r} 26R1 \\ 2\overline{)\ 53} \\ -4 \\ \hline 13 \\ -12 \\ \hline 1 \end{array}$$

3.
$$\begin{array}{r} 27 \\ 2\overline{)\ 54} \\ -4 \\ \hline 14 \\ -14 \\ \hline 0 \end{array}$$

4.
$$\begin{array}{r} 27R1 \\ 2\overline{)\ 55} \\ -4 \\ \hline 15 \\ -14 \\ \hline 1 \end{array}$$

5.
$$\begin{array}{r} 28 \\ 2\overline{)\ 56} \\ -4 \\ \hline 16 \\ -16 \\ \hline 0 \end{array}$$

6.
$$\begin{array}{r} 28R1 \\ 2\overline{)\ 57} \\ -4 \\ \hline 17 \\ -16 \\ \hline 1 \end{array}$$

7. Suppose the next problem is 58 ÷ 2. Use the pattern to predict
the quotient. Will it have a remainder? If so, what might it be?
Explain your reasoning.

_____

PROJECT

Rolling a Divisor

Begin with 20 counters. Roll a number cube and divide the
counters by that number. Draw a picture and write a division
equation to solve. Write a multiplication equation to check your
work. Repeat until you have divided 20 by 1, 2, 3, 4, 5, and 6.
Record your answers and explain your findings.

seven 7

Complete the table. Draw the corresponding picture or write the corresponding division or multiplication equation.

Picture	Division	Multiplication
8. 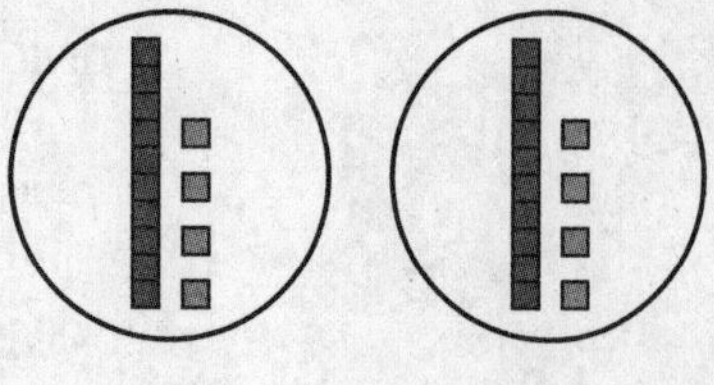		
9.	$4\overline{)84}$ with quotient 21	

Write a multiplication or division equation to solve each problem. If you divide, multiply to check your work. Explain why you chose the operation you did.

10. Evan has 3 dimes and 4 pennies. He shares the money evenly with Sasha. How much does each person get?

I used _____ to solve this problem because _____

_____

_____ .

11. Mr. Smith earns $12 per hour. How much does he earn in 6 hours?

I used _____ to solve this problem because _____

_____

_____ .

Name: _____ Date: _____

Interpreting the Remainder

In the investigation, you explored the ways a remainder can be interpreted. Use models or draw pictures to help. Tell whether you should drop the remainder or add 1 to the quotient.

1. A cooler holds 6 bottles of water. How many coolers does Steven need for 27 water bottles?

_____

_____

2. Yolanda needs 3 meters of ribbon to wrap a box. She has 20 meters of ribbon. How many boxes can she wrap?

_____

_____

3. Ava makes key chains with 5 beads each. How many key chains can she make with 37 beads?

_____

_____

4. At Music Megastore, CDs cost $8 each. How many CDs can Matt buy for $42?

_____

_____

5. A ferry can hold 7 cars. How many trips must it make to carry 25 cars across the river?

_____

_____

6. A roller coaster car holds 6 people. How many cars are needed for 40 people?

_____

_____

At Home

Talk to your family about interpreting remainders. Can you think of a time that your family divided something and interpreted the remainder? Did they divide pieces of pizza? Household chores? Money? What happened and how was the remainder interpreted?

nine   9

Use the information below to help you solve the problems. Tell whether you dropped the remainder or added 1 to the quotient.

> The Rosens and the Blairs are taking a trip to the zoo. There are 9 people in the Rosen family and 8 people in the Blair family.

7. The families rent vans for the trip. They can fit up to 6 people in a van. How many vans do they need?

_____

_____

8. Each person gets two bottles of water to drink during the day. They buy water bottles that come in packs of 8. How many packs of water do they need?

_____

_____

9. A group photograph with the animals costs $8. If everyone contributes $3, how many group photographs can they buy?

$8

_____

_____

10. Finish the story problem below. For A, write a question in which the remainder will be dropped. For B, write a question in which you will add 1 to the quotient. Then solve the problems.

Belinda bakes 20 cookies. 3 cookies fit into each bag.

A. _____

_____

B. _____

_____

Reflecting on What I Learned

New *Vocabulary* I learned:

1. _____

_____

2. _____

_____

3. _____

_____

Explain the difference between a *factor* and a *multiple*. _____

_____

_____

It is said that multiplication and division "undo" each other. What does that mean? Explain, and give specific examples.

_____

_____

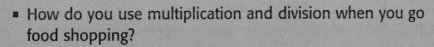

Outside Your Classroom

Where will you see multiplication and division outside the classroom?

- How do you use multiplication and division when you go food shopping?

- How do you know whether to drop the remainder or add 1 to the quotient when you are splitting a pizza with family members?

- You have been given the choice to multiply your savings and divide your spending or multiply your spending and divide your savings. Which would you choose? Why?

Planning a Bowling Party

PROJECT

Use your new knowledge of multiplication and division to plan a day at the bowling alley with two friends. You will all buy the same items and bowl the same number of games.

1. Use the price list to find the cost of renting bowling shoes, bowling one game, and buying food and clothing. You have a budget of $60 to spend on yourself and your 2 friends, and you must rent shoes in order to bowl.

   ■ Think about how you will spend your money.

   ■ How many games do you want to bowl?

   ■ How will you use the math from this unit during your project?

2. Make a table showing how you will spend your money. List each item you want to buy for you and your friends, along with how many you will need. Then make another column for the total cost of each item.

Item	Cost per Item	Me	Friend #1	Friend #2	Total Cost
Shoe rental	$4	1	1	1	$12
One game	$5				
T-shirts	$8				
Food items	$3				
Drinks	$2				

3. Write a report on your project. Include some of the following:

   ■ details of the price list and your budget;

   ■ an explanation of how you made your choices;

   ■ the strategies you used to find the total cost for each item you chose (include a table like the one in Step 2);

   ■ whether or not you have any money left.

UNIT B

Exploring Functions

In this unit, I will:

- Create a variety of patterns using different materials
- Use a function table to organize input and output numbers
- Use function rules to find numbers

Review Concepts
- addition, division, multiplication, and subtraction

Projects
- Study Your Growth Rate
- Create a Function Machine Game

New Vocabulary

function   a relationship in which one number depends on another number

function table   a table of ordered pairs that is based on a rule

input   the number that is increased or decreased to produce the output number

output   the number that results from increasing or decreasing the input number

pattern   a sequence of numbers, figures, or symbols that follows a rule or design

2, 4, 6, 8, 10

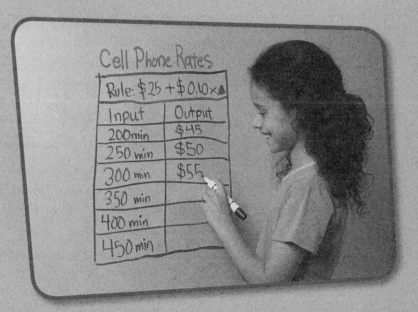

Cell Phone Rates

Rule: $25 + $0.10 × ▲

Input	Output
200 min	$45
250 min	$50
300 min	$55
350 min	
400 min	
450 min	

Home Letter

English

During this math unit, your student will be exploring number relationships in patterns and function tables. To help with learning, here are things to do at home.

- Find number patterns and ask your student to continue the pattern. For example, house numbers on one side of the street are even- or odd-numbered.
- Ask your student to create a table showing daily activities, such as the number of glasses of milk your family drinks in one day, two days, three days, and so on.

Number of Days	Number of Glasses of Milk
1 day	3
2 days	6
3 days	9

Español

Durante esta unidad de matemáticas su estudiante va a explorar las relaciones numéricas en patrones y tablas de funciones. Para ayudar con el aprendizaje, sugerimos estas actividades para hacer en casa:

- Busque patrones numéricos y pídale a su estudiante que continúe el patrón. Por ejemplo, por lo regular las casas de un lado de la calle tienen números pares o impares.
- Pídale a su estudiante que elabore una tabla que muestre actividades diarias, tales como el número de vasos de leche que su familia toma en un día, en dos días, en tres días, etcétera.

Número de días	Número de vasos de leche
1 día	3
2 días	6
3 días	9

Name: _____   Date: _____

Patterns in Numbers

In the investigation, you made repeating and growing patterns using manipulatives.

Now, we will look at some number patterns we find in our daily lives.

1. How many hours are you in school each day?

1 day: _____ hours

2 days: _____ hours

3 days: _____ hours

2. Describe the number pattern.

_____

_____

You can use a table to help you organize data and see a relationship between numbers. This is called a function table.

3. Complete the function table with the number of hours you are in school for three days.

Number of Days	1	2	3		
Number of Hours					

4. Extend the pattern to find the number of hours you are in school for 4 days and 5 days. Add them to the table.

At Home

Make a function table for the number of chairs (output) around your kitchen or dining room table (input). How many chairs would there be around 2 tables? 3 tables? Make a function table for the number of times you brush your teeth each day. How many times do you brush your teeth in 2 days, 3 days, and so on?

fifteen   □ = ▲ — 9   **15**

Sophie is a cashier at a movie theater. She sells movie tickets to five groups of students.

5. If each movie ticket costs $8, what is the total cost for each group?

Number in Group	2	4	6	8	10
Cost of Tickets					

6. How much money did Sophie receive for all the tickets above? _____

The ticket numbers increase by the same number each time. Sophie gave the tickets shown to Sam's group.

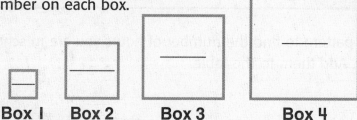

7. Joe received three tickets right after Sam. What were the numbers on his tickets?

_____

8. Paige received three tickets right before Sam. What were the numbers on her tickets?

_____

Jake unloaded 4 boxes of milk cartons. Each box had 25 more cartons than the previous box. The total number of milk cartons in all is 250.

9. How many milk cartons are in each box? Write the number on each box.

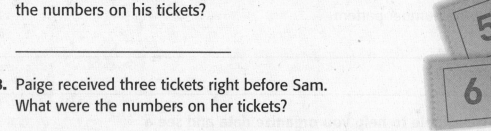

Box 1   Box 2   Box 3   Box 4

10. If each milk carton is 2 cups, how many cups of milk are in each box? Use the function table to help you solve the problem.

Number of Cartons				
Number of Cups				

Name: _____ Date: _____

Addition and Subtraction Functions

Use a different rule to make your own flower garden design. Draw a sketch of the garden and complete the function table to show the rule you used.

Math Words

function

input

output

1.

Rule:	
Input (▲)	Output (□)

Complete each function table below. Describe the patterns in the two tables.

2.

Rule: (▲ + 5)	
Input (▲)	Output (□)
2	7
3	
	9

_____

_____

_____

3.

Rule: (▲ − 3)	
Input (▲)	Output (□)
18	15
17	
	13

_____

_____

_____

Growth Rate

Work with a partner to measure each other's heights. If you could grow 2 inches each year, how tall would you be after 3 years? 5 years? How many years would it take you to be 6 feet tall? How old would you be? Use a function table to show your answers.

seventeen   □ = 100 − ▲

You can use function tables to solve problems. Complete each function table. Use an equation to define the function rule.

4. Each row in an auditorium has 12 more seats than its row number. In which row can a group of 16 people sit together?

_____

Function rule: _____

Input (▲) Row Number	Output (□) Number of Seats
1	13
2	

5. The time in California is 3 hours earlier than the time in New York. What time is it in California when it is 2:00 in New York?

_____

Function rule: _____

Input (▲) New York Time	Output (□) California Time
12:00	9:00
2:00	
	1:00

6. In the library, 15 books from each shelf were donated to charity. How many books were left on a shelf that started with 35 books?

_____

Function rule: _____

Input (▲) Number of Books per shelf Before Donation	Output (□) Number of Books per shelf After Donation
65	50
55	

Use a function table to solve the problem.

7. Juanita has a brother who is 3 years older than she is. Juanita is 10 years old. Make a function table to show their ages. How old will Juanita be when her brother is 18?

_____

8. What function rule did you use for Exercise 7?

_____

2 × ▲ = □   eighteen

Name: _____ **Date:** _____

Multiplication and Division Functions

In the investigation, you wrote a function rule that used multiplication. Let's explore more multiplication and division function rules. Complete the table. Write the rule.

1.

Input (▲)	Output (□)
2	8
3	12
4	16
5	

_____

2.

Input (▲)	Output (□)
100	10
90	9
80	8
70	

_____

3.

Input (▲)	Output (□)
48	6
40	5
32	

_____

4.

Input (▲)	Output (□)
1	3
3	9
	18

_____

5. Write a story problem that uses the function rule in Exercise 4.

_____

_____

In Science

The average person throws away about 5 pounds of garbage each day. Many times, garbage is collected and taken to a landfill. Create a function table that shows how much garbage a person throws away in 1 week, 1 month, and 1 year. What could you do to reduce the amount of trash you throw away each day?

nineteen   □ = ▲ — 10   19

Complete each function table. Use the table to solve the problem. Then write the function rule.

6. You need 3 cups of flour for one batch of muffins. How many cups of flour do you need for 4 batches?

_____

Function rule: _____

Input (▲) Batches	Output (□) Cups
1	3
2	

7. You earn $15 every 3 hours you work. You want to make enough money to buy a $45 video game. How many hours do you need to work to buy the video game?

_____

Function rule: _____

Input (▲) Hours	Output (□) Dollars
3	$15
6	

8. Each apartment building on your block has half as many floors as the number of apartment units. How many floors are there in a building with 20 apartment units? 30 apartment units? 40 apartment units?

_____

Function rule: _____

Input (▲) Apartment Units	Output (□) Floors

Use the sign to complete the problems.

9. The local clothing store is having a clearance sale. You can find the sale prices on the sign. What function rule describes the price relationships?

_____

10. Baseball caps are also on sale. They normally cost $16. What is the sale price for baseball caps?

_____

Clearance Sale		
	Original	Sale Price
Sweaters	$48	$12
Pants	$44	$11
Shirts	$40	$10
Shoes	$36	$9
Baseball caps	$16	

□ = 5 × ▲   twenty

Reflecting on What I Learned

New *Vocabulary* I learned:

1. _____

_____

2. _____

_____

3. _____

_____

What did you learn about function tables and function rules?

_____

_____

List one relationship between input and output numbers and the function rule you learned.

_____

_____

_____

Outside Your Classroom

Where will you use functions outside the classroom?

- You have 50 minutes before dinner. The length of a song is about 3 minutes. Do you have enough time to listen to 5, 10, 15, or 20 songs?

- In the first round of the game, Team A scored 6 points and Team B scored 4 points. After the first round, both teams scored 4 points each round. How many points did each team score at the end of 5 rounds?

- For every 6 cans of soup you buy, you get 2 free cans. How many cans do you need to buy to get 10 free cans of soup?

Create a Function Machine Game

In this unit, you used function tables to find the relationships between sets of numbers. Use this new knowledge to create a game using a function machine.

1. First draw a design of the function machine.

   - Where will you put the input and output numbers?

   - Where will you put the function rules?

   - What materials will you need to make the function machine?

   - How will players use the machine in a game?

2. Create your function machine and write the game rules.

   - How many players can play the game?

   - What is the goal of the game?

   - What are the game rules?

   - What materials other than the function machine do you need to play the game?

   - Are there alternative ways to play the game?

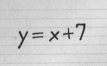
$$y = x + 7$$

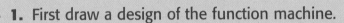

3. Write a report on your project including some of the following:

   - What are some special features about your function machine?

   - What are some of the function rules?

   - Is there a range of input numbers?

   - Include the game rules.

UNIT C

Estimating

In this unit, I will:

- Estimate to find sums and differences
- Estimate the area of classroom objects
- Estimate distance and time traveled by using map routes

New Vocabulary

estimate a number close to an exact value; an estimate indicates *about* how much

$$47 + 22 \text{ is about } 50 + 20 \text{ or } 70$$

round to change the value of a number to one that is easier to work with; to find the nearest value of a number based on a given place value

Review Concepts
- add, area, difference, divide, multiply, product, quotient, subtract, sum

Projects
- Finding containers and estimating quantities
- Planning a Vacation

Game
- Roll to the Target Number

Home Letter

English

During this math unit, your student will be exploring how to estimate for addition, subtraction, multiplication, and division. To help with learning, here are things to do at home:

- Play estimation games by guessing how many things are in one or more jars, bags, or other containers.
- Estimate how much you will spend purchasing two or more of the same item.
- Talk about when it is helpful to estimate (for example, when figuring out if you have enough money to buy something).

In class, your student will be:

- learning strategies to estimate quantities, distances, area, and money;
- using various models and tools to estimate, such as jars with beans, grid squares, and maps.

Español

Durante esta unidad de matemáticas, su estudiante va a explorar cómo estimar para la suma, resta, multiplicación y división. Para ayudar con el aprendizaje, sugerimos estas actividades para hacer en casa:

- Haga juegos de estimación y trate de adivinar cuántas cosas hay en uno o más frascos, bolsas o cualquier otro recipiente.
- Estime cuánto gastaría si comprara dos o más artículos iguales.
- Hable acerca de cuándo es mejor hacer una estimacion (por ejemplo, para calcular si tiene suficiente dinero para comprar algo).

En clase su estudiante va a:

- aprender estrategias para estimar cantidades, área y dinero;
- usar distintos modelos y herramientas para estimar, tales como frascos con frijoles, cuadrículas y mapas.

Name: _____ **Date:** _____

Estimating Sums and Differences

Estimate the number of marbles in a jar.

Jar A   Jar B   Jar C

Math Words

estimate

overestimate

round

underestimate

20 marbles   estimate = ?   estimate = ?

Use the pictures above for Exercises 1–3.

1. Jar B   **2.** Jar C

_____ _____

3. About how many more marbles do you need to fill Jar C to the top?

_____

Estimate the number of balls in the box.

Box A   Box B

44 balls

4. About how many balls are in Box A? _____

5. About how many balls are in Box B? _____

6. About how many balls would fill Box B? _____

Sale Items

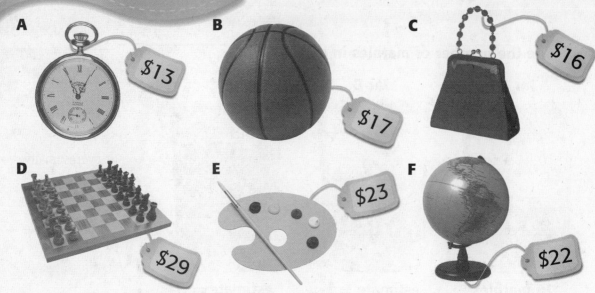

A $13

B $17

C $16

D $29

E $23

F $22

Estimate the total cost.

7. C and D _____

8. B and E _____

9. A and B _____

10. C and F _____

11. You bought B and E. You gave the cashier $50.
About how much change did you get back?

_____

12. If you have $50 to spend, which 3 things could you buy?

_____

13. Paige estimated that the difference in price between F and D
is about $5. Is she correct? If not, did she overestimate or
underestimate?

_____

PROJECT

Container Estimates

Find containers in your house that hold many objects, such as a
box of tissues, a box of noodles, or a bag of carrots. Estimate the
number of things inside the container. Bring one container to class
and put it in the center for others to estimate.

Estimating Products

Use grid squares to estimate the area of a large sheet of paper.

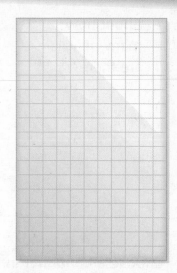

1. Write the number of grid squares for the width and length of the paper. About how many grid squares cover the paper?

_____

_____

Estimate the area of a floor in square tiles.

2. About how many square tiles cover a floor with 2 rows of 37 tiles?

_____

3. About how many square tiles cover a floor with 23 rows of 46 tiles?

_____

The rug hides part of the floor. Estimate the total number of tiles.

4.

About how many tiles cover the floor?

_____

_____

How do you know? _____

_____

_____

About how many tiles are covered by the rug? _____

Estimate how many there are in all.

5. 8 pencil boxes

About how many pencils are there?

_____

6. 14 boxes

About how many cotton swabs are there?

_____

Choose a container in the classroom. Draw it and label the number of items inside. Write your own estimation problem.

7. _____

_____

_____

_____

Estimate the total cost.

8. 1 bicycle = $218

11 bicycles = _____

9. 1 pair of skates = $67

3 pairs of skates = _____

In Science

Did you know that a person throws away about 5 pounds of garbage each day? About how much garbage does your family throw away in one day, one week, one month, and one year?

Name: _____ Date: _____

Estimating Quotients

In the investigation, you estimated to find the number of miles traveled each day. Let's estimate more quotients.

1. If Sheena traveled the same number of miles each day, about how many miles did she travel in one day?

2,706 miles

ARIZONA
Phoenix

Boston

MASSACHUSETTS

It took me 9 days to get to Boston.

$9 \times 3 = 27$
$9 \times 30 = 270$
$9 \times 300 = 2,700$

$2,700 \div 9 =$ _____

Estimate the number of miles.

2. Los Angeles to Orlando
6 days
About how many miles each day?

_____

CALIFORNIA
Los Angeles

2,432 miles

Orlando

FLORIDA

3. Houston to New Orleans
6 hours
About how many miles each hour?

_____

TEXAS

360 miles

Houston

New Orleans

LOUISIANA

	Nashville, TN	Kansas City, MO	Bismarck, ND	Reno, NV
Indianapolis, IN	287 miles	485 miles	1,852 miles	2,073 miles

Use the table to estimate.
Each traveler's route starts in Indianapolis.

4. If Jake traveled 7 hours to Nashville, about how many miles did he travel each hour?

_____

5. Rosa traveled 9 days to Bismarck. About how many miles did she travel each day?

_____

6. Liz traveled 400 miles each day. About how many days did it take her to get to Reno?

_____

7. Sammy traveled about 60 miles each hour. About how long did it take him to get to Kansas City?

_____

8. If Rosa traveled 4 hours each day, who traveled more miles each hour, Rosa or Jake? Explain why.

_____

_____

Estimate.

9. On her vacation, Rosa spent $161 for 5 meals. About how much did she spend for each meal?

_____

10. Sammy spent about $57 for 8 meals. About how much did he spend for each meal?

_____

Reflecting on What I Learned

New *Vocabulary* I learned:

1. _____

_____

2. _____

_____

3. _____

_____

What are two key items I learned about estimating sums, differences, products,

or quotients? _____

_____

_____

List one example of when you would estimate to find a product.

_____

_____

Outside Your Classroom

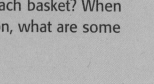

Using estimation is helpful in many situations.

- Where will you use estimation outside the classroom?

  - About how many hours of sleep do you get in one year?

  - Your school made $200 by selling baskets of fruit. What information do you need to know to find out the price of each basket? When you know this information, what are some ways to raise $400?

Planning a Vacation

Use estimation of quantities, distance, area, and money to plan a vacation. Choose a special place you want to go and the fun things you want to do there.

1. First, decide on a place to visit. Then, figure out your travel schedule. (Don't forget that you have to come back!)

   - About how many miles away is this vacation place?

   - About how many hours or days will it take to drive there?

2. Next, estimate how much you will spend on meals and a hotel.

   - About how many nights will you stay at the hotel? About how much will you spend for your hotel stay? (Hint: Round the hotel price to the nearest ten dollars.)

   - About how many meals will you have on your trip? About how much will you spend on meals?

   - What fun and interesting places will you visit? About how much will you spend?

3. Finally, write a travel diary including the following:

   - About how many miles did you travel? About how long did it take?

   - Where did you stay and what fun things did you do?

   - What were the estimated costs? About how much did you spend each day?

Vacation to Miami Plan
1. 486 miles
   about 8 hours, 60 miles each hour
2. Each meal–about $6.00
   3 meals each day = ?

   Total cost for 7 days = ?
3. Zoo $8.00, Art Museum $5.00, Beach $2.00.

Total cost of the trip?

Understanding Fractions

In this unit, I will:

- Find fractions that "make 1"
- Find equivalent fractions by multiplying and dividing
- Compare and order fractions
- Add and subtract fractions with like denominators

Review Concepts
- factor, number line, addition, subtraction, multiplication, and division

Projects
- Making a "How I Spend My Day" circle graph
- Conducting a survey and recording the results

Game
- Coin-Toss Game

New Vocabulary

denominator   the bottom number in a fraction

equivalent fractions   fractions that represent the same number

fraction   a number that represents part of a whole or part of a set

$$\frac{1}{2}, \frac{1}{3}, \frac{1}{4}, \frac{3}{4} \longleftarrow \text{numerators} \atop \longleftarrow \text{denominators}$$

greatest common factor (GCF)   the largest number that divides evenly into two or more numbers

like denominators   when two or more fractions have the same denominator, they have like denominators; in $\frac{1}{4}$ and $\frac{3}{4}$, 4 is the like denominator

numerator   the number above the bar in a fraction; the part of the fraction that tells how many of the equal parts are being used

simplest form   a fraction in which the numerator and the denominator have no common factor greater than 1

Home Letter

English

During this math unit, your student will be exploring fractions. To help with learning, here are some activities to do at home:

- Find fractions on recipe cards and food packages and write equivalent fractions for them or add and subtract fractions with like denominators.
- Talk about activities in terms of fractions, such as: "Let's fill the cereal bowl with $\frac{1}{2}$ cup of cereal and $\frac{1}{4}$ cup of milk."

In class, your student will be:

- using various models and drawings to represent fractions;
- writing fractions in different ways, such as $\frac{8}{8}$ is 1 and $\frac{2}{4}$ is $\frac{1}{2}$;
- comparing, ordering, adding, and subtracting fractions.

Español

Durante esta unidad de matemáticas, su estudiante va a explorar las fracciones. Para ayudar con el aprendizaje, sugerimos estas actividades para hacer en casa:

- Halle fracciones en tarjetas de recetas y empaques de alimentos y escriba fracciones equivalentes a ellas, o sume y reste fracciones con denominadores semejantes.
- Hable acerca de actividades comunes en términos de fracciones, tales como: "Llenemos el tazón de cereal con $\frac{1}{2}$ taza de cereal y $\frac{1}{4}$ de taza de leche".

En clase, su estudiante va a:

- usar distintos modelos y dibujos para representar fracciones;
- escribir fracciones de diferentes formas, tales como: $\frac{8}{8}$ equivale a 1 y $\frac{2}{4}$ es igual a $\frac{1}{2}$;
- comparar, ordenar, sumar y restar fracciones.

Name: _____ Date: _____

Other Names for 1

In the investigation, you found other names for 1.
Let's find more ways to make 1.

A

B

C

D

Math Words

denominator

fraction

numerator

1. Look at the pictures. Write the fractions that make one whole.
   The first one has been done for you.

A	$\frac{1}{6} + \frac{1}{6} + \frac{1}{6} + \frac{1}{6} + \frac{1}{6} + \frac{1}{6} = \frac{6}{6}$ or 1
B	
C	
D	

If you put the shaded parts together, will they make exactly
one whole? Write *yes* or *no*.

2.  _____

3.  _____

4. 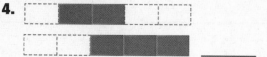 _____

5. _____

Draw lines to divide each whole into equal parts. Write the fraction that equals 1.

6. $1 = \dfrac{}{10}$

7. $1 = \dfrac{}{6}$

8. $1 = \dfrac{}{12}$

9. $1 = \dfrac{}{7}$

Circle the fractions that equal 1. Underline the fractions that are greater than 1. Write an X on the fractions that are less than 1.

10.	11.	12.	13.	14.
$\dfrac{3}{3}$	$\dfrac{1}{4}$	$\dfrac{7}{10}$	$\dfrac{30}{30}$	$\dfrac{100}{100}$
15.	**16.**	**17.**	**18.**	**19.**
$\dfrac{10}{5}$	$\dfrac{8}{11}$	$\dfrac{9}{9}$	$\dfrac{6}{2}$	$\dfrac{18}{18}$

20. How do you know that a fraction is less than 1?

_____

_____

Name: _____ Date: _____

Equivalent Fractions

In the investigation, you used models and multiplied to find equivalent fractions. Now let's find more equivalent fractions.

These drawings both show the fraction $\frac{4}{6}$.

$\dfrac{\text{4 shaded counters}}{\text{6 total counters}}$ 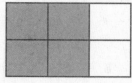 $\dfrac{\text{4 shaded parts}}{\text{6 total parts}}$

1. Show $\frac{2}{3}$ of each diagram. Circle the groups or shade the parts.

$\dfrac{\text{2 groups of shaded counters}}{\text{3 total groups of counters}}$ $\dfrac{\text{2 shaded parts}}{\text{3 total parts}}$

You can divide to find equivalent fractions. $\dfrac{4 \div 2}{6 \div 2} = \dfrac{2}{3}$

Write the fraction for each model. Are the fractions equivalent? Write *yes* or *no*. Explain your answer to a partner.

2.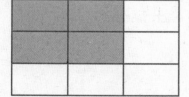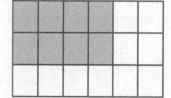

_____   _____

3.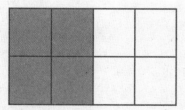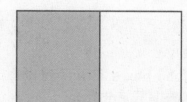

_____   _____   _____

Multiply or divide to find an equivalent fraction.

4. $\frac{1}{6} = \frac{\boxed{}}{12}$ 5. $\frac{1}{2} = \frac{10}{\boxed{}}$ 6. $\frac{8}{12} = \frac{2}{\boxed{}}$ 7. $\frac{6}{18} = \frac{\boxed{}}{3}$

8. $\frac{2}{3} = \boxed{}$ 9. $\frac{2}{5} = \boxed{}$ 10. $\frac{7}{21} = \boxed{}$ 11. $\frac{3}{12} = \boxed{}$

Identify the pattern, then multiply or divide to find the missing fraction in each pattern of equivalent fractions.

12. $\frac{1}{2}, \frac{3}{6}, \boxed{}, \frac{27}{54}$ 13. $\frac{32}{64}, \frac{16}{32}, \frac{8}{16}, \boxed{}$ 14. $\boxed{}, \frac{8}{20}, \frac{32}{80}, \frac{128}{320}$

Make your own pattern of equivalent fractions. Challenge a partner to continue the pattern.

15. _____

16. Five people are sharing a pizza. Show at least three ways to cut the pizza so each person gets an equal share. Write each fraction.

_____   _____   _____

At Home

Look on food boxes, in magazines, in cookbooks, or ask a family member for a recipe. Rewrite the recipe using equivalent fractions. For example, if the recipe uses $\frac{1}{2}$ cup milk, you could write $\frac{2}{4}$ cup milk. Bring the original recipe and your rewritten one to school to share with the class.

Fruit Salad

$\frac{1}{4}$ cup blueberries
$\frac{1}{2}$ cup strawberries
$\frac{3}{4}$ cup grapes
4 bananas sliced
3 apples sliced
Mix together in a large bowl.

Name: _____ Date: _____

Comparing and Ordering Fractions

Use a number line to compare and order fractions.

1. Ana and Edward are walking the same trail. The trail begins at the parking lot and ends at the playground. The trail is 1 mile long. There are signs showing the distance every tenth of a mile. Ana has walked $\frac{2}{5}$ of the trail. Edward has walked $\frac{8}{10}$ of the trail.

Who is closer to the parking lot? _____

Who is closer to the playground? _____

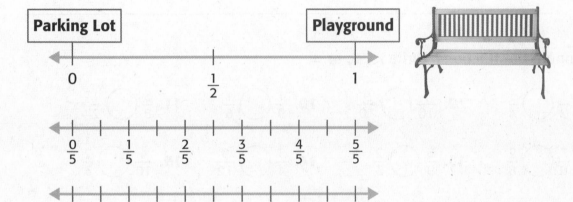

2. If you wanted to put a park bench closest to the parking lot without it being on 0, at which sign might you place the park bench? How do you know? _____

_____

_____

3. If you wanted to put the park bench closest to the playground without it being on 1, at which sign might you place the bench? _____

4. Write a story problem about using the trails.

_____

_____

_____

With a partner, answer each question and explain your choice.
You can use tiles, number lines, or drawings to explain your answer.

5. Which is greater, $\frac{2}{6}$ or $\frac{5}{6}$ of a pizza? _____

_____

6. Which is greater, $\frac{3}{8}$ or $\frac{3}{16}$ of a pound? _____

_____

7. Which is greater, $\frac{5}{8}$ or $\frac{3}{7}$ of a rug? _____

_____

Compare the fractions. Write <, >, or =.

8. $\frac{1}{2}$ ◯ $\frac{1}{4}$ **9.** $\frac{7}{10}$ ◯ $\frac{9}{10}$ **10.** $\frac{1}{9}$ ◯ $\frac{1}{6}$ **11.** $\frac{5}{8}$ ◯ $\frac{1}{2}$

12. $\frac{3}{8}$ ◯ $\frac{2}{8}$ **13.** $\frac{5}{9}$ ◯ $\frac{2}{3}$ **14.** $\frac{3}{4}$ ◯ $\frac{9}{12}$ **15.** $\frac{4}{10}$ ◯ $\frac{2}{3}$

Put these fractions in order from least to greatest.

16. $\frac{1}{2}, \frac{1}{3}, \frac{1}{6}, \frac{5}{6}, \frac{2}{3}, \frac{2}{2}$ _____

17. $\frac{3}{4}, \frac{1}{8}, \frac{7}{12}, \frac{1}{4}, \frac{3}{8}, \frac{1}{12}$ _____

18. $\frac{4}{9}, \frac{2}{3}, \frac{1}{6}, \frac{8}{9}, \frac{1}{3}, \frac{5}{6}$ _____

At Home
Coin-Toss Game
Players take turns tossing a coin ten times. Each player
records the number of times his or her toss lands heads up and then
writes the result as a fraction of total tosses. The player with the
fraction closest to 1 wins. After playing three rounds, list the fractions
in order from greatest to least. Bring your fraction list to school.

Name: _____ Date: _____

Adding and Subtracting Fractions with Like Denominators

Subtract the following fractions. Use fraction tiles, number lines, or drawings to help.

$$\frac{5}{6} - \frac{4}{6} = \frac{1}{6}$$

Math Words

greatest common factor (GCF)

like denominators

simplest form

1. $\frac{9}{10} - \frac{2}{10} =$ _____

2. $\frac{5}{8} - \frac{2}{8} =$ _____

3. $\frac{7}{12} - \frac{4}{12} =$ _____

4. $\frac{6}{14} - \frac{3}{14} =$ _____

5. How is subtracting fractions similar to adding fractions? How is it different?

_____

_____

_____

After we add or subtract fractions, we can write our answer in simplest form. Complete the table to find the fractions in simplest form.

	Fraction	Common Factors	Greatest Common Factor	Simplest Form
	$\frac{8}{12}$	2, 4	4	$\frac{2}{3}$
6.	$\frac{6}{8}$	2		
7.	$\frac{10}{20}$		10	
8.	$\frac{4}{16}$			

9. Add or subtract the fractions. Draw a number line or use fraction tiles to show your work. Write your answer in simplest form.

a. $\dfrac{9}{12} - \dfrac{6}{12} = $ _____

b. $\dfrac{1}{4} + \dfrac{2}{4} = $ _____

c. $\dfrac{1}{8} + \dfrac{2}{8} = $ _____

d. $\dfrac{7}{10} - \dfrac{1}{10} = $ _____

e. $\dfrac{5}{9} + \dfrac{2}{9} = $ _____

10. Match each sum or difference above to a statement. Write the letter of the equation in the correct box.

a sum between $\dfrac{1}{2}$ and 1 _____	a sum between zero and $\dfrac{1}{2}$ _____
a difference between $\dfrac{1}{2}$ and 1 _____	a difference between zero and $\dfrac{1}{2}$ _____

Make a Circle Graph

Make a list of the activities you do in a day. Include the amount of time you spend doing each activity. Write the time as a fraction of a day. Then, make a circle graph to show your data. (HINT: There are 24 hours in 1 day, and the sum of the fractions must equal 1.)

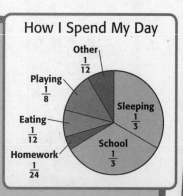

How I Spend My Day

Other $\frac{1}{12}$

Playing $\frac{1}{8}$

Eating $\frac{1}{12}$

Homework $\frac{1}{24}$

School $\frac{1}{3}$

Sleeping $\frac{1}{3}$

Reflecting on What I Learned

New *Vocabulary* I learned:

1. _____

2. _____

3. _____

How do you compare two fractions that have different denominators?

_____

_____

_____

_____

List one thing you learned about equivalent fractions.

_____

_____

_____

Outside Your Classroom

Where will you use fractions outside the classroom?

- How do you cut a pie for your guests?

- What fraction of a day do you spend sleeping? What fraction of the day do you spend watching television?

- You are making a new muffin recipe. How much of each ingredient will you need?

Representing Survey Data

Use your new knowledge about fractions to represent survey data in a circle graph.

1. First, plan and conduct a survey.

   - Choose a survey question that has at least three answer choices to ask 10 people. For example, "What is your favorite sport?" or "What is your favorite color?"

   - Record the results in a tally chart.

   - Turn the results into fractions: $\dfrac{\text{number of votes for choice}}{\text{total number of survey votes}}$

2. Next, make a circle graph to represent the data from your survey.

   - Draw a circle. Draw the sections of your graph for each choice.

   - Label each choice and its fraction part. Make sure fractions are in simplest form.

3. Finally, write a report explaining your survey and results.

   - Include the tally chart and the circle graph in your report. Explain the results. (Sample graphs shown.)

   - Which choice received the most votes? Which received the fewest? What fraction is each?

   - Which two choices added together received more than $\frac{1}{2}$ of the votes? Which choices received about $\frac{1}{3}$ of the votes?

What is your favorite sport?	
Baseball	卌 l
Basketball	l
Soccer	卌 llll
Tennis	llll

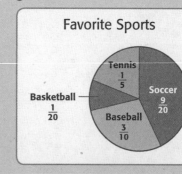

Favorite Sports

Tennis $\frac{1}{5}$

Soccer $\frac{9}{20}$

Basketball $\frac{1}{20}$

Baseball $\frac{3}{10}$

UNIT E
Working with Fractions and Decimals

In this unit, I will:

- Identify the decimal name for parts of one
- Find equivalent decimals and fractions
- Compare and order decimals, fractions, and mixed numbers
- Create a spending plan for $100 and write a report

Review Concepts
- denominator, fraction, equivalent fraction, number line, numerator

Projects
- Decimal Book
- Spending $100

New Vocabulary

decimal   a number that uses place value, numbers, and a decimal point to show part of a whole

decimal equivalents   decimals that represent the same number

0.9 and 0.90

decimal point   a period separating the ones and the tenths in a decimal number

0.8 or $3.77

hundredth   a place-value position; one of one hundred equal parts

In the number 0.05, 5 is in the hundredths place.

mixed number   a number that has a whole number part and a fraction part

$6\frac{3}{4}$

tenth   one of ten equal parts, or $\frac{1}{10}$

In the number 0.25, 2 is in the tenths place.

Home Letter

English

During this math unit, your student will be exploring decimals. To help with learning, here are some activities to do at home.

- Find decimals around your home or while running errands, such as food labels, measuring tools, radio stations, and price tags.
- Compare decimals to 0, $\frac{1}{2}$, and 1. For example, ask: "Is 0.4 closer to 1 or $\frac{1}{2}$?"
- When counting coins, ask students to tell you how many tenths and hundredths there are. "Seventy-three cents is seven tenths, three hundredths."

In class, your student will be:

- using various models and drawings to represent decimals;
- identifying different decimal and fraction names for the same amount.

Español

Durante esta unidad de matemáticas, su estudiante va a explorar los decimales. Para ayudar con el aprendizaje, sugerimos estas actividades para hacer en casa:

- Encuentre decimales, tales como los que aparecen en las etiquetas de los productos alimenticios, las herramientas de medición, las estaciones de radio y las etiquetas de precios, por su casa o mientras hace mandados.
- Compare decimales con 0, $\frac{1}{2}$ y 1. Pregunte: "¿Está 0.4 más cerca de 1 ó de $\frac{1}{2}$?"
- Cuando cuente monedas, pídale a su estudiante que le diga cuántas décimas y centésimas hay. "Setenta y tres centavos son siete décimas y tres centésimas."

En clase, su estudiante va a:

- usar distintos modelos y dibujos para representar decimales;
- identificar distintos nombres para decimales y fracciones en una misma cantidad.

Name: _____ Date: _____

What Is a Decimal?

In the investigation, you used coins and grids to explore decimals and place value. Let's learn more about writing decimals.

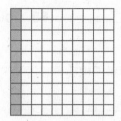
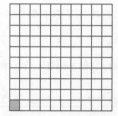

Ones		Tenths	Hundredths
1	.	0	0

Ones		Tenths	Hundredths
0	.	1	0

Ones		Tenths	Hundredths
0	.	0	1

1. How many hundredths in 1? _____   **2.** How many tenths in 1? _____

Write the decimal to match the shaded part of the grid in both standard and word form.

3.

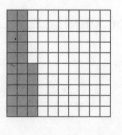

_____

4.

_____

5.

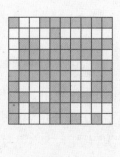

_____

6.

_____

Decimal equivalents name the same part.
Write a decimal equivalent.

7. $0.40 =$ _____

8. $0.9 =$ _____

Write each as a decimal.

9. seventy-nine hundredths _____

10. four-hundredths _____

Write the value of the underlined digit.

11. 0.3<u>7</u> _____

12. 0.<u>8</u> _____

13. <u>9</u>.62 _____

Answer each question. Use base-ten models, grid paper, or drawings.

14. Which is greater, 0.25 or 25? Explain. _____

_____

_____

15. Is 0.58 greater than or less than one-half? How do you know? _____

_____

_____

Decimal Book
Look through newspapers or magazines to find decimals. Write
how the decimal number is used and draw a picture to model it.
Glue the article into your book. On the opposite page, write the
decimal number in word form.

Name: _____ **Date:** _____

Renaming Fractions and Decimals

We can write fractions as decimals or decimals as fractions.

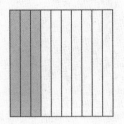

$\frac{3}{10} = 0.3$

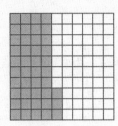

$\frac{43}{100} = 0.43$

Write the decimal for each fraction.

1. $\frac{35}{100}$ _____   **2.** $\frac{6}{10}$ _____   **3.** $\frac{50}{100}$ _____   **4.** $\frac{27}{100}$ _____

5. $\frac{9}{10}$ _____   **6.** $\frac{12}{100}$ _____   **7.** $\frac{88}{100}$ _____   **8.** $\frac{40}{100}$ _____

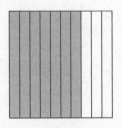

$0.7 = \frac{7}{10}$

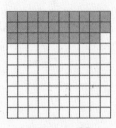

$0.29 = \frac{29}{100}$

Write an equivalent fraction for each decimal.

9. 0.45 _____   **10.** 0.82 _____   **11.** 0.5 _____

12. 0.76 _____   **13.** 0.6 _____   **14.** 0.9 _____

What if the fraction does not have a denominator of 10 or 100? How do we write the fraction as a decimal?

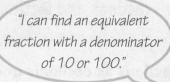

"I can find an equivalent fraction with a denominator of 10 or 100."

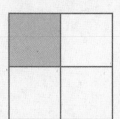

$$\frac{1}{4} \times \frac{25}{25} = \frac{25}{100} \qquad \frac{25}{100} = 0.25$$

$4 \times ? = 100$

Write a decimal for each.

15.

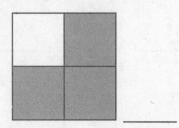 _____

16.

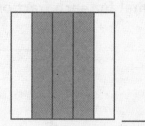 _____

17. $\frac{2}{5}$ _____   **18.** $\frac{1}{20}$ _____   **19.** $\frac{3}{25}$ _____

20. Shade the diagram to show 0.2.

21. Shade the diagram to show 0.8.

22. Shade the diagram to show 0.75.

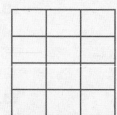

Name: _____ Date: _____

Ordering Fractions and Decimals on a Number Line

Compare the following decimals and fractions.

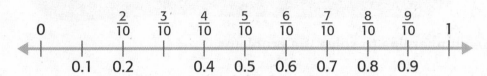

1. Plot these decimal numbers on the number line: 0.3, 0.55, and 0.85.

2. Plot these fractions on the number line: $\frac{4}{100}$, $\frac{1}{10}$, and $\frac{95}{100}$.

3. Is 0.3 less than or greater than $\frac{1}{5}$? _____

4. Which is greater, 0.85 or $\frac{4}{5}$? _____

Use the benchmarks above to help you.

5. Plot these decimals and fractions on the number line below. Then write them in order from least to greatest. $\frac{1}{8}$, 0.25, 0.9, $\frac{5}{8}$, seven-tenths

_____

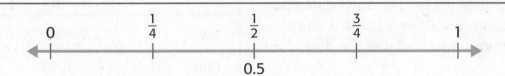

Find the errors on the number line below.

6. Cross out the incorrect fractions or decimals. Plot the numbers correctly.

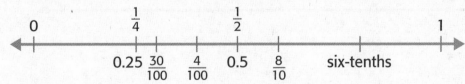

Decimal Book
Look at the decimals you listed in your Decimal Book.
Make a list of the decimals in order from least to greatest.

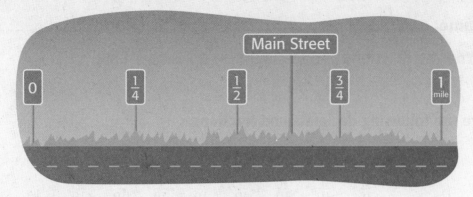

Use the number line to solve the problems.

7. Herb and Lana are city workers. Their job is to install lampposts along Main Street at 0.9, 0.25, and 0.55 mile. Plot the lamppost locations on the street plan.

8. Another city worker, Sophie, is installing fire hydrants along Main Street. She must place fire hydrants at seventy-five hundredths, $\frac{1}{10}$, and three-tenths mile. Plot the fire hydrant locations on the street plan.

Use the table to draw a number line.

9. The table shows the number of bicycles per person in different countries. Draw a number line from 0 to 1 and plot the data.

Bicycles per Capita	
Germany	0.88
U.S.A.	$\frac{49}{100}$
Japan	six-tenths
China	0.37
Netherlands	1.0

10. Which country has the least number of bikes per person? _____

11. Which country has the greatest number of bikes per person? _____

Name: _____ Date: _____

Decimals, Fractions, and Mixed Numbers

In the investigation, you learned how to change mixed numbers to decimals. Use this skill to compare mixed numbers and decimals.

Compare: $3\frac{1}{5}$ and 3.25

First, change the mixed number to a decimal.

$3\frac{1}{5} \times \frac{20}{20} = 3\frac{20}{100}$
or
3.20 or 3.2

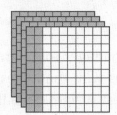

Then, compare decimals.

3.2 < 3.25

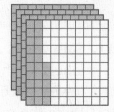

Compare. Write <, >, or =.

1. 0.32 ◯ 0.61   **2.** 1.84 ◯ 0.57   **3.** 2.80 ◯ 2.8

Write each fraction or mixed number as a decimal. Then compare. Write <, >, or =.

4. $\frac{45}{100}$ ◯ 0.23   **5.** $\frac{57}{100}$ ◯ 0.9   **6.** $1\frac{85}{100}$ ◯ 1.72

7. $3\frac{1}{10}$ ◯ 3.01   **8.** $6\frac{27}{100}$ ◯ 7.26   **9.** 2.15 ◯ $2\frac{51}{100}$

In Science

Density is how much space an object takes up related to its weight. The density of water is 1. Any substance with a density less than 1 floats on water. Any substance that has a density greater than 1 sinks. Look at the table. Tell which would float and which would sink.

Substance	Ice	Salt	Oak	Butter	Milk
Density	0.92	2.16	0.7	0.90	1.03

Work with a partner to solve these problems.

All Salmon Fillets
$11.50

10. Ying went to the grocery store. She read the sign on the right. There were only two fish left. One was 5.86 pounds. The other was $5\frac{68}{100}$ pounds. Which fish should she buy to get the better deal? Explain why.

_____

_____

_____

11. Sam works at the grocery store. His manager told him to write the price labels for the vegetable cans. The cans with the lowest weight have the lowest price. The cans with the greatest weight have the highest price. Write the prices for each can in decimal form.

Beans
4.5 oz.

Corn
6.75 oz.

Tomatoes
6.25 oz.

$0.69
$1.50
$1.70

_____   _____   _____

12. Mia set up displays at the grocery store. She had three different heights of shampoo bottles. Which shampoo bottle should she put on each shelf?

$10\frac{1}{4}$ in.
tall

$6\frac{1}{2}$ in.
tall

$8\frac{3}{4}$ in.
tall

6.08 in.

$6\frac{80}{100}$ in.

$9\frac{10}{100}$ in.

Reflecting on What I Learned

New *Vocabulary* I learned:

1. _____

2. _____

3. _____

How do you write a decimal equivalent for a fraction?

_____

_____

_____

_____

List one thing you learned about comparing decimals and fractions.

_____

_____

_____

_____

Outside Your Classroom

Where will you use decimals outside the classroom?

- A recipe uses fractions but your measuring cups use decimals. How can you make sure that you measure the correct amount?

- When shopping, the prices of two boxes of cereal are the same. One box is 12.5 oz and the other is 14.1 oz. How do you know which is the better buy?

- You are trying to find a book in the library. The call number is 595.78. Is it on the shelves between 575.01 and 595.70 or between 595.71 and 620?

Spending $100

Use your knowledge of decimals to make a spending plan.
You have $100. Plan how you will spend it.

1. There are some rules as to how you can spend the money.
You cannot spend the $100 on one item, and you must
buy items from three or four categories. For example, your
categories could be toys, music, books, and activities.

2. Begin by deciding on your categories and writing
them on a sheet of paper.

3. Next, look through catalogs or search the Internet
to find prices. List each item under the correct
category and write the price of each item (rounded
to the nearest dollar). Write the total cost for each
category. These totals are called *subtotals*. Then
add the three or four subtotals to make sure the
total sum equals $100 or less.

Spending Plan	
Clothing	Cost
Shirt	$12.49
Pants	$15
Shoes	$20
Subtotal	$47.50

4. Make a circle graph or a bar graph showing the
subtotal for each category.

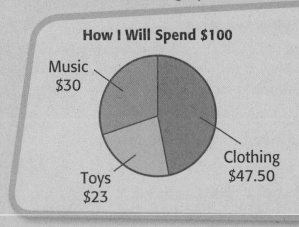

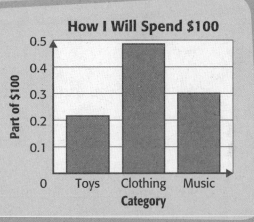

5. Write a report explaining how you spent your money.
Include your lists of items, prices, and the subtotals for
each category. Also, relate each price to the total using a
fraction and a decimal.

UNIT F

Area of Figures

In this unit, I will:

- Find the perimeter and area of rectangles and complex figures using nonstandard, customary, and metric units
- Measure objects in the classroom and find their perimeter and area
- Create paper models of customary and metric square units

Review Concepts
- attributes of a rectangle

Projects
- Measuring the perimeter and area of objects
- Pentomino rectangle puzzles

New Vocabulary

complex figure   a shape that is made up of two or more shapes

customary system (units)   the measurement system that includes units such as foot, pound, quart, and degrees Fahrenheit; also called *standard measurement*

kilometer   a metric unit for measuring length 1,000 meters = 1 kilometer

line segment   a part of a *line* between two *endpoints*; the length of the line segment can be measured

A _____ B

metric system (units)   the measurement system based on powers of 10 that includes units such as meter, gram, liter, and degrees Celsius

millimeter   a metric unit used for measuring length 1000 millimeters = 1 meter

0 mm 10   20   30

Home Letter

English

During this math unit, your student will be finding the perimeter and area of rectangles and complex figures. To help with learning, here are things to do at home.

- Find the perimeter and area of different items in your home with a ruler.
- Look through the newspaper with your student and search for measurements. Which system's units are used more often?
- Help your student make a scale drawing of his or her bedroom. First measure the walls, bed, dresser, etc. Use graph paper to make the drawing. Use metric and customary measuring devices if possible.

Español

Durante esta unidad de matemáticas, su estudiante va a explorar el perímetro y el área de los rectángulos y las figuras complejas. Para ayudar con el aprendizaje, sugerimos estas actividades para hacer en casa:

- Halle el perímetro y el área de distintos objetos de la casa usando una regla.
- Examine el periódico con su estudiante y busquen medidas. ¿Cuál sistema de unidades se usa más?
- Ayude a su estudiante a hacer un dibujo a escala de su habitación. Primero, mida las paredes, la cama, la cómoda, etc. Para hacer el dibujo, utilice un papel para gráficas. De ser posible, utilice instrumentos de medición usuales y métricos.

Name: _____ Date: _____

Square Units: Segments to Squares

Each of these rectangles has an area of 16 units². Find the perimeter for each.

1.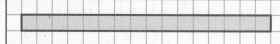

P = _____

2.

P = _____

3.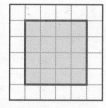

P = _____

4. Explain how you found the perimeter of each rectangle.

_____

_____

_____

5. What do you notice about the perimeters and shapes of these 3 rectangles?

_____

_____

Measure It!

Use what you have learned about finding perimeter and area to measure everyday objects. Choose 3 ways to find the perimeter and area of the given objects using paper clips, geoboards, color tiles, rulers, tape measures, string or yarn. Create a table that lists the objects, the perimeters, and the areas, and which method you used. Be sure to measure to the nearest whole unit.

How many square units is the area of each figure below?

6.

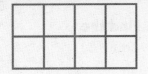

A = _____

7.

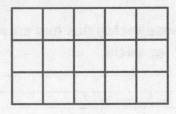

A = _____

8.

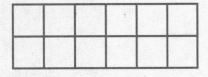

A = _____

9.

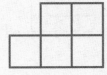

A = _____

10.

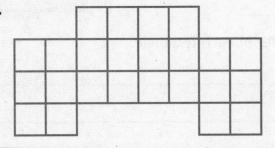

A = _____

11. Describe what you see happening to the area and perimeter in the figures below.

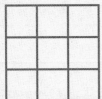 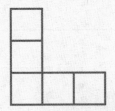

P = _____   P = _____   P = _____

A = _____   A = _____   A = _____

_____

_____

Name: _____   Date: _____

Finding Area with Customary and Metric Units

In the investigation, you made area models that represent customary and metric units of measure. Use these units to find the area of the following shapes.

1.

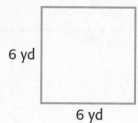

6 yd

6 yd   _____

2. 2 m

6 m   _____

3.

24 in.

36 in.   _____

4.

16 cm

32 cm   _____

Math Words

area

centimeter

customary units

kilometer

metric units

millimeter

At Home

Look at the front page of your newspaper. Use customary and metric measurements to find out how much area is used by news articles and how much is used by pictures and headlines. Do the same thing for the front of the Sports section. Compare the area measurements by making a chart.

**Find the measurement of the missing side. The area is given.
Draw in grid lines as needed.**

5. Area = 42 in²

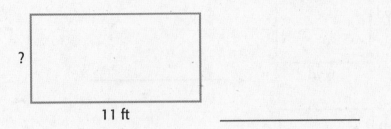

6 in.

?

_____

6. Area = 33 ft²

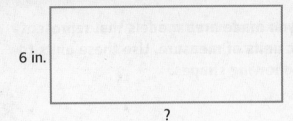

?

11 ft

_____

7. Area = 24 m²

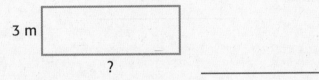

3 m

?

_____

8. Area = 16 cm²

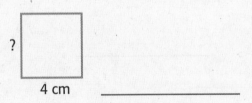

?

4 cm   _____

9. Draw a figure below with an area of 12 yd². Be sure to label
the sides with the correct measurements and units.

10. Draw a figure below with a base of 8 cm and an area of
64 cm². What shape did you draw? Explain.

_____

_____

_____

_____

Name: _____ Date: _____

Finding Area of Complex Figures

Use both the addition and subtraction methods
to find the area of the figures below.

Math Word

complex figure

1.

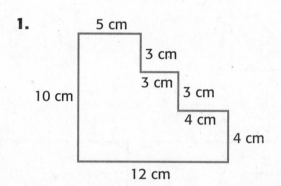

Addition Method _____

_____

_____

Subtraction Method _____

_____

_____

_____

2.

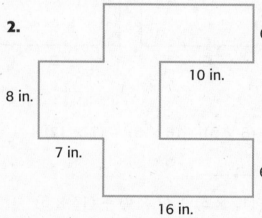

Addition Method _____

_____

_____

Subtraction Method _____

_____

_____

3. Explain how you found the area using the subtraction method
for Exercise 2.

_____

_____

_____

_____

_____

Match each math sentence with the correct division of the complex figure below.

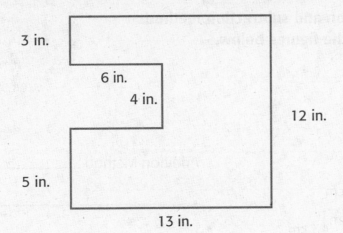

3 in.

6 in.

4 in.

12 in.

5 in.

13 in.

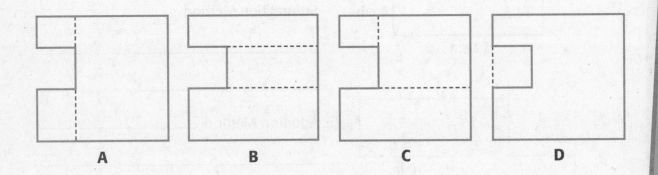

A   B   C   D

4. $(6 \times 3) + (7 \times 7) + (13 \times 5)$

_____

5. $(6 \times 3) + (6 \times 5) + (7 \times 12)$

_____

6. $(13 \times 12) - (6 \times 4)$

_____

7. $(13 \times 3) + (7 \times 4) + (13 \times 5)$

_____

PROJECT

Finding Area

Find an object that is a complex figure in your classroom to add to your table. Use color tiles to find the area. Then use a ruler. Compare your results.

5

5   7   10

5   5   P = 64

20

Reflecting on What I Learned

New *Vocabulary* I learned:

1. _____

_____

2. _____

_____

3. _____

_____

4. List all the metric units of measure you know.

_____

5. Describe the relationship between perimeter and area when the perimeters of two rectangles are the same, but the areas are different.

_____

_____

_____

Outside Your Classroom

Where do you see perimeter and area in the world around you?

- How much floor space do you need to build a full basketball court?

- How much floor space do you need to build an indoor volleyball court?

Your after-school job is to sweep the school hallways. You are offered a choice on how to be paid. You can be paid by the total number of square feet you sweep, or by the total number of square meters you sweep.

- Which payment method would you pick? Explain why and include the math used to make your decision.

sixty-five   6 $\lfloor$ 8 $\rceil$ 9   P = 65   **65**

Pentomino Rectangle Puzzles

Use your knowledge of perimeter and area to create pentomino puzzle pieces and then use the puzzle pieces to make pentomino rectangles.

Pentominos are shapes made from 5 squares. The five squares must lie flat, and whole sides of squares must touch. Corner to corner connections are not allowed.

This is a pentomino.   **This is not a pentomino.**

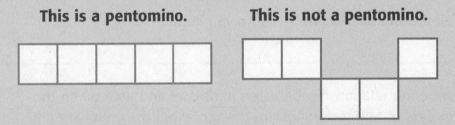

1. Using five color tiles, find the 12 possible pentomino shapes.

   ■ Trace the 12 pentomino shapes that you created onto a clean piece of grid paper and cut them out. These will become the puzzle pieces for the next part of the project.

2. Create two different rectangles using all 12 pentomino puzzle pieces. Trace the rectangles onto your piece of grid paper and record the area and perimeter of each rectangle puzzle. Use a table to organize your work.

Sketch of Rectangle	Perimeter	Area

   ■ Can you create any other shapes with the puzzle pieces? If so, draw a diagram.

UNIT G

Time and Temperature

In this unit, I will:

- Relate time to fractions
- Compare days, hours, minutes, and seconds
- Find elapsed time
- Read temperature in degrees Fahrenheit and degrees Celsius

Review Concepts
- multiplication, division, fractions, graphing, measurement

Projects
- Ways We Use Time
- Make a Perfect-Day Timeline

New Vocabulary

Celsius (°C)   the unit used to measure temperature in the metric system

elapsed time   the difference in time between the start and the end of an event

Fahrenheit (°F)   the unit used to measure temperature in the customary system

half past   30 minutes past the hour

2:30

hour   a unit of time equal to 60 minutes

4:00

minute   a unit used to measure time

1 hour = 60 minutes
1 minute = 60 seconds

quarter past   15 minutes past the hour

quarter to   15 minutes before the hour

8:15

1:45

temperature   a measure of how hot or how cold something is

thermometer   a tool used to measure temperature

Home Letter

English

During this math unit, your student will be exploring time and temperature. To help with learning, here are things to do at home.

- Use time words to describe events.
- Estimate about how much time passes between the beginning and the ending of events, such as family gatherings, errands, or television programs.
- Find the time and temperature in different time zones.
- Help your student create a schedule of family activities.

In class, your student will be:

- reading, writing, and comparing times;
- finding elapsed time;
- reading thermometers using Fahrenheit and Celsius scales.

Español

Durante esta unidad de matemáticas, su estudiante va a explorar el tiempo y la temperatura. Para ayudar con el aprendizaje, sugerimos estas actividades para hacer en casa:

- Use palabras que se refieran al tiempo para describir eventos.
- Estime cuánto tiempo transcurre entre el principio y el final de eventos como reuniones familiares, mandados o programas de televisión.
- Encuentre la hora y la temperatura en las distintas zonas horarias.
- Ayude a su estudiante a crear un calendario de actividades familiares.

En clase, su estudiante va a:

- leer, escribir y comparar tiempos;
- encontrar el tiempo transcurrido;
- leer termómetros por medio de las escalas Fahrenheit y Celsius.

Name: _____ **Date:** _____

Days, Hours, Minutes

In the investigation, you made a graph showing the time you spend doing different activities in one day.

1. Which activity would you like to spend more time doing? Which activity would you like to spend less time doing? Redraw your graph to show how you would like to spend your day differently. Make sure to include labels for the activity, the time, and the fraction of the day.

2. Name three things you do that take about 1 hour.

_____

_____

3. Name three things you do that take about 1 minute.

_____

_____

Ways We Use Time

How do we use time each day? What words do we use to talk about time? Make a book featuring different words and phrases we use to describe time.

Timely Words

When units of time are related, we say they are equivalent.

4. Complete the chart to show equivalent times.

Equivalent Units of Time
365 days = 1 year
12 months = 1 year
52 weeks = 1 year
7 days = 1 week
_____ hours = 1 day
_____ minutes = 1 hour

Name the equivalent time.

5. $\frac{2}{7}$ of a week = _____ days

6. $\frac{1}{2}$ year = _____ weeks

7. _____ day = 8 hours

Write >, <, or = to make each statement true.

8. $\frac{1}{4}$ of a day _____ 12 hours

9. 3 months _____ $\frac{1}{2}$ of a year

10. 24 hours _____ $\frac{1}{7}$ of a week

11. 735 days _____ 2 years

Solve each problem. You may use a circle graph to help.

12. On Brian's vacation, he drove $\frac{1}{4}$ of a day for 3 days. How many hours did he drive in all? _____

13. Brian spent about 3 hours eating at restaurants the first day. What fraction of the day did Brian spend eating? _____

14. About $\frac{1}{6}$ of the day, Brian listened to music on the car radio. About how many hours did Brian listen to music during the day? _____

15. Brian spent about 2 hours visiting the beach along the way. What fraction of the day did Brian stay at the beach? _____

Name: _____ **Date:** _____

Parts of an Hour

Write the number of minutes that are shaded.
Then name the fraction of the hour.

1.

2.

3.

_____ _____ _____

_____ _____ _____

We can use the number of minutes before or after an hour to
read time. We can also use fractions to read time.

We read:

We say:
six fifteen

15 minutes past 6

quarter past 6

Write the different ways we can say the time
shown on the clocks to the right.

4. _____

_____

_____

5. _____

_____

Look for a pattern. Then draw the time on the last clock face.
Write that time in three different ways.

6.

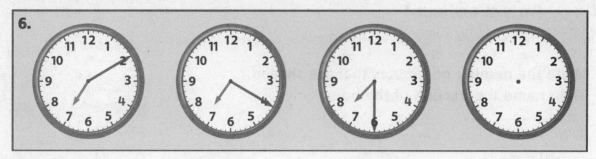

7.

8.

Complete the schedule. Write in the correct times.

9. The train left Mayfield at half past 2. It arrived at Clarksville at quarter past 3.

10. The train left Clarksville at 10 minutes to 4. It arrived at Hook Lake at quarter to 5.

11. All of the times listed are in the afternoon. Would you add A.M. or P.M. to each time on the schedule? _____

Train Schedule		
	Depart	Arrive
Mayfield to Clarksville		
Clarksville to Hook Lake		

 4:05 5:17 seventy-two

Name: _____ Date: _____

Elapsed Time

In the investigation, you found elapsed time. Now find more elapsed times.

1. Rosa started her homework at 4:10. She stopped at 5:15. How long did she do her homework?

4:10 to 5:10 is 1 hour.
5:10 to 5:15 is 5 minutes.

It took Rosa 1 hour and 5 minutes to do her homework.

What is another way to find the elapsed time?

_____

_____

Math Word

elapsed time

Write the elapsed time.

2.

_____

3.

_____

4.

_____

5.

_____

Write the start or end time.

6. Start: 3:00 P.M.
(40 minutes later)

End: _____

7. Start: 7:30 A.M.
(1 hour 20 minutes later)

End: _____

8. Start: _____
(2 hours 30 minutes later)

End: 9:15 P.M.

Complete the zoo-field-trip schedule using the information below. Draw hands on the clocks to show the start and end times of each activity.

9. The bus ride from the school to the zoo is 1 hour and 20 minutes.

10. The dolphin show lasts 2 hours and 15 minutes.

11. The reptile exhibit takes about 30 minutes to see.

Zoo Field Trip		
Activity	**Start Time**	**End Time**
Bus Ride to Zoo	7:00 A.M.	
Dolphin Show	8:30 A.M.	
Reptile Exhibit		11:30 A.M.
Lunch	11:35 A.M.	
Zoo Train	12:15 P.M.	
Tour Zoo	1:10 P.M.	
Bus Ride to School		5:25 P.M.

12. Lunch lasts for 25 minutes.

13. The zoo train ride is 50 minutes long.

14. To walk through the rest of the zoo takes about 2 hours and 10 minutes

15. The bus ride to the school takes 5 minutes longer than the ride to the zoo.

At Home
Make a schedule of your family's activities for one day. Mark the times of each activity and note the elapsed times.

Name: _____ Date: _____

Temperature: Fahrenheit and Celsius

In the investigation, you measured temperature and made a thermometer. Now, use your thermometer to answer these questions.

Math Words

Celsius (°C)

Fahrenheit (°F)

temperature

thermometer

1. Which number of degrees is across from 0°C?

_____

2. Which is warmer, −15°C or −15°F?

_____

3. Which is cooler, 40°C or 40°F?

_____

4. What might the temperature be on a very hot day?

Degrees Celsius _____

Degrees Fahrenheit _____

5. What might the temperature be on a very cold day?

Degrees Celsius _____

Degrees Fahrenheit _____

In Science

As the ice water from your investigation melts, continue to record the temperatures. What happens when you put both cups in a warm spot? in a cooler spot? by a sunny window? in a dark room? Compare the temperature changes of the water in the two cups.

Write the temperature in °F and °C. Then, tell what each student should wear to school.

6.

°F   °C

110°
100°   40°
90°   30°
80°
70°   20°
60°

Frank in Florida

Temperature:_____

What should Frank wear?

_____

_____

7.

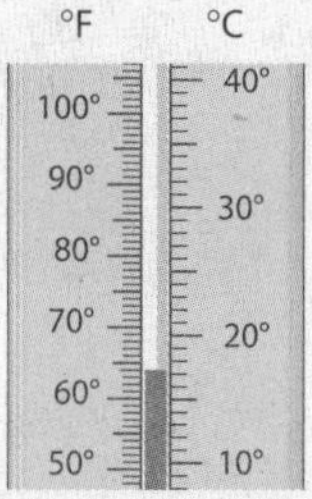

°F   °C

          40°
100°
90°   30°
80°
70°   20°
60°
50°   10°

Callie in California

Temperature:_____

What should Callie wear?

_____

_____

8.

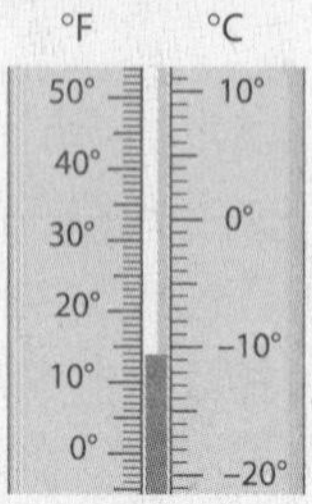

°F   °C

50°   10°
40°
30°   0°
20°
10°   −10°
0°   −20°

Matt in Minnesota

Temperature:_____

What should Matt wear?

_____

_____

The chart shows the temperature changes during the day.

9. How much did the temperature change between 5:00 A.M. and 10:00 A.M.?

_____

10. Between which two times was there the greatest temperature drop? How many degrees did the temperature drop?

Time	Temperature
5:00 A.M.	41°F
10:00 A.M.	52°F
12:00 P.M.	65°F
3:00 P.M.	68°F
7:00 P.M.	58°F
10:00 P.M.	46°F

Reflecting on What I Learned

New *Vocabulary* I learned:

1. _____
   _____

2. _____
   _____

3. _____
   _____

What units do you use when talking about time? about temperature?

_____

_____

List one relationship between fractions and time you learned.

_____

_____

Outside Your Classroom

Where will you see time and temperature outside the classroom?

- About how much of your day do you spend at home?

- About how long does it take you to get from your house to school?

- What kind of clothes should you bring for a camping trip?

Make a Perfect-Day Timeline

Use your knowledge of elapsed time and temperature to make a timeline of your perfect day.

1. First, make a schedule of the activities you would like to do and the times you would do them.

   - What time do you wake up and what time do you go to sleep?

   - What activities do you do throughout the day? Where do you go? When do you go? How long are you there?

   - What time do you eat meals?

2. Using a long strip of paper, make a timeline of your perfect day.

   - How will you divide your paper into different times of the day? Will you divide it by hours? half hours? other units?

   - What symbols will you use to show the different activities?

3. Write a report about your project. Include some of the following.

   - What is the month, day, and date?

   - What is the temperature?

   - About what fraction of the day is the elapsed time for each activity?

   - Include the schedule of your activities.

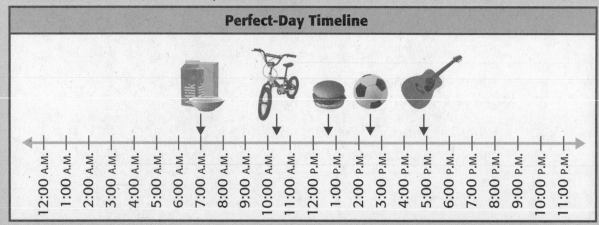

Perfect-Day Timeline

6:30 7:48

UNIT H

Length, Volume, and Weight/Mass

In this unit, I will:

- Find the lengths of objects in inches and centimeters
- Find the volumes of rectangular prisms
- Explore capacity using customary and metric units
- Use a balance to find the weight and mass of objects
- Compare measurements

Review Concepts
- measuring with a ruler, rectangular prisms, multiplication

Project
- Make a Measurement Book

New Vocabulary

capacity the amount a container can hold

cubic unit a unit for measuring volume, such as a cubic inch or cubic centimeter

mass measure of the amount of matter in an object

volume the number of cubic units needed to fill a three-dimensional figure or solid figure

weight a measurement that tells how heavy an object is

customary system (units) the measurement system that is used more in the United States; includes:	metric system (units) the measurement system based on powers of 10; includes:
1 cup = 8 ounces	1 liter = 1,000 milliliters
1 gallon = 16 cups	
1 gallon = 4 quarts	1 meter = 100 centimeters
1 quart = 4 cups	
1 pint = 2 cups	1 kilogram = 1,000 grams
1 pound = 16 ounces	
1 ton = 2,000 pounds	
1 foot = 12 inches	
1 yard = 3 feet	

Home Letter

English

During this math unit, your student will be exploring measurements of length, capacity, and weight using customary and metric units.
To help with learning, here are some activities to do at home.

- Practice measuring items around the house using a ruler.
- Examine labels on drink bottles and containers. Note the capacity.
- Go to a supermarket and compare the weights of different foods. Look at the labels and identify the weight in customary and/or metric units.

In class, your student will be:

- using different measuring tools to find an object's length;
- using centimeter cubes to find the volume of boxes and rectangular prisms;
- using a balance to find and compare weights of items.

Español

Durante esta unidad de matemáticas, su estudiante va a explorar las mediciones de longitud, capacidad y peso por medio de unidades de medida usuales y métricas. Para ayudar con el aprendizaje, sugerimos estas actividades para hacer en casa.

- Practique el medir artículos alrededor de la casa con una regla.
- Examine las etiquetas de diversas botellas y recipientes. Observe su capacidad.
- Vaya a un supermercado y compare los pesos de distintos alimentos. Mire las etiquetas e identifique el peso en unidades usuales y/o métricas.

En clase, su estudiante va a:

- usar distintas herramientas de medición para hallar la longitud de un objeto;
- usar cubos de 1 centímetro para hallar el volumen de cajas y prismas rectangulares;
- usar una balanza para hallar y comparar el peso de distintos artículos.

Name: _____ **Date:** _____

Length: Customary and Metric

In the investigation, you measured body parts to the nearest inch and centimeter. Now measure to a fraction of an inch.

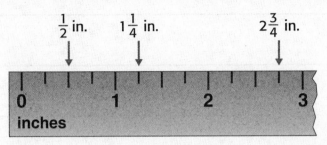

$\frac{1}{2}$ in. $1\frac{1}{4}$ in. $2\frac{3}{4}$ in.

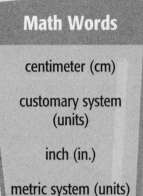

Math Words

centimeter (cm)

customary system (units)

inch (in.)

metric system (units)

1. Measure the ribbon to the nearest inch, $\frac{1}{2}$ inch, and $\frac{1}{4}$ inch.

_____   _____   _____

2. Draw a line that is 4 inches long.

3. Draw a line that is $3\frac{1}{2}$ inches long.

4. Draw a line that is $3\frac{3}{4}$ inches long.

5. Which of the lines you drew is closest to the length of the ribbon?

_____

6. What can you do to get the most accurate inch measurement?

_____

In Science
Will a sock fit your foot? Make a fist and wrap the sock around the widest part. If the sock meets toe to heel when wrapped, the sock should fit. Test this with a piece of string.

**List at least two objects that have a length close to the
given measurement.**

7. 12 inches _____

8. 8 feet _____

9. 10 centimeters _____

10. 1 yard _____

11. 2 centimeters _____

12. 5 meters _____

13. Draw the following:
a. a line that measures 4 inches

b. a line that measures 10 centimeters

14. Look at the lines you drew. Is 1 inch greater than or less than
2 centimeters? How do you know?

_____

_____

_____

_____

Measurement Book
Create your own measurement book. Measure different objects
and record the dimensions in inches and in centimeters.

Name: _____ Date: _____

Capacity: Customary and Metric

Build different rectangular prisms and find their volumes.

1. Make as many different rectangular prisms as possible using eight centimeter cubes. Record the dimensions and volume of each.

Length	Width	Height	Volume

2. Make as many different rectangular prisms as possible using twelve centimeter cubes. Record the dimensions and volume of each.

Length	Width	Height	Volume

Math Words

capacity

cubic unit

cup (c)

gallon (gal)

liter (L)

milliliter (mL)

pint (pt)

quart (qt)

volume

Sometimes a container is not a rectangular prism. You can use customary and metric units of capacity to describe its volume.

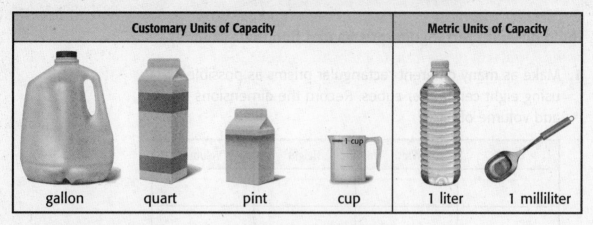

Customary Units of Capacity				Metric Units of Capacity	
gallon	quart	pint	cup	1 liter	1 milliliter

Use the benchmarks above to match each item with its capacity.

A. 1 cup	B. 55 gallons	C. 20 gallons
D. 4,000 gallons	E. 25 milliliters	F. 1 milliliter

3.

4.

5.

6.

7.

8.

Measurement Book

Food and drink containers are often labeled in units of capacity. Visit a grocery store, look at advertisements, or find items in your refrigerator. Add photos or drawings of items with different capacities to your measurement book.

In the investigation, you used a balance to find the weight of classroom objects using nonstandard units. Let's look at the weight of objects using customary units.

Math Words

gram (g)

kilogram (kg)

mass

ounce (oz)

pound (lb)

ton

weight

1. About 10 pennies weigh an ounce. List three items that could be measured in ounces.

   _____

   _____

2. A pound is equal to 16 ounces.
   List three items that could be measured in pounds.

   _____

   _____

3. A ton is equal to 2,000 pounds.
   List three items that could be measured in tons.

   _____

   _____

   _____

Let's look at the mass of objects using metric units.

4. A large paper clip weighs about a gram.
   List three items that could be measured in grams.

   _____

   _____

   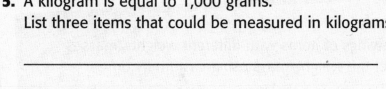

5. A kilogram is equal to 1,000 grams.
   List three items that could be measured in kilograms.

   _____

   _____

Look at each picture. Describe the weight/mass using the terms *greater than, less than,* **or** *equal to.*

6.

The bear is

_____.

7.

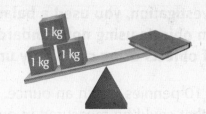

The book is

_____.

8.

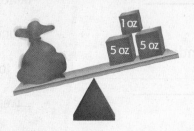

The bag is

_____.

9.

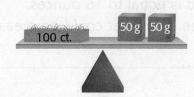

The box of paper clips is

_____.

Circle the greater weight/mass.

10. 3 tons   25 pounds

11. 700 grams   1 kilogram

12. 1 pound   34 ounces

13. 4 kilograms   5,000 grams

14. 5,000 ounces   1 ton

15. 1 ton   1 kilogram

PROJECT

Measurement Book
Add photos or drawings of items with different weights/masses to your book. Label the weight/mass using customary or metric units.

86 ounces = $5\frac{3}{8}$ **pounds**   eighty-six

Reflecting on What I Learned

New *Vocabulary* I learned:

1. _____

_____

2. _____

3. _____

_____

What are two key items I learned about metric and customary units?

_____

_____

_____

Describe one relationship between length, width, height, and volume you learned.

_____

_____

Outside Your Classroom

Where will you see length, capacity/volume, and weight/mass outside the classroom?

- About how much material would you need to make a curtain for your bedroom window?

- If you need to fill an aquarium with water, how would you pick the size of bucket or glass to use?

- When would you use volume to measure something? When would you use weight?

Sandbox Builder

In this unit, you measured length, volume, and weight/mass in both customary and metric units. Use this knowledge to design a sandbox.

1. Use the centimeter cubes to plan your sandbox. Explore different shapes and sizes.

- What shape is your sandbox?

- What will be the length and width of your sandbox?

- How high will your sandbox be?

2. Let each cube represent 1 cubic foot.

- Draw a diagram of your sandbox on grid or dot paper.

- Label the dimensions in feet.

3. You need sand for your sandbox.

One bag of sand covers 1 cubic foot.

Each bag of sand weighs 50 pounds.

Use the math in this unit and the information above to answer these questions:

- How much sand will you need?

- How much will the sand weigh altogether?

4. Write a report on your project. Include some of the following.

- What are the dimensions of your sandbox? Did you use customary or metric units?

- How much wood do you need to buy at the hardware store to build the sandbox?

- What measurements did you use to calculate how many bags of sand to buy?

UNIT 1

Graphs: Creating and Interpreting

In this unit, I will:

- Create surveys and interview people
- Create bar graphs and double bar graphs to compare data
- Read and create line graphs that show data changes over time
- Interpret data shown on different kinds of graphs

Review Concepts
- addition, subtraction, multiplication, scale

Projects
- What Do You Know About Your Class?
- Design a New School Room

Games
- Card Keepers

New Vocabulary

bar graph a graph that compares data by using bars of different lengths or heights to show the values

data numbers or symbols, sometimes collected from a survey or experiment, to show information; datum is singular; data is plural

double bar graph a bar graph that compares two related groups of data

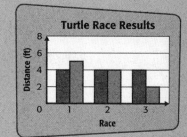

line graph a graph that uses points connected by line segments to represent data

point an exact location in space

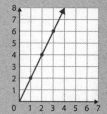

survey a method of collecting data

tally chart a way to keep track of data using tally marks to record the number of responses or occurrences

What is Your Favorite Color?	
Color	Tally
Blue	~~HHH~~ III
Green	IIII

Home Letter

English

During this math unit, your student will be reading, creating, and interpreting data from different types of graphs. To help with learning, here are things to do at home.

- Find different types of graphs in newspapers, magazines, brochures, and other printed materials.
- Talk about how the graphs are organized and what information they contain.
- Encourage your student to make graphs for daily activities, such as the time spent reading a book or the number of each kind of coin that you have in your pockets.

In class, your student will be:

- conducting surveys and recording data;
- reading, creating, and interpreting graphs;
- designing a new school room.

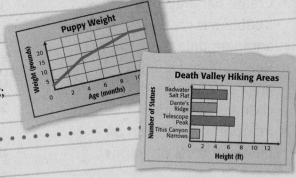

Español

Durante esta unidad de matemáticas su estudiante va a leer, crear e interpretar datos de diferentes tipos de gráficas. Para ayudar con el aprendizaje, sugerimos estas actividades para hacer en casa:

- Encuentre diferentes tipos de gráficas en periódicos, revistas, folletos y otros materiales impresos.
- Hable acerca de cómo están organizadas las gráficas y qué información contienen.
- Anime a su estudiante a que haga gráficas de sus actividades diarias, tales como el tiempo que pasa leyendo un libro o el número de monedas de cada tipo que tiene usted en sus bolsillos.

En clase, su estudiante va a:

- llevar a cabo encuestas y registrar datos;
- leer, crear e interpretar gráficas;
- diseñar un nuevo salón de clases.

Name: _____   Date: _____

Bar Graphs

In the investigation, you conducted a survey and recorded the data in a tally chart. Now, you will make a bar graph representing the results.

Plan your graph.

1. What will be the title of your bar graph?

_____

_____

2. How will you label the edges of the graph?

_____

_____

3. What will be the scale of the graph?

_____

_____

4. Create your bar graph.

> **Math Words**
>
> bar graph
>
> data
>
> survey
>
> tally chart

Use the chart and bar graph to answer the questions.

Favorite Bike Colors	
Colors	Votes
Black	3
Yellow	8
Blue	7
Red	10

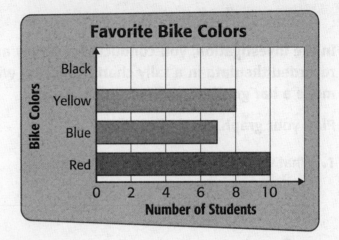

Favorite Bike Colors

5. What is the title of the bar graph? _____

6. Which bar is missing from the graph? _____

7. Compare the chart and the graph. Complete the graph so that it represents the same data shown in the chart.

8. List the bike colors in order from greatest to least number of votes.

_____

9. How many students are represented in the survey? _____

10. How many more students chose red than yellow? _____

11. Which two colors added together received the same number of votes as red? _____

12. Which color represents a number of votes that is 5 fewer than the number of yellow votes? _____

What Do You Know About Your Class?

Survey other students in your class to get to know them better. Interview at least 5 girls and 5 boys. Record your data in a tally chart and a bar graph.

Name: _____ **Date:** _____

Double Bar Graphs

In the investigation, you represented data in a double bar graph. This graph compares a fourth-grade class's favorite sports.

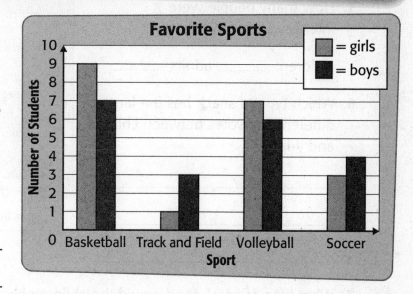

Favorite Sports

= girls

= boys

1. How can you tell the difference between the girls' bars and the boys' bars?

   _____

   _____

   _____

   _____

2. Do more girls or boys like soccer best? _____

3. How many more girls than boys chose basketball as their favorite sport? _____

4. How many girls and how many boys are represented in the graph? Explain how you found your answer.

   _____

   _____

   _____

Math Word

double bar graph

In Sports

Ask students to gather data about a sports game from a newspaper or the Internet. Have them make a tally chart to total the scores for two teams for each inning, period, or quarter. Then use grid paper to create a double bar graph from the data.

Use the graph to answer the questions below.

5. How many people were interviewed for this survey?

children: _____ adults: _____

6. Which type of snack has the largest difference in votes between children and adults?

_____

_____

_____

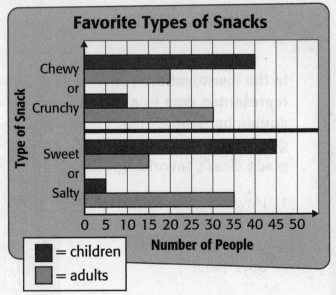

Favorite Types of Snacks

Type of Snack: Chewy or Crunchy, Sweet or Salty

Number of People: 0 5 10 15 20 25 30 35 40 45 50

■ = children
■ = adults

7. What type of snack food would the children like best?

_____

_____

Complete the graph.

8. Add the bars to show this data.

	Boys	Girls
Pockets	15	2

Use the graph to answer these questions.

9. Which jacket part has the greatest difference between boys' and girls' preferences?

_____

10. How many more boys prefer a pullover jacket than girls? _____

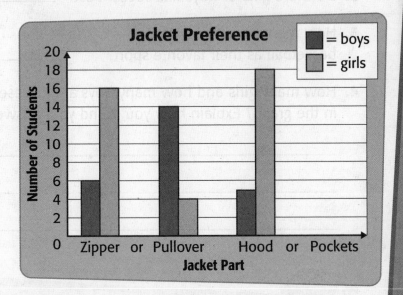

Jacket Preference

■ = boys
■ = girls

Number of Students: 0 2 4 6 8 10 12 14 16 18 20

Jacket Part: Zipper or Pullover Hood or Pockets

Name: _____ **Date:** _____

Line Graphs

In the investigation, you used a line graph to show the distance mountain climbers traveled. A line graph shows how data changes over time.

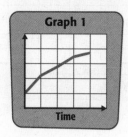

Graph 1

Time

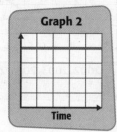

Graph 2

Time

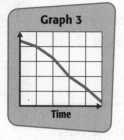

Graph 3

Time

1. Which graph shows data that decreases over time? _____

2. Which graph shows data that increases over time? _____

3. Which graph shows data that stays the same over time? _____

Look at the data shown by this line graph.

4. What does this graph tell you?

_____

_____

_____

_____

_____

_____

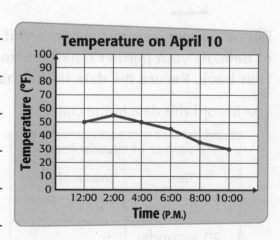

Temperature on April 10

Temperature (°F)

100
90
80
70
60
50
40
30
20
10
0

12:00 2:00 4:00 6:00 8:00 10:00
Time (P.M.)

Each year the gardener keeps track of the height of one of his plants.

5. About how tall was the plant in 2003?

   _____

6. Between which two years was there the greatest increase in height?

   _____

   About how much of an increase was it?

   _____

7. When does the line graph show that the height stayed about the same? _____

8. Tony, the gardener, predicts the height in 2008 and 2009. Add these to the graph.

   2008: 85 inches   2009: 95 inches

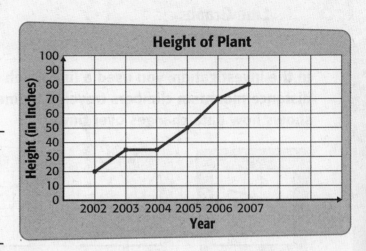

Height of Plant

With a partner, record the number of words you can read in different lengths of time. As your partner times you, mark the beginning and ending words in your book. Record the data in the chart given.

9. Record the data in the chart.

Number of Words Read	
Time	**Number of Words**
10 seconds	
20 seconds	
30 seconds	
40 seconds	
50 seconds	

10. Predict the number of words you will read in one minute. Make a line graph showing the data.

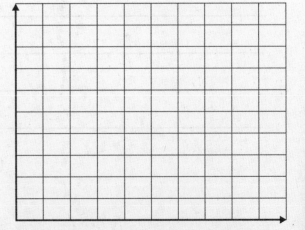

Reflecting on What I Learned

New *Vocabulary* I learned:

1. _____

_____

_____

2. _____

_____

3. _____

Describe one difference between a double bar graph and a line graph.

_____

_____

List one relationship between a tally chart and a graph you learned.

_____

_____

Outside Your Classroom

Where will you see surveys, data, and graphs outside the classroom?

- How could you show your growth in height throughout your life?

- How could you find and show how many boys or girls in your classroom prefer dogs or cats as pets?

- How could you show the number of students in each grade at your school?

Design a New School Room

Use your knowledge of graphs and surveys to collect data for a new school room.

1. First, create a survey asking at least ten people what new room they would like in the school. Give them choices for their answers.

   - How will the room be used? (e.g., computer room, game room, art gallery)

   - Who will use the room? (e.g., students, teachers, visitors)

   - What will be in the room? (e.g., games, computers, books, musical instruments)

How will you record the responses to your survey questions? How will you organize and display the data in a graph?

2. Use grid paper to draw a room design based on the results from your survey.

   - How large will the room be? What is the area and the perimeter?

   - Will the room have computers, play equipment, books, or other items?

3. Write a report on your project including some of the following:

   - What information from your survey and graphs helped you design the room?

   - Include your room design.

   - Include a copy of your graph.

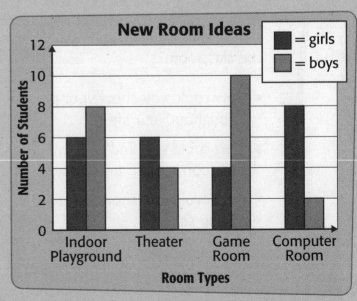

UNIT J

Transformations

In this unit, I will:

- Examine figures for line and rotational symmetry
- Tell if two figures are congruent
- Explore reflecting, translating, and rotating figures

Review Concepts
- polygons, two-dimensional figures

Projects
- Make an Alphabet of Symmetry book
- Make transformation patterns
- Design a flag

Game
- Congruent Match

New Vocabulary

congruent figures two figures having the same size and the same shape

line of symmetry a line on which a figure can be folded so that its two halves match exactly

point an exact location in space that is represented by a dot

reflection a figure that is flipped over a line to create a mirror image of the figure

rotation rotating a figure about a point

rotational symmetry a figure has rotational symmetry if, after a rotation of the figure about a point, the figure lies in its original position

similar figures that have the same shape but different sizes

transformation a movement of a figure that does not change the size or shape of the figure

translation sliding a figure in a straight line horizontally, vertically, or diagonally

Home Letter

English

During this math unit, your student will be exploring congruence, symmetry, and transformations. To help with learning, here are some activities to do at home.

- Look at items around the house and in nature that have symmetry (e.g., butterfly).
- Draw a figure on paper. Have your student draw a figure that is similar (same shape) and a figure that is congruent (same size and shape).
- Examine things in a mirror. Talk about how the reflections are opposite.

In class, your student will be:

- drawing figures that have line symmetry and rotational symmetry;
- labeling movements of figures as translations, reflections, or rotations.

Español

Durante esta unidad de matemáticas su estudiante va a explorar la congruencia, la simetría y las transformaciones. Para ayudar con el aprendizaje, sugerimos estas actividades para hacer en casa:

- Observe cosas en la casa y en la naturaleza que tengan simetría (p.ej., mariposa).
- Dibuje una figura en un papel. Pídale a su estudiante que dibuje una figura que sea similar (de la misma forma) y una figura que sea congruente (del mismo tamaño y de la misma forma).
- Examine diversos objetos frente a un espejo. Hable acerca de cómo el reflejo muestra lo opuesto.

En clase, su estudiante va a:

- dibujar figuras que tengan simetría lineal y simetría de rotación;
- identificar los movimientos de las figuras como traslaciones, reflexiones o rotaciones.

Name: _____ Date: _____

Symmetry

Draw figures that have symmetry.

1. Color in grid squares so that the dotted line is a line of symmetry.

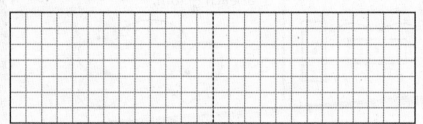

Math Words

line of symmetry

reflection

rotational symmetry

2. Draw a figure that has only one line of symmetry. Identify the line of symmetry.

3. Draw a figure that has 2 lines of symmetry. Show the lines of symmetry.

4. Draw a figure that has 3 or more lines of symmetry. Show the lines of symmetry.

5. Draw a figure that has both line and rotational symmetry.

6. Is there a relationship between the number of lines of symmetry a shape has and rotational symmetry? Explain your answer.

_____

_____

A shape must look the same in 2 or more positions to have rotational symmetry.

A rectangle has rotational symmetry. When turned around a center point, it looks the same at each $\frac{1}{2}$ turn.

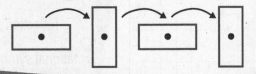

A heart does not have rotational symmetry. When turned around a center point, it looks different at each $\frac{1}{4}$ turn.

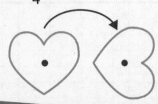

Does the shape have rotational symmetry? Write *yes* or *no*.

7.

_____

8.

_____

9.

_____

10.

_____

11.

_____

12.

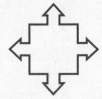

_____

Alphabet of Symmetry

Create an Alphabet of Symmetry book. Write a letter of the alphabet on each page of the book. Write both the capital and the lowercase letters. Then label each as having line symmetry, rotational symmetry, or both. Write a paragraph summarizing your findings.

Name: _____ **Date:** _____

Congruence

Practice drawing congruent and similar figures.

Complete the table.

Math Words

congruent figures

similar

	Congruent	Similar
1.		
2.		
3.		
4.		

In Art

Draw a figure on paper. Then use your drawing to design a picture that is made up only of figures that are congruent or similar to your figure. Color your picture.

Decide if each figure to the right is congruent or similar to the figure on the left.

Write _congruent, similar,_ or _neither._

5.

_____ _____ _____

6.

_____ _____ _____

7.

_____ _____ _____

Answer these questions.

8. Evelyn and Tanya both drew similar rectangles. Are all rectangles similar? Explain. _____

_____

9. Heidi has two square rugs. One of the rugs is larger than the other rug. Are the rugs similar? Explain.

_____

10. Are all triangles similar? Explain. _____

_____

11. Pamela said that all circles are congruent. Is she correct? Explain.

_____

_____

Name: _____ Date: _____

Rotations, Reflections, and Translations

In the investigation, you explored different types of transformations.

Rotations can be described using angle degrees. A circle has a total of 360°.

90° rotation ($\frac{1}{4}$ turn)

180° rotation ($\frac{1}{2}$ turn)

270° rotation ($\frac{3}{4}$ turn)

360° rotation (1 full turn)

Reflections can have a horizontal or vertical reflection line.

horizontal reflection line

vertical reflection line

Translations can be left, right, up, down, or diagonal.

The triangle was translated 2 units right.

The rectangle was translated 3 units down.

Label each transformation as a *rotation, reflection,* or *translation.* Then describe the transformation in more detail.

1.

_____

2.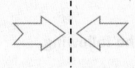

_____

3.

_____

4.

_____

5.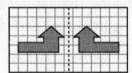

_____

6.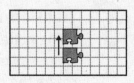

_____

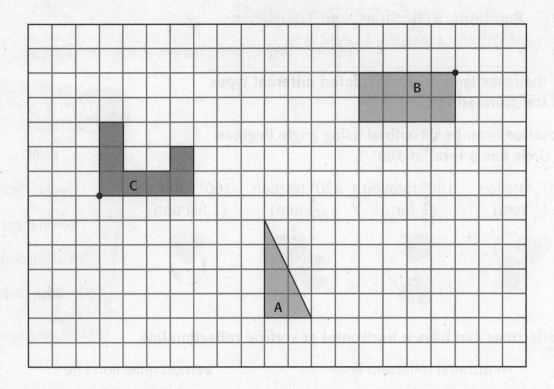

Complete the following.

7. Reflect Figure A over a vertical reflection line. Draw the new figure. Label it X.

8. Translate Figure B two units left and then rotate it 90°. Draw the new figure. Label it Y.

9. Rotate Figure C 180° and then translate it three units down. Draw the new figure. Label it Z.

10. On grid or dot paper, draw a figure. Then show a translation, rotation, and reflection of the figure. Label each transformation.

Transformation Patterns
Using pattern blocks, have students create patterns using one shape. Instruct them to translate, rotate, or reflect their shapes to create the patterns. Have students present their patterns to the class, and have classmates determine how the patterns were made.

Reflecting on What I Learned

New *Vocabulary* I learned:

1. _____

_____

2. _____

_____

3. _____

_____

What are the 3 types of transformations?

_____

_____

Describe the relationship between transformations and congruence that you learned.

_____

_____

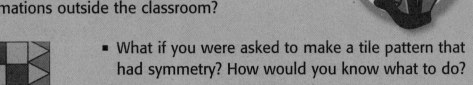

Outside Your Classroom

Where will you see symmetry, congruence, and transformations outside the classroom?

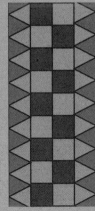

- What if you were asked to make a tile pattern that had symmetry? How would you know what to do?

- What if you were sorting items? How could you use congruence and similarity?

- Where in nature do you see symmetry?

- How could you use transformations to paint a decorative border around your room?

Design a Flag

In this unit you worked with symmetry, congruence, and transformations.

Use this new knowledge to design a flag. The flag can be decorative or it can be symbolic.

1. First, decide what you want on your flag. Explore different ideas.

   - Will your flag be a decoration for a season or a holiday?

   - Will your flag represent you, your family, your class, or a state or country? Will your flag have pictures or words?

   - What color or colors do you want on your flag?

   - How big will your flag be?

2. Next, use the math in this unit to design the flag. On poster board, draw the outline of your flag.

   - Your flag should have symmetry.

   - Use congruent and similar figures.

   - Include transformations in your design.

3. Write a report on your project including some of the following:

   - What kind of flag did you design? What shape is it?

   - What type of symmetry does your flag have? Does is show congruence?

   - Are there one or more lines of symmetry?

   - Which transformations did you use in your design?

   - Describe where on your flag these transformations can be seen.

Acknowledgements

Student Edition Photo Credits

Cover Mazer Creative Services; United States coin images from the United States Mint; **i** Corbis/PictureQuest; **xiv** Image Source Pink/Getty Images; **xix** Mazer Photo Studio; **xv** (t)Masterfile, (b)PunchStock; **xvi** (tl), (tr)Getty Images, (bl)Ed-Imaging, (br)Ryan McVay/Getty Images; **xvii** Ryan McVay/Getty Images; **xviii** Travel Ink Photo Library/Index Stock Imagery; **xx** Thinkstock Images/Jupiter Images; **xxi** Mazer Creative Services, **1** CORBIS; **2** Mazer Creative Services; **4** (tl)Getty Images, (tr)Stockbyte/Getty Images, (bl)PunchStock, (br)Getty Images; **5** Amos Morgan/Photodisc Green/Getty Images; **7** Masterfile; **12** Mark Karrass/Corbis; **13** Mazer Creative Services; **15** RTimages/Alamy; **19** PhotoAlto; **21** Image Source Pink/Getty Images; **A5** (T)Ed-imaging, (b)Rubberball/Jupiter Images; **23** Mazer Creative Services; **24** Brian Hagiwara/Brand X Pictures/Getty Images; **25** (all) Mazer Creative Services; **26** (tl)Travel Ink Photo Library/Index Stock Imagery, (tc)Ryan McVay/Getty Images, (tr)Comstock Images/Alamy, (bl)Getty Images, (bc)IndexOpen, (br)Jupiter Images; **28** (tl), (tr) Mazer Creative Services, (bl), (br)CORBIS; **29** Ed-Imaging; **31** Masterfile; **33** Mazer Creative Services; **34** Ingram Publishing/SuperStock; **39** Brand X Pictures/PunchStock; **43** Mazer Creative Services; **44** (tl)Getty Images; (tr)Ryan McVay/Getty Images; (c)Getty Images; (b)Ryan McVay/Getty Images, **45** Mazer Creative Services; **46** Michael Houghton/StudiOhio; **50** Thinkstock Images/Jupiter Images; **55** Comstock Images/Alamy; **57** (l)Ryan McVay/Photodisc/Getty Images, (r) Mazer Creative Services; **65** Brand X Pictures/PunchStock; **68** Mazer Creative Services; **78** (l)CORBIS, (cl)Burke/Triolo Productions/Getty Images, (cr)Ryan McVay/Getty Images, (r)C Squared Studios/Getty Images; **80** The McGraw-Hill Companies, Inc./Ken Karp; **84** (tl)Lew Robertson/CORBIS, (tr)Stockbyte/Getty Images, (ctl)CORBIS, (ctr)Group 5/Alamy, (cbl)image 100/CORBIS, (cbr)Jupiter Images, (bl)The McGraw-Hill Companies, Inc./Ken Karp, (br)The McGraw-Hill Companies, Inc./Ken Cavanagh; **85** (t)Brand X Pictures/PunchStock, (b)C Squared Studios/Getty Images; **88** Dejan/fstop/Alamy; **96** Corbis/PictureQuest; **100** Siede Preis/Getty Images; **108** John Foxx/Stockbyte/Getty Images.

Scope and Sequence

Geometry

Concept	Kindergarten	Grade 1	Grade 2	Grade 3	Grade 4	Grade 5
Attributes and Properties of Two- and Three-Dimensional Figures						
Identify attributes of two-dimensional figures	◐	◐	◐	○	○	◐
Identify attributes of three-dimensional figures	◐	◐	◐	○	○	◐
Sort and describe properties of two-dimensional figures	◐	◐	◐	○	○	○
Sort and describe properties of three-dimensional figures	◐	◐	◐	◐	○	○
Relate two- and three-dimensional figures	◐	◐	◐	○	○	○
Classify and measure angles				○	○	○
Identify and define polygons	◐	◐	◐	◐	○	○
Classify quadrilaterals		◐	◐	◐	○	○
Classify triangles					○	○
Congruent figures				◐	◐	○
Similar figures				●	◐	○
Right triangles and parts					○	○
Points, lines, planes				○	○	○
Coordinate Geometry						
Position and direction	◐	○	◐	◐		
Graph ordered pairs, Coordinate plane			○	○	○	○

● IMPACT Mathematics   ○ Macmillan Mathematics   ◐ Both IMPACT Mathematics and Macmillan Mathematics

Transformations and Symmetry

Concept	Kindergarten	Grade 1	Grade 2	Grade 3	Grade 4	Grade 5
Transformations and Symmetry						
Translation (slide)		●	●	●	◐	●
Reflection (flip)		●	●	◐	◐	●
Rotation (turn)		●	●	●	●	●
Transformations on the coordinate plane						●
Symmetry (line and rotation)		◐	◐	◐	◐	●
Tessellations						●

Concept	Kindergarten	Grade 1	Grade 2	Grade 3	Grade 4	Grade 5
Drawings and Constructions						
Nets					●	◐

Measurement

Concept	Kindergarten	Grade 1	Grade 2	Grade 3	Grade 4	Grade 5
Measurable Attributes of Objects and Units of Measure: Length, Weight (Mass), Capacity (Volume)						
Nonstandard units	◐	●	◐	◐	◐	◐
Customary units		●	◐	◐	◐	◐
Metric units			◐	◐	◐	◐
Compare and order objects by length, weight, volume	◐	●	◐	◐	◐	●
Convert units within a system				◐	◐	◐

Measurement (continued)

Concept	Kindergarten	Grade 1	Grade 2	Grade 3	Grade 4	Grade 5
Measurable Attributes of Objects and Units of Measure: Time and Temperature						
Temperature (Celsius, Fahrenheit)	○	○	○	○	◐	●
Estimate time	○	◐	◐	◐	◐	◐
A.M., P.M.			○	○	◐	◐
Calendar	○	◐	○	○	◐	○
Tell time		◐	○	◐	◐	◐
Convert time				○	◐	◐
Units of time		◐	◐	◐	◐	◐
Elapsed time		◐	○		◐	◐
Sequence of events, order events	○	◐	○	○	◐	◐
Measurable Attributes of Objects and Units of Measure: Money						
Recognize and count coins		◐	◐	◐	◐	◐
Recognize and count bills			◐	◐	◐	◐
Compare money amounts		◐	◐	◐	◐	◐
Find values of coins and bills		◐	◐	◐	◐	◐
Make change		●	◐	◐	◐	◐
Measurement Formulas and Techniques						
Use formulas					◐	◐
Perimeter				◐	◐	◐

● IMPACT Mathematics   ○ Macmillan Mathematics   ◐ Both IMPACT Mathematics and Macmillan Mathematics

Concept	Kindergarten	Grade 1	Grade 2	Grade 3	Grade 4	Grade 5
Estimate area			•	•	•	•
Compare areas	•	•	•	•	•	•
Area of square		•	•	•	•	•
Area of rectangle		•	•	•	•	•
Area of parallelogram				•	•	•
Area of triangle				•	•	•
Area of trapezoid				•	•	•
Area of composite figures			•	•	•	•
Surface area of cube				•	•	•
Surface area of rectangular prism						•
Surface area of pyramids, cones						•
Estimate volume			•	•	•	•
Volume of cube				•	•	•
Volume of rectangular prism				•	•	•
Angle measurement in degrees					•	•
Indirect measurement	•		•			

Patterns, Relationships, and Algebraic Thinking

Concept	Kindergarten	Grade 1	Grade 2	Grade 3	Grade 4	Grade 5
Patterns						
Sort and classify	◐	◐	◐	○	○	○
Number patterns	◐	◐	◐	◐	◐	○
Extend a pattern, predict	◐	◐	◐	◐	◐	◐
Create a pattern	◐	◐	◐	◐	◐	○
Describe a pattern	◐	◐	◐	◐	◐	◐
Use addition/subtraction patterns	◐	◐	◐	◐	◐	◐
Use multiplication patterns				◐	○	○
Use division patterns				◐	◐	○
Functions and Relations						
Function Machine, input/output				○	○	◐
Function tables				◐	◐	◐
Function rules and equations			○	○	◐	◐
Definition of function				●	●	◐
Coordinate Plane, ordered pairs					○	◐
Graphs of functions						◐
Model real-world data					○	○
Symbols, Expressions, and Equations						
Write and solve number sentences using symbols, +, −, =, <, >	◐	◐	◐	◐	◐	◐
Use formulas					○	◐
Variables, expressions, equations		◐	○	◐	◐	◐

● IMPACT Mathematics ○ Macmillan Mathematics ◐ Both IMPACT Mathematics and Macmillan Mathematics

Concept	Kindergarten	Grade 1	Grade 2	Grade 3	Grade 4	Grade 5
Order of operations						◐
Evaluate expressions					◐	◐
Write expressions and equations			●	◐	◐	◐
Equivalent expressions, simplify						●

Solve Equations and Inequalities

	Kindergarten	Grade 1	Grade 2	Grade 3	Grade 4	Grade 5
Addition/subtraction equations				◐	◐	◐
Multiplication/division equations				◐	◐	◐
Multi-step equations					●	◐
Use formulas to solve problems					◐	◐
Write inequalities with variables		◐	◐	◐	◐	◐
Addition/subtraction inequalities		●	●			
Multiplication/division inequalities				●	●	

Graph Linear and Non-Linear Equations and Inequalities

	Kindergarten	Grade 1	Grade 2	Grade 3	Grade 4	Grade 5
Coordinate Plane, ordered pairs					○	○
Model real-world data with equations					○	○

Analyze Change

	Kindergarten	Grade 1	Grade 2	Grade 3	Grade 4	Grade 5
Describe qualitative change (e.g., grow taller)	●		◐	○	○	○
Describe quantitative change (e.g., grow 2 inches in one year)	●		◐	○	○	○
Change in one variable relates to change in another				○	○	◐
Use graphs to analyze change			○	○	○	○

Number, Operation, and Quantitative Reasoning

Scope and Sequence

Concept	Kindergarten	Grade 1	Grade 2	Grade 3	Grade 4	Grade 5
Understand, Represent, and Relate Numbers: Whole Numbers						
One-to-one correspondence	◐	◐				
Ordinal numbers	◐	○	○	○	○	○
Count, read, write, name, rename						
Numbers to 20	◐	◐	◐	◐	◐	◐
Numbers to 100	○	◐	◐	◐	◐	◐
Numbers to 1,000			◐	◐	◐	◐
Numbers to 10,000				○	◐	◐
Numbers to 1 million					◐	◐
Numbers to 1 billion and above						◐
Count backward, forward	◐	◐	◐	◐	◐	◐
Skip count		◐	◐	◐	◐	
Write Roman numerals					○	◐
Equivalent forms (word, expanded, standard)	◐	◐	◐	◐	◐	◐
Place value		◐	◐	◐	◐	◐
Power and exponents						○
Compare and order whole numbers	◐	◐	◐	◐	◐	◐
Represent on a number line	◐	◐	◐	◐	◐	◐
Even and odd numbers		◐	◐	◐	◐	○
Divisibility				◐	◐	◐
Factors				◐	◐	◐
Prime and composite numbers						◐
Prime factorization						○

● IMPACT Mathematics   ○ Macmillan Mathematics   ◐ Both IMPACT Mathematics and Macmillan Mathematics

R8 Scope and Sequence

Concept	Kindergarten	Grade 1	Grade 2	Grade 3	Grade 4	Grade 5
Greatest common factor (GCF)						●
Least common multiple (LCM)						●

Understand, Represent, and Relate Numbers: Fractions

Concept	Kindergarten	Grade 1	Grade 2	Grade 3	Grade 4	Grade 5
Fractional parts of a whole	●	●	●	●	●	●
Fractional parts of a set	●	●	●	●	●	●
Fractional parts of measurements, time		●	●	●	●	●
Read and write fractions		●	●	●	●	●
Compare and order fractions		●	●	●	●	●
Represent fractions on a number line				●	●	●
Equivalent fractions			●	●	●	●
Simplify fractions						●
Least common denominator (LCD)						●
Mixed numbers and improper fractions					●	●
Relate fractions to decimals				●	●	●

Understand, Represent, and Relate Numbers: Decimals

Concept	Kindergarten	Grade 1	Grade 2	Grade 3	Grade 4	Grade 5
Models decimals				●	●	●
Read and write decimals			●	●	●	●
Represent decimals on a number line					●	●
Compare and order decimals			●	●	●	●
Equivalent decimals				●	●	●
Round decimals				●	●	●

Number, Operation, and Quantitative Reasoning *(continued)*

Concept	Kindergarten	Grade 1	Grade 2	Grade 3	Grade 4	Grade 5
Understand, Represent, and Relate Numbers: Ratio, Rate, Proportion						
Ratio and probability						◕
Unit price				◕	◑	◕
Scale drawings						●
Understand, Represent, and Relate Numbers: Percent						
Concept of percent					◑	◕
Understand, Represent, and Relate Numbers: Integers						
Concept of integers, negative numbers						◕
Read and write integers						◕
Graph integers on a number line						◕
Compare and order integers						◕
Understand Operations						
Model addition	◑	◑	◑	◕	◕	◑
Model subtraction	◑	◑	◑	◑	◑	◑
Relate addition and subtraction (inverse)		◑	◑	◑	◑	◑
Model multiplication		◑	◕	◑	◑	◑
Model division		◕	◕	◑	◑	◑
Relate multiplication and division (inverse)				◑	◑	◑
Check subtraction by adding	◑	◑	◑	◑	◕	◑
Check division by multiplying				◑	◑	◑

● IMPACT Mathematics   ◕ Macmillan Mathematics   ◑ Both IMPACT Mathematics and Macmillan Mathematics

Scope and Sequence

Concept	Kindergarten	Grade 1	Grade 2	Grade 3	Grade 4	Grade 5
Understand Properties						
Order of Operations		●	●	●	●	◐
Associative and Commutative Properties	◐	◐	◐	◐	◐	◐
Distributive Property					○	○
Identity Properties		◐	◐	◐	◐	◐
Zero Product Property				◐	◐	◐
Use Operations: Whole Numbers						
Add whole numbers						
Basic facts	◐	◐	◐	◐	◐	◐
Fact families		◐	◐	◐	◐	◐
Algorithm		◐	◐	◐	◐	◐
Three or more addends		●	◐	◐	◐	◐
Subtract whole numbers						
Basic facts	◐	◐	◐	◐	◐	◐
Fact families		◐	◐	◐	◐	◐
Algorithm		◐	◐	◐	◐	◐
Multiply whole numbers						
Basic facts			○	◐	◐	◐
Fact families				◐	◐	◐
Algorithm				◐	◐	◐

Number, Operation, and Quantitative Reasoning *(continued)*

Concept	Kindergarten	Grade 1	Grade 2	Grade 3	Grade 4	Grade 5
Use Operations: Whole Numbers *(continued)*						
Divide whole numbers						
Basic facts			◐	◐	◐	◐
Fact families				◐	◐	◐
Algorithm				◐	◐	◐
Remainders					◐	◐
Use Operations: Fractions						
Add and subtract fractions and mixed numbers					●	
Like denominators				○	◐	○
Unlike denominators					◐	○
Use Operations: Decimals						
Add and subtract decimals						
Money amounts	●	◐	◐	◐	◐	◐
Non-money amounts					○	◐
Use Operations: Mental Math Strategies						
Mentally add and subtract			◐	◐	◐	◐
Mentally multiply and divide				●	◐	◐
Add/subtract multiples of powers of 10		◐	◐	◐	◐	◐

● IMPACT Mathematics   ○ Macmillan Mathematics   ◐ Both IMPACT Mathematics and Macmillan Mathematics

Scope and Sequence

Concept	Kindergarten	Grade 1	Grade 2	Grade 3	Grade 4	Grade 5
Multiply multiples of powers of 10				●	●	◑
Divide multiples of powers of 10				●	●	◑
Use compensation					●	●
Break numbers apart			◑	◑	◑	◑
Use Distributive Property					●	●
Multiply/divide by powers of 10						●

Estimate: Estimation and Rounding						
Rounding			●	◑	◑	●
Front-end estimation					◑	●
Compatible numbers				●	◑	●
With whole numbers			◑	◑	◑	●
With fractions					●	●
With decimals					●	●
Area and volume				●	●	●
Select best method of computation—estimate or exact				●	◑	●

Probability and Statistics

Concept	Kindergarten	Grade 1	Grade 2	Grade 3	Grade 4	Grade 5
Collect, Organize, and Display Data						
Use data to solve problems	◐	◐	○	○	◐	◐
Organize data with a table		◐	○	○	◐	◐
Organize data with a graph	◐	◐	○	○	◐	○
Tally charts	●	◐	○	○	◐	○
Frequency tables		○	○	◐	○	○
Samples					○	○
Surveys		◐	○	○	○	○
Represent Data						
Select an appropriate display					○	◐
Pictographs		●	○	◐	○	○
Bar graphs		◐	○	◐	◐	○
Line plots		○	◐	◐	◐	○
Line graphs			◐	○	◐	○
Venn diagrams	●		●	○	○	○
Interpret Data and Make Predictions						
Use data	◐	◐	○	◐	◐	◐
Collect data	◐	◐	○	◐	◐	◐
Mode						○

● IMPACT Mathematics   ○ Macmillan Mathematics   ◐ Both IMPACT Mathematics and Macmillan Mathematics

Scope and Sequence

Concept	Kindergarten	Grade 1	Grade 2	Grade 3	Grade 4	Grade 5
Median						●
Range			●	●	●	●
Outliers						●
Make predictions from graphs				●	●	
Make predictions from a sample					●	●
Probability						
Certain, probable, impossible		●	●	●	●	●
Compare likelihoods			●	●	●	●
Predict outcomes	●	●	●	●	●	●
Outcomes and sample space				●	●	●
Simple event				●	●	●
Independent and Dependent events; Compound events						●
Experimental probability						●
Theoretical probability				●	●	●
Probability and ratio						●
Simulations						●
Tree diagrams					●	●
Combinations					●	●

Problem Solving, Reasoning, Communicating

Legend: **I** = IMPACT Mathematics · **M** = Macmillan Mathematics · **B** = Both IMPACT Mathematics and Macmillan Mathematics

Concept	Kindergarten	Grade 1	Grade 2	Grade 3	Grade 4	Grade 5
Problem Solving						
Find a pattern	B	I	B	B	I	B
Use a four-step plan	M	M	M	M	I	B
Solve a simpler problem		I	I	I	I	I
Act it out/Do an experiment/ Use a simulation	B	B	B	I	I	B
Guess and check	B	B	B	B	I	B
Draw a picture or diagram	B	B	B	I	I	I
Make a table		B	M	B	B	B
Work backward		I	B	B	I	I
Make a list		I	M	I	I	I
Make a model	I	I	I	I	I	I
Make a graph	I	M	B	B	I	B
Write an equation		I	B	B	B	I
Use logical reasoning		I	B	I	I	I
Choose a strategy	I	B	B	B	I	B
Select an operation		I	B	B	B	B
Conduct a poll or survey		B	M	M	I	B
Use and evaluate formulas					I	I
Check for reasonableness		B	B	I	I	I
Decide whether to estimate or compute an exact answer	I	I	I	I	B	I
Identify missing or extra information	I	I	B	B	B	B
Solve multi-step problems			M	B	I	B
Eliminate possibilities					B	B

● IMPACT Mathematics ● Macmillan Mathematics ◐ Both IMPACT Mathematics and Macmillan Mathematics

Concept	Kindergarten	Grade 1	Grade 2	Grade 3	Grade 4	Grade 5
Interpret a remainder					●	●
Select a representation					●	●
Use data	●	●	●	●	●	●

Reasoning and Proof

Concept	Kindergarten	Grade 1	Grade 2	Grade 3	Grade 4	Grade 5
Logical reasoning in problem solving		●	●	●	●	●
Make generalization		●	●	●	●	●
Construct mathematical arguments		●	●	●	●	●
Justify conclusions		●	●	●	●	●
Spatial reasoning		●	●	●	●	●
Create problems	●	●	●	●	●	●
Inductive reasoning		●	●	●	●	●
Deductive reasoning		●	●	●	●	●
Make and test conjectures					●	●
Venn diagrams	●		●	●	●	●

Communicate Mathematical Thinking

Concept	Kindergarten	Grade 1	Grade 2	Grade 3	Grade 4	Grade 5
Explain ideas/reasoning	●	●	●	●	●	●
Compare ideas	●	●	●	●	●	●
Describe thinking; justify thinking	●	●	●	●	●	●
Write informal mathematical arguments		●	●	●	●	●
Read mathematics		●	●	●	●	●
Work in groups	●	●	●	●	●	●

Glossary/Glosario

Cómo usar el glosario en español:

1. Busca el término en inglés que desces encontrar.
2. El término en español, junto con la definición, se encuentran en la columna de la derecha.

A

acute angle An *angle* with a measure greater than 0° and less than 90°.

ángulo agudo Un *ángulo* que mide más de 0° y menos de 90°.

acute triangle A *triangle* with all three *angles* less than 90°.

triángulo acutángulo Un *triángulo* cuyos tres *ángulos* miden menos de 90°.

addend Any numbers being added together.

sumando Cualquier número que se suma a otro.

add (adding, addition) An operation on two or more *addends* that results in a *sum*.

$$9 + 3 = 12$$

suma (sumar, adición) Operación en dos o más *sumandos* que resulta en una *suma*.

$$9 + 3 = 12$$

algebra A branch of mathematics that uses symbols, usually letters, to explore relationships between quantities.

álgebra Rama de las matemáticas que usa símbolos, generalmente letras, para explorar relaciones entre cantidades.

Glossary/Glosario

angle A figure that is formed by two *rays* with the same *endpoint*.

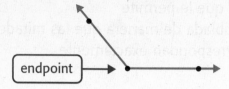

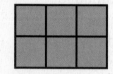

area The number of *square units* needed to cover the inside of a region or plane figure without any overlap.

area = 6 square units

Associative Property of Addition
The property states that the grouping of the *addends* does not change the *sum*.

$$(4 + 5) + 2 = 4 + (5 + 2)$$

Associative Property of Multiplication
The property that states that the grouping of the *factors* does not change the *product*.

$$3 \times (6 \times 2) = (3 \times 6) \times 2$$

ángulo Figura formada por dos *rayos* con el mismo *extremo*.

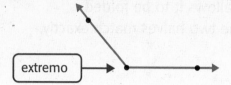

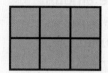

área El número de *unidades cuadradas* necesarias para cubrir el interior de una región o figura plana.

área = 6 unidades cuadrados

propiedad asociativa de la adición
Propiedad que establece que la agrupación de los *sumandos* no altera la *suma*.

$$(4 + 5) + 2 = 4 + (5 + 2)$$

propiedad asociativa de la multiplicación Propiedad que establece que la agrupación de los *factores* no altera el *producto*.

$$3 \times (6 \times 2) = (3 \times 6) \times 2$$

balance An equation is balanced if both sides of the equals sign have the same value.

bar graph
A graph that compares data by using bars of different lengths or heights to show the values.

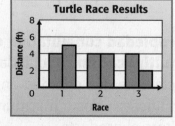

equilibrar Una ecuación está equilibrada si ambos lados del signo de igualdad tienen el mismo valor.

gráfica de barras Gráfica que compara los *datos* usando barras de distintas longitudes o alturas para mostrar los valores.

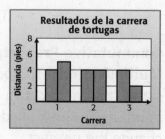

bilateral symmetry
The property of a figure
that allows it to be folded
so the two halves match exactly.

simetría bilateral
Propiedad de una
figura que le permite
ser doblada de manera que las mitades
se correspondan exactamente.

capacity   The amount
a container can hold,
measured in units of
dry or liquid measure.

capacidad   Cantidad
de material líquido o
seco que puede
contener un envase.

Celcius (°C)   The unit used to measure
temperature in the metric system.

Celsios (°C)   Unidad que se usa para
medir la temperatura en el sistema
métrico.

centimeter (cm)   A *metric unit* for
measuring *length* and *height*.

100 centimeters = 1 meter

centímetro (cm)   Unidad métrica de
longitud y altura.

100 centímetros = 1 metro

circle   A closed figure in which
all points are the same distance
from a fixed point, called the
center.

círculo   Figura cerrada en la
cual todos los puntos equidistan
de un punto fijo llamado
centro.

Commutative Property of Addition
The property that states that the order
in which two numbers are added does
not change the *sum*.

12 + 15 = 15 + 12

propiedad conmutativa de la adición
Propiedad que establece que el orden en
el cual se suman dos o más números no
altera la *suma*.

12 + 15 = 15 + 12

**Commutative Property of
Multiplication**   The property that
states that the order in which two
numbers are multiplied does not
change the *product*.

7 × 2 = 2 × 7

**propiedad conmutativa de la
multiplicación**   Propiedad que
establece que el orden en el cual se
multiplican dos o más números no
altera el *producto*.

7 × 2 = 2 × 7

Glossary/Glosario

compatible numbers   Numbers in a problem or related numbers that are easy to work with mentally.

720 and 90 are compatible numbers for division because 72 ÷ 9 = 8.

complex figure   A shape that is made up of two or more shapes.

composite number   A whole number that has more than two factors.

12 has the factors 1, 2, 3, 4, 6, and 12.

cone   A three-dimensional figure with a curved surface, a circular base, and one *vertex*.

congruent figures   Two figures having the same size and the same shape.

coordinate   One of two numbers in an *ordered pair*.

In (1, 5), the 1 is the number on the *x*-axis. The 5 is on the *y*-axis.

coordinate plane or grid   A graph that displays a set of points and gives the position of a point on a line.

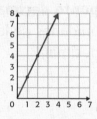

cube   A three-dimensional figure with six *congruent* square *faces*.

cubic unit   A unit for measuring *volume*, such as a cubic inch or a cubic centimeter.

customary system   The measurement system that includes units such as foot, pound, quart, and degrees Fahrenheit. Also called *standard measurement*.

números compatibles   Números en un problema o números relacionados con los cuales es fácil trabajar mentalmente.

720 y 90 son números compatibles en la división porque 72 ÷ 9 = 8.

figura compleja   Figura compuesta por dos o más formas.

número compuesto   Número entero con más de dos factores.

12 tiene los factores 1, 2, 3, 4, 6 y 12.

cono   Figura tridimensional con una superficie curva, una base circular y un *vértice*.

congruentes figuras   Dos figuras con la misma forma y el mismo tamaño.

coordenada   Uno de los dos números de un *par ordenado*.

(1, 5)   El 1 es el número en el eje *x* y el 5 está en el eje *y*.

gráfica de coordenadas o cuadriculado   Gráfica que representa un conjunto de puntos y da, en términos numéricos, la posición de un punto sobre una recta.

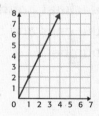

cubo   Figura tridimensional con seis *caras* cuadradas *congruentes*.

unidad cúbica   Unidad de *volumen*, como la pulgada cúbica o el centímetro cúbico.

sistema inglés   Sistema de medición que incluye unidades como el pie, la libra, el cuarto de galón y los grados Fahrenheit. También llamado medición estándar.

cylinder A three-dimensional figure having two *parallel congruent* circular bases and a curved surface connecting the two bases.

cilindro Figura tridimensional que tiene dos bases circulares *paralelas* y *congruentes* y una superficie curva que las une.

D

data Numbers or symbols, sometimes collected from a *survey* or experiment, to show information. Datum is singular; data is plural.

datos Números o símbolos que muestran información, algunas veces reunidos de una *encuesta* o un experimento.

decimal equivalents Decimals that represent the same number.

0.3 and 0.30

decimales equivalentes Decimales que representan el mismo número.

0.3 y 0.30

decimal A number that uses *place value*, numbers, and a *decimal point* to show part of a whole.

decimal Número que utiliza el *valor de posición*, números y un punto decimal para indicar una parte de un entero.

decimal point A period separating the ones and the *tenths* in a decimal number.

0.8 or $3.77

punto decimal Punto que separa las unidades de las *décimas* en un número decimal.

0.8 o $3.77

denominator The bottom number in a *fraction*.

In $\frac{5}{6}$, 6 is the denominator.

denominador El número inferior en una *fracción*.

$\frac{5}{6}$ 6 es el denominador.

diameter A *line segment* that connects two points on a circle and passes through the center of a *circle*.

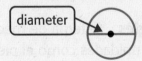

diámetro Un *segmento de recta* que pasa por el centro de un *círculo*.

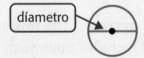

digit A symbol used to write numbers. The ten digits are 0, 1, 2, 3, 4, 5, 6, 7, 8, and 9.

Distributive Property of Multiplication To multiply a *sum* by a number, multiply each *addend* by the number and add the *products*.

$$4 \times (1 + 3) = (4 \times 1) + (4 \times 3)$$

division (divide) An operation on two numbers in which the first number is split into the same number of equal groups as the second number.

dividend A number that is being divided.

$3\overline{)19}$ 19 is the dividend.

divisor The number by which the *dividend* is being divided.

$3\overline{)19}$ 3 is the divisor.

double bar graph A *bar graph* that compares two related groups of *data*.

dígito Símbolo que se usa para escribir números. Los diez dígitos son 0, 1, 2, 3, 4, 5, 6, 7, 8 y 9.

propiedad distributiva de la multiplicación Para multiplicar una *suma* por un número, puedes multiplicar cada *sumando* por el número y sumar los *productos*.

$$4 \times (1 + 3) = (4 \times 1) + (4 \times 3)$$

división (dividir) Operación en dos números en que el primer número se separa en tantos grupos iguales como indica el segundo número.

dividendo El número que se divide.

$3\overline{)19}$ 19 es el dividendo.

divisor El número entre el cual se divide el dividendo.

$3\overline{)19}$ 3 es el divisor.

gráfica de barras dobles *Gráfica de barras* que compara dos grupos de *datos* relacionados.

edge The *line segment* where two *faces* of a *solid figure* meet.

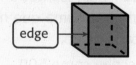

elapsed time The difference in time between the start and the end of an event.

arista El *segmento de recta* donde concurren dos *caras* de una *figura sólida*.

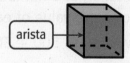

tiempo transcurrido La diferencia en tiempo entre el comienzo y el final de un evento.

endpoint The point at either end of a *line segment* or the point at the beginning of a ray.

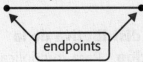

extremo El punto en cualquiera de los dos lados en que termina un *segmento de recta* o el punto al principio de un rayo.

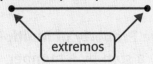

equation A sentence that contains an equals sign (=), showing that two *expressions* are equal.

ecuación Enunciado matemático que contiene el signo de igualdad, =, el que indica que el lado izquierdo del signo de igualdad tiene el mismo valor que el lado derecho.

equilateral triangle A *triangle* with three *congruent* sides.

triángulo equilátero *Triángulo* con tres lados *congruentes*.

equivalent fractions *Fractions* that represent the same number.

$$\frac{3}{4} = \frac{6}{8}$$

fracciones equivalentes *Fracciones* que representan el mismo número.

$$\frac{3}{4} = \frac{6}{8}$$

estimate A number close to an exact value. An estimate indicates *about* how much.

$47 + 22$ is about $50 + 20$ or 70.

estimación Número cercano a un valor exacto. Una estimación indica *aproximadamente* cuánto.

$47 + 22$ es aproximadamente $50 + 20$; o 70.

expanded form/expanded notation The representation of a number as a sum that shows the value of each digit.

536 is written as $500 + 30 + 6$.

forma desarrollada/notación desarrollada Representación de un número como una suma que muestra el valor de cada dígito.

536 se escribe como $500 + 30 + 6$.

expression A combination of numbers, variables, and at least one operation.

expresión Combinación de números, variables y por lo menos una operacion.

Glossary/Glosario

face The flat part of a 3-dimensional figure.

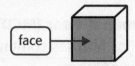

cara La parte llana de una figura tridimensional.

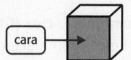

fact family A group of related facts using the same numbers.

$$5 + 3 = 8 \qquad 5 \times 3 = 15$$
$$3 + 5 = 8 \qquad 3 \times 5 = 15$$
$$8 - 3 = 5 \qquad 15 \div 3 = 5$$
$$8 - 5 = 3 \qquad 15 \div 5 = 3$$

familia de operaciones Grupo de operaciones relacionadas que usan los mismos números.

$$5 + 3 = 8 \qquad 5 \times 3 = 15$$
$$3 + 5 = 8 \qquad 3 \times 5 = 15$$
$$8 - 3 = 5 \qquad 15 \div 3 = 5$$
$$8 - 5 = 3 \qquad 15 \div 5 = 3$$

factor A number that divides a whole number evenly. Also a number that is multiplied by another number.

factor Número que divide exactamente a otro número entero. También es un número multiplicado por otro número.

Fahrenheit (°F) The unit used to measure temperature in the customary system.

Fahrenheit (°F) Unidad que se usa para medir la temperatura en el sistema inglés.

fraction A number that represents part of a whole or part of a set.

$$\frac{1}{2}, \frac{1}{3}, \frac{1}{4}, \frac{3}{4}$$

fracción Número que representa parte de un todo o parte de un conjunto.

$$\frac{1}{2}, \frac{1}{3}, \frac{1}{4}, \frac{3}{4}$$

frequency table A table for organizing a set of *data* that shows the number of times each result has occurred.

tabla de frecuencias Tabla para organizar un conjunto de *datos* que muestra el número de veces que ha ocurrido cada resultado.

function A relationship in which one number depends on another number.

función Relación en que una cantidad depende de otra cantidad.

function table A table of ordered pairs that is based on a rule.

tabla de funciones Tabla de pares ordenados que se basa en una regla.

gram (g) A *metric unit* for measuring mass.

gramo (g) Unidad métrica de masa.

Greatest Common Factor (GCF) The greatest of the common factors of two or more numbers.

The greatest common factor of 12, 18, and 30 is 6.

máximo común divisor (MCD) El mayor de los factores comunes de dos o más números.

El máximo común divisor de 12, 18, y 30 es 6.

grid A group of horizontal and vertical lines, that intersect, forming squares.

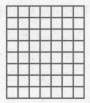

cuadrícula Grupo de rectas horizontales y verticales que se intersecan formando cuadrados.

hexagon A *polygon* with six *sides* and six *angles*.

hexágono *Polígono* con seis lados y seis *ángulos*.

hour (h) A unit of time equal to 60 *minutes*.

1 hour = 60 minutes

hora (h) Unidad de tiempo igual a 60 *minutos*.

1 hora = 60 minutos

hundredth A place value position. One of one hundred equal parts.

In the number 0.05, 5 is in the hundredths place.

centésima Un valor de posición. Una parte de cien partes iguales.

En el número 0.05, 5 está en el lugar de las centésimas.

Identity Property of Addition
For any number, zero plus that number is the number.

3 + 0 = 3 or 0 + 3 = 3

propiedad de identidad de la adición
Para todo numero, cero más el numero es el número.

3 + 0 = 3 o 0 + 3 = 3

Identity Property of Multiplication
If you multiply a number by 1, the product is the same as the given number.

$$8 \times 1 = 8 = 1 \times 8$$

propiedad de identidad de la multiplicación   Si multiplicas un número por 1, el producto es igual al número dado.

$$8 \times 1 = 8 = 1 \times 8$$

impossible   An event that cannot happen. It has a probability of zero.
It is impossible to choose yellow.

imposible   Un evento que no puede suceder, cuya probabilidad es cero.

improper fraction   A fraction with a *numerator* that is greater than or equal to the *denominator*.

$$\frac{17}{3} \text{ or } \frac{5}{5}$$

fracción impropia   Fracción con un *numerador* mayor que o igual al *denominador*.

$$\frac{17}{3} \text{ o } \frac{5}{5}$$

inch (in.)   A *customary unit* for measuring *length*. The plural is *inches*.

pulgada (pulg)   *Unidad inglesa* de *longitud*.

input   The number that is increased or decreased to produce the output number.

entrada   Número que se aumenta o disminuye para producir otro número.

intersecting lines
Lines that meet or cross at a point.

rectas secantes
Rectas que se intersecan o cruzan entre sí.

is greater than >   An inequality relationship showing that the number on the left of the symbol is greater than the number on the right.

$$5 > 3 \quad \text{5 is greater than 3.}$$

es mayor que >   Relación de desigualdad que muestra que el número a la izquierda del símbolo es mayor que el número a la derecha.

$$5 > 3 \quad \text{5 es mayor que 3.}$$

is less than <   The number on the left side of the symbol is smaller than the number on the right side.

$$4 < 7 \quad \text{4 is less than 7.}$$

es menor que <   El número a la izquierda del símbolo es más pequeño que el número a la derecha.

$$4 < 7 \quad \text{4 es menor que 7.}$$

isosceles triangle
A *triangle* with at least 2 sides of the same length.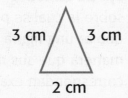

triángulo isósceles
Un *triángulo* que tiene por lo menos 2 lados del mismo largo.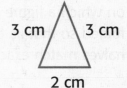

kilogram (kg) A *metric unit* for measuring mass.

kilometer (km) A *metric unit* for measuring length.

kilogramo (kg) *Unidad métrica* de masa.

kilómetro (km) *Unidad métrica* de longitud.

like denominators When two or more fractions have the same *denominator* they have *like denominators*.

denominador común El mismo *denominador* que se usa en dos o más *fracciones*.

like fractions Fractions that have the same denominator.

$$\frac{1}{5} \text{ and } \frac{2}{5}$$

fracciones semejantes Fracciones que tienen el mismo denominador.

$$\frac{1}{5} \text{ y } \frac{2}{5}$$

likely An event that will probably happen.

It is likely you will choose a red cube.

posible Un evento que probablemente sucederá.

Es posible que elijas un cubo rojo.

line A straight set of points that extend in opposite directions without ending.

recta Conjunto de puntos dispuestos rectamente en direcciones opuestas y sin fin.

line graph A graph that uses points connected by *line segments* to represent data.

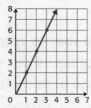

gráfica lineal Gráfica que usa puntos unidos por *segmentos de recta* para representar datos.

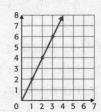

line of symmetry A *line* on which a figure can be folded so that its two halves match exactly.

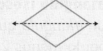

eje de simetría *Recta* sobre la cual se puede doblar una figura de manera que sus mitades se correspondan exactamente.

Glossary/Glosario

line plot A graph that uses columns of Xs above a *number line* to show frequency of data.

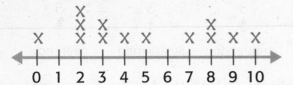

esquema lineal Gráfica que usa columnas de X sobre una *recta numérica* para representar frecuencias de datos.

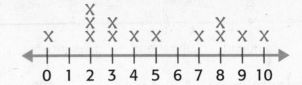

line segment A part of a *line* between two *endpoints*. The length of the line segment can be measured.

segmento de recta Parte de una *recta* entre dos *extremos*. La longitud de un segmento de recta se puede medir.

line symmetry A figure has *line symmetry* if it can be folded so that the two parts of the figure match, or are *congruent*.

simetría lineal Una figura tiene *simetria lineal* si puede doblarse de modo que las dos partes de la figura correspondan o sean *congruentes*.

mass The amount of matter in an object. Two examples of units of measure would be gram and kilogram.

masa Cantidad de materia de un cuerpo. Dos ejemplos de unidades de medida son la libra y el kilogramo.

median The middle number in a group of numbers arranged in numerical order.

The median of 3, 5, 6, 7, and 8 is 6.

mediana El número central de un grupo de números ordenados numéricamente.

La mediana de 3, 5, 6, 7, y 8 es 6.

metric system (SI) The measurement system based on powers of 10 that includes units such as meter, gram, and liter.

sistema métrico (sm) Sistema de medición que se basa en potencias de 10 y que incluye unidades como el metro, gramo, y litros.

millimeter (mm) A *metric unit* used for measuring *length*.

1,000 millimeters = 1 meter

milímetro (mm) *Unidad métrica de longitud.*

1,000 milímetros = 1 metro

minuend The first number in a subtraction sentence from which a second number is to be subtracted.

$$8 \quad - \quad 3 \quad = \quad 5$$

minuend   subtrahend   difference

minute (min) A unit used to measure time.

1 minute = 60 seconds

mixed number A number that has a *whole number* part and a *fraction* part.

$$6\frac{3}{4}$$

mode The number(s) that occurs most often in a set of numbers.

7, 4, 7, 10, 7, and 2
The mode is 7.

multiple A multiple of a number is the *product* of that number and any whole number.

15 is a multiple of 5 because $3 \times 5 = 15$.

multiply (multiplication) An operation on two numbers to find their *product*. It can be thought of as repeated *addition*.

minuendo El primer número en un enunciado de sustracción del cual se restará un segundo número.

$$8 \quad - \quad 3 \quad = \quad 5$$

minuendo   sustraendo   diferencia

minuto (min) Unidad de tiempo.

1 minuto = 60 segundos

número mixto Número compuesto por una *parte entera* y una parte *fraccionaria*.

$$6\frac{3}{4}$$

moda Número o números que ocurre(n) con mayor frecuencia en un conjunto de números.

7, 4, 7, 10, 7, y 2
La moda es 7.

múltiplo Un múltiplo de un número es el *producto* de ese número y cualquier otro número entero.

15 es múltiplo de 5 porque $3 \times 5 = 15$.

multiplicar (multiplicación) Operación en dos números para calcular su *producto*. También se puede interpretar como una *adición* repetida.

negative number Numbers less than zero.

net A flat pattern that can be folded to make a three-dimensional figure.

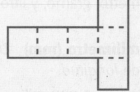

número negativo Números menores que cero.

red Patrón llano que se puede doblar para formar una figura tridimensional.

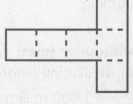

number line   A line with numbers on it in order at regular intervals.

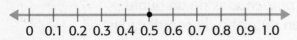

numerator   The number above the bar in a *fraction*; the part of the fraction that tells how many of the equal parts are being used.

recta numérica   Recta que representa números como puntos.

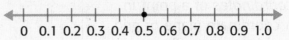

numerador   El número que está encima de la barra de *fracción*; la parte de la fracción que te indica cuántas partes iguales están siendo usadas.

obtuse angle   An *angle* that measures greater than 90° but less than 180°.

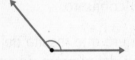

obtuse triangle
A *triangle* with one
obtuse angle.

octagon   A *polygon* with 8 sides.

ángulo obtuso   *Ángulo* que mide más de 90° pero menos de 180°.

triángulo obtusángulo
Triángulo con un
ángulo obtuso.

octagon   *Polígono* de 8 lados.

operation   A mathematical process such as addition (+), subtraction (–), multiplication (×), or division (÷).

operación   Proceso matemático como la adición (+), la sustracción (–), la multiplicación (×) o la división (÷).

order of operations   Rules that tell what order to follow use in evaluating an expression:
(1) Do the operations in parentheses first.
(2) Multiply and divide in order from left to right.
(3) Add and subtract in order from left to right.

orden de las operaciones   Reglas que te indican qué orden seguir cuando evalúas una expresión:
(1) Evalúa primero las operaciones dentro de los paréntesis ( ).
(2) Multiplica o divide en orden de izquierda a derecha.
(3) Suma o resta en orden de izquierda a derecha.

ordered pair A pair of numbers that are the *coordinates* of a point in a coordinate plane or grid in this order (horizontal coordinate, vertical coordinate).

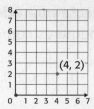

origin The point (0, 0) on a *coordinate* graph where the vertical axis meets the horizontal axis.

outcome A possible result of an experiment.

outlier A number in a set of data that is much larger or much smaller than most of the other numbers in the set.

output The number that results from increasing or decreasing the input number.

par ordenado Par de números que son *coordenadas* de un punto en un plano de coordenadas o cuadriculado, en este orden (coordenada horizontal, coordenada vertical).

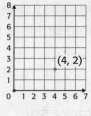

origen El punto (0, 0) en una *gráfica de coordenadas* donde el eje vertical interseca el eje horizontal.

resultado Resultado posible de un experimento.

valor atípico Número en un conjunto de datos que es mucho mayor o mucho menor que la mayoría de los otros números del conjunto.

salida Número que resulta del aumento o disminución del número de entrada.

parallel lines Lines that are the same distance apart. Parallel lines do not meet.

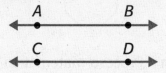

parallelogram A quadrilateral with four sides in which each pair of opposite sides are parallel and equal in length.

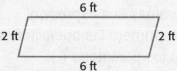

pentagon A *polygon* with five sides.

rectas paralelas Rectas separadas por la misma distancia. Las rectas paralelas no se intersecan.

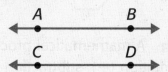

paralelogramo Cuadrilátero de cuatro lados en el cual cada par de lados opuestos son paralelos y de la misma longitud.

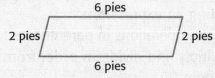

pentágono *Polígono* de cinco lados.

Glossary/Glosario

perimeter The distance around a shape or region.

perímetro Distancia alrededor de una figura o región.

period The name given to each group of three digits on a place-value chart.

período Nombre dado a cada grupo de tres dígitos en una tabla de valores de posición.

perpendicular lines *Lines* that meet or cross each other to form *right angles*.

rectas perpendiculares *Rectas* que se intersecan o cruzan formando *ángulos rectos*.

place value The value given to a *digit* by its position in a number.

valor de posición El valor dado a un *dígito* según su posición en un número.

plane figure A two-dimensional figure that lies entirely within one plane such as a triangle or square.

figura plana Figura bidimensional que yace completamente en un plano como un triángulo o un cuadrado.

point An exact location in space. Also refers to a decimal place.

punto Ubicación exacta en el espacio. También se refiere a un lugar decimal.

polygon A closed *plane figure* formed using *line segments* that meet only at their *endpoints*.

polígono *Figura plana* cerrada formada por *segmentos de recta* que sólo concurren en sus *extremos*.

positive number Numbers that are greater than zero.

número positivo Números mayores que cero.

prime number A whole number with exactly two *factors*, 1 and itself.

número primo Número entero que tiene exactamente dos *factores*, 1 y sí mismo.

7, 13, and 19

7, 13, y 19

probability   A number between 0 and 1 that measures the likelihood of an event happening.

probabilidad   Número entre 0 y 1 que mide la posibilidad de que ocurra un evento.

product   The answer or result of a multiplication problem. It also refers to expressing a number as the product of its factors.

producto   Repuesta o resultado de un problema de multiplicación. También se refiere a la expresión de un número como el producto de sus factores.

pyramid   A three-dimensional figure with a *polygon* as a base and triangular shaped *faces* that share a common *vertex*.

pirámide   Figura sólida con un *polígono* como base y *caras* triangulares que comparten un *vértice* común.

Q

quadrilateral   A shape that has 4 sides and 4 *angles*.
square, rectangle, and parallelogram

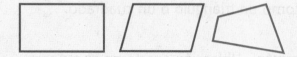

cuadrilátero   Figura con 4 lados y 4 *ángulos*.
cuadrado, rectángulo y paralelogramo

quotient   The result of a *division* problem.

cociente   Respuesta o resultado de un problema de *división*.

R

ray   A part of a *line* that has one *endpoint* and extends in one direction without ending.

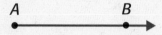

rayo   Parte de una *recta* que tiene un *extremo* y que se extiende en una dirección.

rectangle   A *quadrilateral* with four *right angles*; opposite sides are equal and *parallel*.

rectángulo   *Cuadrilátero* con cuatro *ángulo rectos*; los lados opuestos son iguales y *paralelos*.

rectangular prism A three-dimensional figure with six faces that are rectangles.

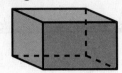

reflection A figure that is flipped over a line to create a mirror image of the figure.

remainder The number that is left after one whole number is divided by another.

rhombus A *parallelogram* with four *congruent* sides.

right angle An *angle* with a measure of 90°.

right triangle
A *triangle* with one *right angle*.

rotation A type of transformation in which a figure is turned about a central point.

rotational symmetry A figure has rotational symmetry if, after a rotation of the figure about a point, the figure lies in its original position.

round To change the value of a number to one that is easier to work with. To find the nearest value of a number based on a given *place value*.

prisma rectangular Figura tridimensional de seis caras rectangulares.

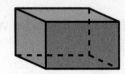

reflexión Figura que se vuelca sobre una línea para crear una imagen especular de la figura.

residuo Número que queda después de dividir un número entero entre otro número entero.

rombo *Paralelogramo* con cuatro lados *congruentes*.

ángulo recto *Ángulo* que mide 90°.

triángulo rectángulo
Triángulo con un *ángulo recto*.

rotación Un tipo de transformación en el que una figura gira con relación a un punto central.

simetría de rotación Una figura posee simetría de rotación si después de rotarla sobre un punto la figura yace en su posición original.

redondear Cambiar el valor de un número a uno con el cual es más fácil trabajar. Calcular el valor más cercano a un número basado en un *valor de posición* dado.

scalene triangle   A *triangle* with no *congruent* sides.

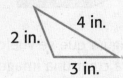

similar   Figures that have the same shape but different sizes.

simplest form   A *fraction* in which the *numerator* and the *denominator* have no common factor greater than 1.

solid figure   A solid figure has three dimensions: length, width, and height.

sphere   A three-dimensional figure that is set of all points that are the same distance from a given point, called the center.

square   A rectangle with four *congruent* sides.

square unit   A unit for measuring area.

standard form/standard notation
The usual way of writing a number that shows only its *digits*, no words.

537   89   1642

subtract (subtraction)   An operation on two numbers that tells the difference, when some or all are taken away. Subtraction is also used to compare two numbers.

14 − 8 = 6

triángulo escaleno   *Triángulo* sin lados *congruentes*.

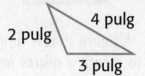

similar   Figuras que tienen la misma forma pero que no tienen el mismo tamaño.

forma reducida   *Fracción* en la cual el *numerador* y el *denominador* no tienen un factor común mayor que 1.

figura sólida   Figura sólida de tres dimensiones: largo, ancho y alto.

esfera   Figura tridimensional formada por el conjunto de todos los puntos equidistantes de un puntodado llamado centro.

cuadrado   Rectángulo de cuatro lados *congruentes*.

unidad cuadrada   Unidad para medir el área.

forma estándar/notación estandard   Manera habitual de escribir un número que sólo muestra sus *dígitos*, sin palabras.

537   89   1642

restar (sustracción)   Operación en dos números que indica la diferencia, cuando algunos o todos son eliminados. La sustracción también se usa para comparar dos números.

14 − 8 = 6

subtrahend A number that is subtracted from another number.

$$14 - 5 = 9$$

subtrahend

sum The answer to an addition problem.

survey A method of collecting *data*.

sustraendo Un número que se sustrae de otro número.

$$14 - 5 = 9$$

sustraendo

suma Respuesta o resultado de un problema de adición.

encuesta Método para reunir *datos*.

tally chart A way to keep track of *data* using tally marks to record the number of responses or occurrences.

What is Your Favorite Color?	
Color	Tally
Blue	ℍℍ |||
Green	||||

tally mark(s) A mark made to keep track and display *data* recorded from a survey.

temperature A measure of how hot or how cold something is.

tenth One of ten equal parts or $\frac{1}{10}$.

thermometer A tool used to measure temperature.

transformation A movement of a figure that does not change the size or shape of the figure.

tabla de conteo Manera de llevar la cuenta de los *datos* usando marcas de conteo para anotar el número de respuestas o sucesos.

¿Cuál es tu color favorito?	
Color	Conteo
Azul	ℍℍ |||
Verde	||||

marcas(s) de conteo Marca que se hace para llevar un registro y representar *datos* reunidos de una encuesta.

temperatura Medida de qué tan frío o caliente está algo.

décima Una de diez partes iguales o $\frac{1}{10}$.

termómetro Herramienta para medir la temperatura.

transformación Movimiento de una figura que no cambia el tamaño o la forma de la figura.

translation Sliding a figure in a straight line horizontally, vertically, or diagonally.

trapezoid A *quadrilateral* with exactly one pair of *parallel* sides.

tree diagram **a.** A diagram of all the possible *outcomes* of an event or series of events or experiments.
b. A diagram of all the possible combinations of two or more objects or events being put together.

triangle A *polygon* with three sides and three *angles*.

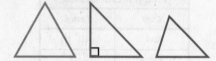

triangular prism A prism whose bases are triangular with *parallelograms* for sides.

triangular pyramid A pyramid whose base is a *triangle*.

traslación Deslizar una figura horizontal, vertical o diagonalmente en línea recta.

trapecio *Cuadrilátero* con exactamente un par de lados *paralelos*.

diagrama de árbol **a.** Diagrama de todos los *resultados* posibles de un evento o series de eventos o experimentos.
b. Diagrama de todas las combinaciones posibles de dos o más objetos o eventos que se combinan.

triángulo *Polígono* con tres lados y tres *ángulos*.

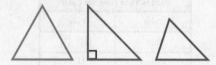

prisma triangular Prisma cuyas bases son triangulares con *paralelogramos* como lados.

pirámide triangular Pirámide cuya base es un *triángulo*.

(U)

unlikely An event that is improbable or it will probably *not* happen.

It is unlikely you will choose a yellow tile.

improbable Evento que es improbable o que es probable que *no* suceda.

Es improbable que elijas ena baldosa amarilla.

Glossary/Glosario

variable   A letter or symbol used to represent an unknown quantity.

vertex   The point where two rays meet in an *angle*.

volume   The number of cubic units needed to fill a 3-*dimensional figure* or solid figure.

variable   Letra o símbolo que se usa para representar una cantidad desconocida.

vértice   Punto en donde dos rayas se juntan en un *ángulo*.

volumen   Número de unidades cúbicas necesarias para llenar una *figura tridimensional* o sólida.

weight   A measurement that tells how heavy an object is.

peso   Medida que indica la pesadez de un cuerpo.

x-axis   The horizontal axis (↔) in a coordinate graph.

x-coordinate   The first number in an *ordered pair* that indicates how far to the left or the right of the *y*-axis a point is. In (2, 3), 2 is the *x*-coordinate.

eje x   El eje horizontal (↔) en una gráfica de coordenadas.

coordenada x   El primer número en un *par ordenado* que indica la distancia a la izquierda o a la derecha del eje *x* a la cual se encuentra un punto. En (2, 3), 2 es la coordenada *x*.

y-axis   The vertical axis (↕) in a coordinate graph.

y-coordinate   The second number in an *ordered pair* that indicates how far above or below the *x*-axis a point is. In (2, 3), 3 is the *y*-coordinate.

eje y   El eje vertical (↕) en una gráfica de coordenadas.

coordenada y   El segundo número en un *par ordenado* que indica la distancia hacia arriba o hacia abajo del eje *x* a la cual se encuentra un punto. En (2, 3), 3 es la coordenada *y*.

Zero Property of Multiplication
The property that states any number multiplied by zero is zero.

$$0 \times 5 = 0 \qquad 5 \times 0 = 0$$

propiedad del producto nulo de la multiplicación   Propiedad que establece que cualquier número multiplicado por cero es igual a cero.

$$0 \times 5 = 0 \qquad 5 \times 0 = 0$$

Index

Magenta text references teacher pages   **Black** text references student pages

Magenta text references teacher pages   **Black** text references student pages